THE APPLICATION OF ARTIFICIAL INTELLIGENCE TECHNIQUES TO CIVIL AND STRUCTURAL ENGINEERING

Edited by
B. H. V. TOPPING

CIVIL-COMP PRESS

published by

CIVIL-COMP PRESS

10 Saxe-Coburg Place
Edinburgh

© *Civil-Comp Limited*

British Library Cataloguing in Publication Data
The application of artificial intelligence techniques to civil and structural engineering
1. Civil engineering – Data processing
2. Artificial intelligence
1. Topping, B. H. V.
624'.028'563   TA345
ISBN 0-948749-06-7

Printed in Scotland
by
MEIGLE PRINTERS
Market Street, Galashiels

CONTENTS

*Papers presented at CIVIL-COMP 85, The Second International Conference on Civil and Structural Engineering Computing, 3rd – 5th December, 1985, The Institution of Civil Engineers, London. All other papers presented at CIVIL-COMP 87, The Third International Conference on Civil and Structural Engineering Computing, 22nd – 24th September, 1987, The Institution of Civil Engineers, London.

I EXPERT SYSTEM SHELLS, INTERFACES AND KNOWLEDGE ELICITATION

SOME EXPERIENCES FROM EVALUATING EXPERT SYSTEM SHELL PROGRAMS AND SOME POTENTIAL APPLICATIONS

R J Allwood, BSc, PhD, CEng, MICE,
D J Stewart, BSc, CEng, MICE and
Professor E G Trimble, BSc, CEng, MICE, MIStructE, MIMechE,
Department of Civil Engineering,
University of Technology, Loughborough

Nine expert system shell programs have been evaluated recently on a SERC funded research grant. A full report is available but this paper reports on some of the lessons learned from the study. Knowledge representation is discussed and problems identified, particularly in handling numeric variables and in deriving factors to represent uncertainty. Attention is also drawn to new developments in controlling conversations with client users which greatly help "user friendliness". Some criticisms are made of the present systems and some comparisons made between shells and the language Prolog.

INTRODUCTION

This paper springs from a 12 month project funded by the Science and Engineering Research Council completed in August 1985 to evaluate commercially available expert system shell programs to help researchers in construction management choose the most suitable shell for their application. The nine shells examined are shown in Table 1 and a full report on the study including benchmark tests is available from the first named author (Ref.1). The purpose of this paper is to draw attention to some lessons learned from the study which may be of value to anyone interested in applying expert systems in construction. We also draw upon our practical experience of constructing knowledge bases particularly a recent commission from the Building Research Establishment to develop a system for diagnosing causes of dampness in buildings.

SOME PROBLEMS OF KNOWLEDGE REPRESENTATION

An expert system consists of knowledge about some "domain" of expertize stored on a file and a shell program which asks questions of a user and uses the answers to make inferences from the stored knowledge. Not suprisingly, each shell stores knowledge in a different form and it is unlikely that a standard form will appear anymore than a standard programming language will appear. However some basic styles are clear and potential users should not be dissuaded from starting to assemble knowledge by the fear of having to re-code it. Changing shells would require effort but probably much less than that expended in gathering the knowledge to start with. Distinct styles of knowledge representation are adopted according to whether the application is concerned with a deterministic problem in which the answers are always yes or no or whether some element of uncertainty is to be allowed. We have no doubt that if it is at all possible uncertainty should be avoided. It is certainly an important advance of artificial intelligence research to have shown that there are appropriate inference methods for dealing with uncertainty in a reasonably consistent fashion. However, this requires factors to represent the uncertainty which strictly can only be obtained from large statistical samples. These are rarely available and, additionally, the coding and testing of an uncertain system has many possibilities for errors due to the virtually infinite combination of

answers a user might give. Uncertainty can so often be just another name for ignorance. It may be better to face up to that, unearth the knowledge needed to make the problem definite and so simplify the resulting expert system.

Representing Deterministic Knowledge

The most basic level of logical inference is "propositional logic". This is a classical logic in which the absolute truth or falsity of a statement can be determined in a mechanical and predictable way. Each basic element is a proposition such as: "the road is a major road". These propositions can be joined using the connectives AND, OR, NOT to form larger propositions and rules such as:

IF "the road is a major road" AND "the road is on an embankment" AND "the height of the embankment is greater than 6m" THEN "a safety barrier must be provided".

Production rule systems represent knowledge as a set of rules in this IF ... THEN format. They use propositional logic to establish the truth of the "antecedent" statements, ie those before THEN. If the antecedent conditions evaluate to true, the rule sets the value of the "consequent" statement. If the rule fails, the consequent may yet be proved by another rule in the knowledge base.

The disadvantage of propositional logic is that it is impossible to reason about items within the propositions. This may lead to many similar questions such as:

"Is it true that "the height of the embankment is > 6 m.?"
"Is it true that "the height of the embankment is > 3 m.?"

because it treats every statement about the height of the embankment as a separate proposition.

To overcome this problem, more sophisticated systems break down the propositions into smaller elements. Two levels of sophistication can be distinguished. As the first level, propositions including numeric terms and simple relations such as "greater than",

SHELL	PRICE (ex vat)	COMPUTERS	DEVELOPER
Xi	£495	IBM PC	Expertech Limited 172, Bath Road, Slough
ESP ADVISOR	£600-£4000	IBM PC Apricot Sirius VAX	Expert Systems Int. 9 West Way, Oxford
APES and Micro-prolog	£575	IBM PC Apricot MSDOS and CPM86 micros	Logic Based Systems Limited 40 Beaumont Avenue Richmond Surrey
TESS	£650	IBM PC	Helix Expert Systems Ltd 11 Ludgate Circus London, EC4M 7LQ
SAVOIR	£3000-£10000	IBM PC Apricot Sirius PRIME, VAX	ISI Limited 11 Oakdene Road, Redhill Surrey
EX-TRAN 7	£1995-£18000	IBM PC-XT-AT Sun GRID Compass VAX(UNIX)	Intelligent Terminals Limited 30 Hanover Street Glasgow
KES	£4000-£24000	IBM PC-XT VAX	Software Architecture & Engineering Inc., 16 New Park Road Chichester West Sussex
ENVISAGE	£12000	VAX(VMS) ICL 2900	Systems Designers Plc Pembroke House
SAGE	£2500	IBM PC VAX	Pembroke Broadway Camberley, Surrey (also from ICL)

TABLE 1   BASIC DETAILS OF SHELLS EVALUATED

"less than" etc. can be handled. At the second, a more general predicate logic able to match non-numeric terms is implemented.

In the first, a rule can include a numeric test such as:
   "embankment height > 6".

The system will ask for and store a numeric value for "embankment height", and will automatically be able to determine the truth of the overall proposition. ESP/ADVISOR, and the deterministic sections of KES.PS, SAVOIR, and ENVISAGE employ this type of logic.

The fuller predicate logic systems allow propositions to contain variables representing non-numeric items, with more general relationships holding between them. The relations cannot be processed in the same automatic way that the numeric relations are. Instead the knowledge base author has to define when a relation and its arguments are going to yield a value of true. These non-numeric variables might be used in rules such as:

   "X needs parapet if
      X built-on structure and
      X is-subject-to BE5-conditions"

where X is some object, which may be related to some other objects: "parapet", "structure", "BE5-conditions" by the relations "needs", "built-on", "is-

subject-to". To find if there is a true instance of an X which needs a parapet, the system needs to find instances of facts in the database such as:

"road built-on structure", "road is-subject-to BE5-conditions".

APES and Xi provide a predicate logic.

EX-TRAN 7 uses a very different representation to any of the systems mentioned above. It uses decision trees to represent the rules. The same deterministic rules can be represented as in ESP/ADVISER for example, but they look very different, even less like English, e.g.

```
road_tp :
    major : v_height :
                < 6 : nobarrier
                >= 6 : barrier
    minor : nobarrier
```

The system chains forward through the decision tree following the appropriate path out of each decision node. This tree could be interpreted in an English style similar to the rules used in the example above, i.e. "if road type is major and verge height is greater than or equal to 6 metres, then a barrier is needed".

Representing Uncertain Knowledge

The systems mentioned above all use classical logic, where all truth values evaluate to true or false. In some domains such a crisp view of truth and falsity is not practical and some measure of truth or uncertainty needs to be associated with statements. Such facilities will clearly be useful in predictive systems which might produce conclusions like:

"the earthworks will be completed by September"
- probability 0.9

The uncertainty in the knowledge could be from a number of different sources.

i) The rules may be uncertain, i.e. the same antecedent conditions can be indicative of different conclusions e.g.

Damp patches on the walls indicates either:
- rising damp or
- condensation

ii) The evidence may be uncertain, some measure of certainty may need to be expressed about some subjective assessment:
Are the roof tiles in good weatherproof condition?

The systems evaluated in this study used three main methods of dealing with uncertainty:
1) fuzzy logic.
2) Shortliffe type certainty factors.
3) Bayes theorems.

Fuzzy Logic

Fuzzy logic measures the truth of a statment as a number between 0 and 1, and may therefore sometimes very loosely be referred to as a probability. There are some fairly standardised methods for combining these truth measures for example:

Proposition A is true with value 0.7
Proposition B is true with value 0.5

If we have a rule such as: If A and B then C,

the truth value of C is taken to be the minimum probability of all the antecedents, i.e. 0.5.

If the rule states: If A or B then C,

the truth value of C is taken to be the maximum probability of all the antecedents, i.e. 0.7.

Most of the systems dealing with uncertainty provide these implementations of the fuzzy logic operators for combining their probabilistic statements. There is no theoretical justification for taking the maximum or minimum values in every case. It works in the classical logic case where the truth values are 0.0 and 1.0 and does not usually provoke any objecttions from users. These operators are provided in KES.PS, SAGE, ENVISAGE, and SAVOIR, which also has some alternative implementations.

Shortliffe Type Certainty Factors

Certainty factors described by Shortliffe (Ref.2) were used in MYCIN. The only system in the study that provided this type of uncertain reasoning was KES.PS. This system allows the knowledge base author to attach a certainty factor in the range -1 to +1 to the rule, e.g.

if vertical rise = significant,
& quantities = small,
& space available = limited,
then lifting equipment = midget cranes <0.75>

This means that the rule leads to that conclusion with a certainty of 0.75. A certainty factor of less than 0.0 indicates against the conclusion with that certainty, e.g. <-0.25> would mean that midget cranes are unsuitable with certainty 0.25. In practice experts will tend to write rules which prove rather than disprove things. However, there may be a number of rules in the knowledge base variously proving and disproving the conclusion. The final tally of the likelihood of a given hypothesis is found by simply adding the positive factor, called the measure of belief, to the negative factor, called the measure of disbelief. When two rules both prove or disprove a conclusion the uncertainties are combined using formulae of the following form:

$$mb' = s * (1 - mb)$$ (mb = measure of belief)
      s = the rule's certainty factor)

These formulae make the measures of belief approach their legal bounds asymptotically, as corroborating evidence is added.

The user is allowed to qualify his answers with a certainty factor. This factor is then used to reduce the rule's certainty by simply multiplying the two factors together. For example, if the user responds to the question "is the space limited?", with a certainty of 0.5 the overall certainty factor of the rule becomes 0.5 * 0.75 = 0.375. Where there are many antecedent conditions in a rule, the fuzzy operators described above are used to tally the user's belief in the evidence i.e. if the conditions are connected by AND's the minimum certainty factor is taken.

The Use of Bayes Theorem in Inference Networks

Inference nets are used by many shells including, from our evaluation set, SAVOIR and its predecessor Micro-Expert, KES.BAYES, ENVISAGE and TESS. They can be seen as an alternative to production rules e.g.

IF A AND B THEN C
becomes
C DEPENDS ON A AND B.

There is however a fundamental difference in the processing of such statements. The production rule does not give a value to C if A or B fail. The inference network statement always leads to a value for C once A and B have been established. A "network" consists of many such statements and a set of questions about A,B, etc. The choice of logical operations permitted on A and B sometimes includes the simple operators AND, OR, NOT etc, but the real interest in inference nets lies in the use of Bayes' theorem for modifying the probabilities of uncertain hypotheses according to the existence of evidence. The Reverend Thomas Bayes (1702-1761) considered how worldly evidence could be used to prove the existence of God and his posthumous theorem has now become a basis of modern decision theory. In its application to inference nets the theorem is used to calculate a modified probability of the result C as the existence of items of evidence A and B is proved disproved.

The typical use of Bayes theorem in an inference network can be summarized by the following example which follows the format of ENVISAGE.

```
C DEPENDS ON
    A AFFIRM 5 DENIES .1
    B AFFIRM 3 DENIES .2
  PRIOR 0.1
```

In brief, Bayes theorem takes the PRIOR probability given for C and modifies it using the AFFIRM factor if A or B are true or the DENIES factor if A or B are false. Either factor may be greater or less than one. From our study we feel that there are some misunderstandings about the application of Bayes theorem to inference networks particularly in the estimation of suitable weighting factors. A varied nomenclature has been adopted to describe the factors. We like the terms AFFIRM and DENIES which convey well the sense of the weighting they give to the truth or falsity of the evidence.

From our practical experience it would seem that experts prefer to offer certainty factors for a line of reasoning rather than determine Bayes weighting factors since the necessary statistical data is rarely available to help derive factors.

Uncertain Response by User

Several systems allow the user to respond on a scale of −5 to +5 to indicate uncertainty about whether an item of evidence is true or false. Bayes theorem does not itself allow for this case and some pragmatic interpolation schemes have been introduced by system writers. Some of these have been found to yield unsymmetric answers when two equally weighted items of evidence are answered with equal but opposite values, i.e. if A=4 and B=4 the result is not the same as that from A=5 and B=5. Several authors, eg Forsyth, have pointed out that users can also have quite different perceptions of "unknown" let alone a scale of "unknowns". A response of +3 could thus represent a number of levels of uncertainty about truth. We would recommend not allowing graded responses on this scale unless absolutely necessary. One alternative is to set up a menu of defined intermediate appearances of an item of evidence and use system facilities to associate a particular probability to the related variable.

COMPREHENSIBILITY OF KNOWLEDGE BASES

We were disappointed at the difficulty of comprehending knowledge bases coded for the majority of shells. It is an anticipated feature of expert systems that a non-computer expert should be able to read a knowledge base and make contributions to it. This is hardly possible with many of the shells we have looked at particularly those using inference networks. Perhaps the system developers could consider writing a translator program to convert the esoteric forms into one resembling English or a graphical representation of the network.

CONTROL OF CONVERSATION WITH A CLIENT USER

An interesting feature of the newer shell programs is the addition to the knowledge base of sophisticated facilities to control the sequence of questions asked of the user. The basic technique used in expert systems to make inferences is to work backwards from the "goals" (answers) through the questions relevant to each goal until the truth of that goal is proved or disproved. This is an efficient

technique and reduces the number of questions to be put to the user but can lead to irrelevant and detailed questions being put about most unlikely goals before getting to the more likely ones. From our experience of constructing practical knowledge bases it is useful to be able to put to the user some preliminary questions about his problem and use these (and later questions) to direct the system to concentrate on the most likely goals and to discard quickly the disproven goals. A technique used in some shells is to introduce so called "demons" which are statements that start or stop investigations whenever specified answers are given or conditions met. Potential researchers are warned that there is a considerable challenge in comprehending the opportunities that demons offer!

HANDLING LARGE KNOWLEDGE BASES

A file containing the knowledge for a particular domain can grow quite alarmingly. This creates problems rather similar to those of handling a large BASIC program. All variables in a knowledge base are global which requires a disciplined approach to choosing names. Expert systems do not process their statements in a sequential fashion. The backward searching technique coupled with the interference by demons means that at any time during a consultation any statement may be invoked if it refers, even indirectly, to variables currently under investigation.

Few facilities are provided by the suppliers of shell programs to assist knowledge authors keep track of their use of variables. When a knowledge base extends to several hundred rules or the equivalent some assistance is needed. The simplest, provided by some shells, is a list of names used and the number of the rule(s) in which each variable appears. This is helpful but what is probably necessary is some form of structuring of the knowledge base into sections corresponding to subroutines. A graphic representation of the knowledge tree relating to each goal is also helpful but only the very expensive AI workstations provide the software to generate these automatically.

SHELLS VERSUS LANGUAGES

An expert system could be written in any programming language but some are more convenient than others. Some languages such as Prolog and Lisp are initially attractive because of built-in data handling facilities and may be made more convenient still with a library of routines designed for expert system work. A shell may be seen as one step further towards a tailored programming system with of course a reduction in generality.

Because of the special place that Prolog now seems to have in AI work, particularly in the UK, we offer some observations on its use for expert systems learned from our study. It is a most versatile language for data-base type applications but for expert systems work we note the following difficulties with most implementations of the language.

The states of "false" and "unknown" are not distinguished;
the qualification of "answered"/unanswered" is not provided;
numeric work is limited to integers;
The search method is blind depth-first which may not be the most appropriate;
uncertainty is not catered for;
it is slow and uses much memory.

POTENTIAL APPLICATIONS OF EXPERT SYSTEMS

Before assessing the potential of expert systems in construction it is worth noting the following current work.

Design Of Building Services

Work is proceeding at the Building Services Research and Information Association and at the Polytechnic of the South Bank. The former is aimed at the initial decision stages while the latter is more broadly based.

Interpretation Of Regulations

Work is being done by the University of Sydney on sunlight requirements, by Birmingham Polytechnic on a British standard for measuring building work and by the water industry on regulations and codes of practice relating to water distribution management.

Estimating Procedures And Cost Control

Work is proceeding at Salford University and Portsmouth Polytechnic. Funding at Portsmouth is very substantial.

Evaluating Contractors' Safety Practice
Selection Of Earth-Moving Plant
The Decision to bid or not

These domains are being developed successfully at Stanford University, California.

Claims Analysis

This work is proceeding at the University of Colorado supported by the Construction Engineering Research Laboratory of the U.S. Army Corps. The purpose of the system is to assess the vulnerability of a client to a claim from his contractor. It is intended to provide guidance as to when legal advice is needed. It is expected to be educational in that it alerts users to the points that need to be watched in the administration of their contracts.

Building Defects Diagnosis

Work is proceeding at the Building Research Establishment on a system to diagnose the cause of damp penetration in buildings. The authors have an involvement in this project and believe it will be valuable in releasing experienced staff for new work. We believe that a similar approach will be useful in the investigation of building defects of a wide range of different types.

Buildability

Work is proceeding at the University of Reading.

Intelligent project management systems

It seems that the Digital Corporation has had some success in this domain with particular regard to the design and manufacture of computers. The PLANIT community club is developing a somewhat similar approach. There is notional potential for these developments in the construction industry. However, our behavioural studies, suggest that less sophisticated methods would be more effective.

CATEGORIES OF POTENTIAL APPLICATIONS

The study we have undertaken so far indicates that, with currently available shells there are several categories of application which are feasible now. They include

- Codifying and accumulating knowledge about topics that have hitherto been largely undefined (e.g. selecting appropriate construction plant)

- Ensuring that nothing gets overlooked (e.g. the check points in a building design, adjusted for each design type)

- Providing positive guidance in interpreting regulations (e.g. Building Regulations and Fire Regulations)

- Providing pointers to strategic design. (e.g. the selection of the most appropriate type of heating system prior to the development of the detail design)

GOALS OF POTENTIAL APPLICATIONS

There has been a lot of speculation about the potentials of expert systems. Much of it has been ill-founded as it has failed to take account of the important limits of such systems as currently devised. Essentially an expert system will efficiently find one or more pre-defined goals. A goal can be a diagnosis or a piece of advice. The following example goals may help to clarify this.

- Use network analysis and short-interval planning

- Use management contracting

- The fault lies in the winding drum

- You should bid. This advice is given at the level of +4 in the range -5 (meaning certainly do not bid) to +5 (meaning certainly you should bid).

- Use check list number 6 (as part of advice in implementing a system of cost planning)

- Use a tower crane with a luffing jib.

- Use a water-borne central heating system.

- The cause is damp penetration. Probability 90%.

- The fault lies in thermostat number 4. Probability 80%.

- For this assignment employ Mr John Smith.

- Use leasing (to finance a capital purchase).

The range of possible applications that comply with the need to pre-define goals is nevertheless large and readers should be able, with the aid of the examples, to define their own potential systems. There is one further important condition namely that the expertize that supports the choice of a goal (from a list of possible goals) must be accessable to the person who wishes to assemble the system. Very often expertize will exist in intuitive unstructured form and its elicitation will be difficult. In fact it may only be possible to produce a system that yields the same results as the expert; it is unlikely that his real thought processes will be reproduced.

One last point that needs to be stressed is that, although an expert system can be employed to assist in the design process this is only feasible if the possible components are pre-defined. Furthermore a hierarchy of components can be defined. Thus an expert system could first select waterborne heating as the best form of heating and go on to select appropriate designs of radiator, prime heat source and method of control. Conceptually there is no limit to the number of levels of hierarchy.

REFERENCES

Allwood, R.J., Stewart, D.J., Hinde, C & Negus, B. "Evaluation of Expert system shell programs for Construction Industry Applications" Department of Civil Engineering, University of Technology, Loughborough, 1985.

Shortliffe, E., "Computer based medical consultation: MYCIN", American Elsevier, 1976.

FURTHER READING

Michie D.(ed) "Introductory Readings in Expert Systems", Gordon & Breach, 1982.

Naylor, C. "Build your own Expert System", Sigma Technical Press, 1983.

Barr, A., Feigenbaum, E.A., et al. "The handbook of Artificial Intelligence", Pitman, London 1981.

Hayes-Roth, F., Waterman, D.E., Lenat, D.B. "Building Expert Systems", Adison-Wesley, 1983.

Forsyth, R. "Expert Systems", Chapman and Hall, 1984.

EXPERT SYSTEM DEVELOPMENT – PROBLEMS IN PRACTICE

Steve Rowlinson
Department of Civil & Structural Engineering,
University of Hong Kong
formerly Construction Study Unit,
Brunel University, London

This paper reports on work funded by the Science and Engineering Research Council and undertaken in the Construction Study Unit (formerly at Brunel University but now at Bath University) to develop an expert system to advise on procurement strategy, i.e. contractual and organisational arrangements to be entered into by the construction client. A brief description of the background to the research and development is given in order to familiarise the reader with the salient features of the domain studied.

A critical appraisal of the project highlights the main decision points in the research process and the alternatives considered. Problems encountered and strategies for overcoming these are discussed. Of particular interest are the use of a rapid prototyping strategy, knowledge acquisition and representation and the use of shells and their adequacy. Research staff appointment is also briefly discussed.

A description of the final system and its mode of operation is included as are criteria for testing the system. It is hoped that test results will be available for presentation at the conference. The paper concludes with a discussion of a scenario for development of future systems.

BACKGROUND

The problem addressed by the research reported in this paper is the choice of an appropriate contract strategy for industrial building clients. To date the process of building procurement has been somewhat haphazard for most clients despite the attempts of government and industry bodies to bring some order and logic to the process. A major stumbling block has been the lack of agreement by experts on appropriate stategies and this has stemmed in part from the research in the area being undertaken in an uncoordinated manner. A number of studies have been undertaken over the past 25 years which have sought to provide information on the performance of different procurement forms. The most recently reported research in the U.K. was undertaken by NEDO, the Faster Building for Industry report (ref 1), and indicated that clients were not sufficiently aware of the alternatives offered to them by the construction industry and, if they were aware, had great difficulty in choosing between the available options.

Research Base

The method adopted here is based upon research undertaken at Brunel University under the sponsorship of the Science and Engineering Research Council (ref 2). The three year research programme into the comparative performance of different procurement forms in Great Britain adopted a contingency view of the construction process. The idea that one procurement form, such as project management, is best is rejected in favour of the view that the most appropriate form is contingent on both the client body's characteristics and those of the project. Contract strategy is based on both the organisation structure of the building team and the decisions made concerning method of payment and selection of the team.

The research concentrated on the industrial client who undertakes construction as part of his product development process and so regards the building as a means of production (although a number of developers do engage in this field and see the building as an investment). This market sector accounted for 17% of U.K. new construction in 1985 and has in the past complained of the long lead times for new construction work (refs 3,4) and the inadequacy of advice offered by the industry (ref 5). As a consequence of this, and the relative lack of complexity in many of the buildings, the adoption of alternative procurement forms, such as design build, has been spearheaded by this sector.

Identification of Need

Whilst conducting the research many clients were interviewed and a good proportion of these admitted that they knew and understood little of the options available to them as far as contract strategy was concerned. Two key facts emerged: clients had little time available to adequately explore and understand the way that the construction industry worked; the majority of clients took their advice from a sole source. This state of affairs led to a consideration of how the would-be client could be educated as to what the construction industry could offer and how advice on the best course of action could be given.

Existing literature, such as client guides produced by the Department of Environment and CIRIA (refs 6,7), was obviously having a limited effect and so a different approach was required. The expert system was chosen as an alternative medium worthy of investigation as a means of advising and educating the client.

The User

The primary user of the system was defined as the prospective building client who has limited knowledge of the construction industry. The user would be at a very early phase in the development of a project with little more than an outline concept of the building that he requires. The user would be drawn from the manufacturing sector of industry, the domain in which the original research was based.

EXPERT SYSTEMS

Expert systems are best referred to at present as knowledge based systems (KBS) as the degree to which they reflect expertise is subject to debate. There are many unresolved fundamental issues to be addressed in the design and construction of such systems, not least of which are those concerning knowledge; its elicitation, representation and formalisation (refs 8,9,10). The issue of whether or not KBS are truly expert is not addressed; Dreyfus (ref 11) with his model of the stages of skill acquisition and Born (ref 12) with his criticism of the nature of conception of artificial intelligence have written copiously on the subject. Suffice it to say that developers of KBS applications must be aware of the debate concerning such matters in describing and propounding their systems. Although, justifiably, some KBS systems have been criticised for a less than rigorous approach to validation it must be borne in mind that they are intended to operate in the real world and, like the experts that they try to mimmick, are not infallible.

The Model

This paper seeks to record experience gained in developing a system and higlight potential problem areas, decisions made and strategies adopted. A fundamental issue to be addressed at the start of any KBS project is the type of advice model required; will it be a problem-solving, decision support or critiqueing system. Each has their own advantages in different situations with different users (ref 13). Problem solving implies scenario evaluation and diagnosis whereas an advisory

system implies scenario generation or planning; a retrospective rather than predictive output. The system described here is a scenario generator and tackles a similar problem to that addressed by Brandon (ref 14) but in a rather different manner. Most applications in the construction management field (by the nature of management) are likely to follow this pattern. BREDAMP, developed by Allwood and Trimble at Loughborough University in conjunction with the BRE, is a notable exception.

DECISIONS

At the inception of a KBS project it is important to define a real problem which exists and which has a client or other body interested in seeing a solution to it. Researchers' whims are not a sound basis for successful development of real world projects and, pertinently, are unlikely to attract funding.

Formulation

The orientation of the system must be determined: there are many views on a particular problem. A clear understanding of who will use the system and what form of advice is required are essential from the outset. In the present example, for instance, the user could be a principal adviser to a building client (and thus have considerable domain expertise), a client (with little knowledge of the building industry) or a contractor's marketing manager (aiming to impress his prospective client). It is highly likely that much of the knowledge base for any of the applications would be common but the means of presenting the system, the explanations and the reasoning would be quite different. Thus an early decision is important.

The source of funding or sponsorship imposes constraints on the development problem. Sponsorship by a research funding body allows exploration of a wider field of investigation with (probably) more time overall to produce results. This allows a more open approach to explore new avenues and prospective solutions to the problem. Work commissioned by a client with a specific need implies more directed research and the need to produce expedient solutions on schedule rather than elegant solutions.

Estimating a budget is problematic in that the length of time required to produce a KBS system is difficult to determine. Many factors complicate the estimation: the choice or availability of hardware and software; the compatibility of these with the problem under investigation; the level of useability required of the final version. There are still few experienced knowledge engineers around so their availability and remuneration levels are imponderables. Under-estimation is highly undesirable as a half-finished system will result in much wasted effort and frustration: determining a balance between what is needed and what the sponsor will fund is not a good strategy - better to underspend or not commence than not complete.

A decision related to the previous comments on funding is the determination of the level of development required of the final system. Basden (ref 8) indicates three levels of development: demonstrator, working and usable status. These imply increasing commitment of resources to achieve their goals and so this decision is crucial in terms of funding and ultimate credibility.

Technical Considerations

Shell selection

Shell selection is an issue that must be addressed at an early stage but one which raises some philosophical issues when applied to projects sponsored by research funding bodies. In such projects the appointed researcher is generally expected to receive a training in research methods and so may be guided rather than directed by the grant holder. Thus, should a decision on the shell to be used be made before the appointment of the researcher or after his appointment when he has had opportunity to submit his own ideas on the efficacy of alternatives? This is a question which is very much dependent on the experience of the grant holder and researcher and the grant holder's preferred style of leadership and supervision. Allwood recommends making the decision at the time of application for funding (ref 15) but in either event it is necessary to have some guidance on the capabilities of various shells and, in this particular application, Allwood again supplied much useful information (ref 16).

Related to the choice of shell is the form of knowledge representation used; the shell effectively determines this. The production rule-based system has been used most frequently in applications to date and has been found to be suitable for many diagnostic applications. These rules can be heuristics or causal, thus expertise and theoretical knowledge can be combined. Basden discusses the pros and cons of causal and heuristic models when discussing SCCES (ref 18). Where inheritance of properties, or "family characteristics", is important then alternative shells incorporating frames (and production rules) are more powerful but, at present, such applications are not well developed and so choice is limited to more expensive software and hardware. Frame based systems may well be of greater use in management applications along with those rule-based shells which offer alternative search strategies and the ability to deal with fuzzy relationships. The reasoning behind this is that management applications recognise a family of possible answers to a problem (rather than discrete solutions), deal with uncertain and incomplete data and often contain hierarchical levels within the problem. It appears that

knowledge engineers prefer to make use of KBS development environments (such as LOOPS and ROSIE) whenever possible as these provide maximum flexibility in choosing an appropriate knowledge representation formalism. The disadvantage of using such systems is that they require expensive, dedicated work-stations and are thus less portable than microcomputer-based systems. In order to develop useable systems economically it appears that, for the present at least, microcomputer-based systems will remain the norm in Construction Management applications. This strategy nevertheless fits in well with the general trend towards the use of IBM compatible systems in office automation by the industry as a whole.

Rules

Rule types are an important consideration in system design; default and priority change rules as well as causal and heuristic rules may be necessary. Default rules allow the system to be utilised when information is missing or unavailable and act so as to mimic the expert's assumptions in building a model of the problem. Such rules need to be carefully explained and allow the user to assess the certitude of the default chosen and change it if he/she sees fit. Such rules, when invoked, should be apparent to the user; too often they are hidden and reduce the system's credibility. Priority change rules deal with incompatibilities between requirements and the way in which a system operates most efficiently, i.e. they explicitly allow sub-optimal solutions. To implement these effectively it may be necessary to use a shell such as Savoir which has a forward-chaining mode.

Domain

Typically, deep and narrow domains have been recommended as suitable for expert system development (refs 8:471,15). The rationale behind this is that a wider domain approaches the areas of common sense and the human ability to take extraneous, real world factors into account, i.e. the context of the situation, a concept beyond the limits of present KBS's. However, management problems are wide in a different sense, they recognise multiple, sub-optimal solutions as existing and thus have both many feasible solutions and paths to these solutions.

Advice

It may seem paradoxical to state that accuracy of results is not an over-riding concern of an expert system: one would expect an expert's advice to be correct. The point about advisory systems however is that they aim to identify all the relevant factors affecting a problem and provide suggested strategies. The success of these strategies depends on the management of the project through to completion, not the initial advice taken. Therefore, by highlighting the relevant variables likely to affect the strategy, by use of how and why explanations, the user may be better prepared for the project in hand.

Critique

Advice strategies may be definitive or multiple but, as a novel departure, they may also be 'critiques'. Langlotz defines a critique as "an explanation of the significant differences between the plan that would have been proposed by the expert system and the plan proposed by the user" (ref 13). The system thus assumes a more passive role and responds to the prior decision of the user. The advantage of such a system is that it generates less user hostility but acts as an effective reminder to the user, performing as an interactive checklist. This approach was not considered during the proposal stage of this project and so not implemented as resources did not allow. Future management KBS's may well benefit from such an approach which incorporates the same knowledge as other systems but interacts with the user in a less threatening manner.

Staffing

The appointment of a researcher to conduct a KBS project is an important area for discussion. In the University environment a main goal, in the past, has been to train the individual in research methods and techniques. Bearing this in mind, allowance has to be made for a more protracted development cycle than in industry-funded projects. The distinction is between directed and directive supervision and makes skill requirements and competences difficult to determine. A graduate of a non-construction discipline can display the ability to challenge the industry's assumptions and thus enhance the knowledge acquisition and formulation process. A construction professional can bring his understanding of the construction process to bear and gather knowledge quickly and efficiently. His intimate knowledge of the domain can help avoid misunderstandings and poor communications (c.f. Tavistock report, ref 18) and it is likely that a relatively recent graduate will have an aptitude for computer programming, a useful if not essential attribute. A computer scientist may produce a working system most efficiently and with an effective interface to the user. A psychologist may extract and formulate the knowledge in the most appropriate manner and build more understanding in depth into the system.

The above propositions indicate that drawing up a person specification for such a post is difficult, the right person may come from any of a number of backgrounds. In general, however, the appointee should have some computing skills (unless provision is made for a programmer to be employed), a research orientation rather than purely production orientation and either a knowledge of the domain or understanding of KBS concepts. These pre-requisites reduce the training/learning process to an acceptable level without demanding too great a specialisation of the researcher. They are based on a philosophy which encourages exploration of new ideas without losing sight of the ultimate goal. Additionally, the ability to meet and interview people is important (experts are often in heavy demand and demanding of others) as is the ability to record data and observations in a methodical manner along with the capacity to deal with new concepts and take an open-minded approach to problems.

STRATEGIES AND PROBLEMS

This section examines the strategies adopted and problems encountered in the production of the KBS.

Rapid Prototype

The knowledge acquisition process involved semi-structured interviews, literature reviews and rapid (or iterative) prototyping. The intention of such an approach is to build a demonstration system as quickly as possible and then critique this system and so successively refine the knowledge base. This can be regarded as "knowledge demolition", an expert or panel of experts reacting to each new version as it is presented to them in order to identify the shortcomings of the system and suggest improvements in advice, reasoning and presentation. The advantage of this is that a tangible result can be seen at an early stage in the project and the nature of most knowledge representation languages suggests that additions and amendments to knowledge bases can be undertaken quite simply. The reality is somewhat different.

A major pitfall is that rapid prototyping may lead to the use of an inappropriate knowledge representation strategy (often determined by the shell chosen) which must be changed on critiqueing the model. This may lead to the need to change shells and so start the process of knowledge representation afresh in a different language, as happened during this project. This creates difficulties for the researcher in that the learning process starts all over again (new software). Even if there is no need to change shells the constant changing, updating and recompilation of knowledge bases becomes irksome and, combined with a change of shell, leads to demoralisation. In order to avoid such problems an alternative shell with facilities for flexible representation strategies could be chosen. More time will be spent in learning to programme with the shell but less frustration will occur in the long run. Another, not inconsiderable, disadvantage of this approach is that it quickly becomes tiresome for the expert if more than a small number of iterations are required.

Shell Use

The main reason for using expert system shells is to facilitate the rapid production of a working system and to aid the learning process concerning KBS concepts and principles. They allow time to be spent on mining and organising knowledge rather than the production of inference engines from scratch. Herein lies one of the problems with using such tools, they act as a strait-jacket on one's thinking and force the researcher to fit his problem to the shell. Whilst this is an interesting discipline it is not the aim of research and thus, a flexible, multi-functional shell is to be preferred in most cases as a development tool. This point is, of course, linked to the original problem of shell selection and other decisions during the formulation phase.

Another problem associated with shells is their often strict and unnatural syntax (compared with, say, Fortran or Basic) which imposes a new and frustrating discipline on the user. Whilst running shells on microcomputers the compilation and checking processes are found to be very slow and the constant checking, rewriting and recompilation are psychologically quite wearing. This aspect is another factor which militates against the use of a rapid prototyping system.

The change from one shell to another, as happened in this project, compounds many of the problems raised above; the learning process, changes and frustrations are more than doubled. An additional aim of the project was to be able to transfer the system from one machine to another (say IBM AT to Apricot Xi) for ease of testing on prospective users. The transfer of uncompiled knowledge bases provided few problems compared with the procedures for actually installing the compilers on different machines. The lack of compatibility here was a minor headache which could have been avoided by the manufacturers with more care taken over their user manuals. These in the main were poor, as with almost all software. Whether this is by design, in order to make introductory courses essential, or not is a matter of conjecture but it is a point that should be addressed by software houses in the future. It is also to be regretted that much software is not supported for use on the Apple Mackintosh which is the leader in the provision of excellent, easy to use facilities for the operator.

Shell Adequacy

Available shells have different facilities to offer the user and one important function missing until recently on many shells is the ability to interface effectively with other software or languages. This becomes particularly important as the size of a knowledge base expands and a need to perform mathematical procedures arises or databases need to be accessed. Such facilities should be recognised at an early phase in the project

development and so used as a guide in selecting a suitable shell. Many shells are unidirectional, locked into a backward-chaining mode and this, although easing their use, restricts the user to a particular type of representation of knowledge. Shells which allow priorities to be assigned to different goals (such as Savoir's firing of actions) and incorporate the ability to chain forwards, backwards and make use of frame concepts are to be preferred.

First Principles

The design strategy adopted in this system was one of going back to first principles, identifying the most important factors affecting procurement, rather than relying on rules generated from empirical study of performance. This approach allows a number of levels of information to be elicited from the user and fitted into a framework which generates user advice. This is then compared with client data and at this stage the empirical data can be compared with the advice offered to generate further advice on how these interact and what managerial actions and monitoring must be undertaken. This design is shown schematically in Fig. 1. The system incorporates an understanding of how the procurement process should operate from a theoretical standpoint and uses empirical rules to indicate where possible problems and conflicts may occur. Thus the process is one of synthesis rather than diagnosis.

OUTCOMES

Testing

The system is being tested with the assistance of experienced project managers but, at the time of writing, no conclusions have been drawn. The system is between demonstration and working status and so the testing process is based around assessment of the "soundness" of the advice and the reasoning process. A system at useable status would be tested for the adequacy of its interface with the user and general acceptability, its validity in terms of advice would already be assured.

Criteria

Notwithstanding the foregoing discussion a number of criteria have been identified as of importance to such a system. They are as follows.

The domain expert should exhaustively test the system to check for the inclusion of all variables that he considers to be relevant to the problem. This may be undertaken at the working status level. At the same time the appropriateness of the advice given, in all circumstances, can be reviewed.

At the working phase the clarity of displayed questions and advice and clarity and adequacy of explanations can be assessed, preferably by

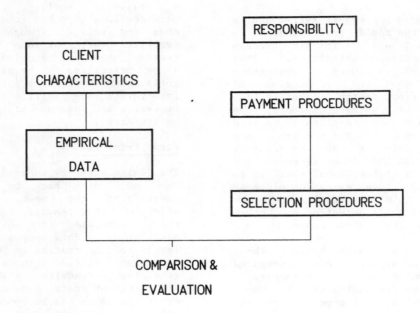

Fig 1: Design Strategy

the end user who has most need of these facilities. The domain expert's input is, of course, still necessary to ensure consistency and accuracy of any proposed changes. During this phase likely user reactions can be assessed, these provide the acid test of whether or not a system has reached useable status.

Features

The knowledge base has been developed from theoretical considerations, to improve its general applicability but heuristic knowledge, based on empirical findings has been included. Default rules have been included to model expertise in making assumptions in order to build up a feasible model of the problem. Much thought has gone into developing a coherent explanation facility which will at once be both comprehensible and comprehensive.

DEVELOPMENT SCENARIO

For future developments a scenario can be generated which indicates the factors which to a great part determine the feasibility or otherwise of a proposed project. This scenario includes the following elements.

1   A client interest and sponsor is essential if the project is to proceed in terms of financial and practical viability. Demonstrator projects in construction management have little merit as research tasks.

2   Extensive pre-planning and in-depth consideration of possible solutions is required before a comprehensive proposal can be drafted. This requires èither some previous experience on the part of the proposer or extensive

consultations with established workers in the field if this is to be effective.

3   A clear definition of the training needs of the researcher is required to determine the most appropriate development strategy. This will be dependent on the type of funding in prospect (research funding body or industry sponsorship) and will have a significant effect on the expected overall duration of the project. A decision here is dependent on the goals of the sponsor and proposer.

4   Choice of an appropriate shell is crucial and cannot proceed without due consideration of points 2 and 3.

5   Allocation of resources should be generous in order to enable in-depth investigation of the system to be produced. In a relatively new field of development, with only tentatively established procedures, scope must be allowed for more basic research and investigation to be undertaken as part of the project.

CONCLUSIONS

A KBS has been developed to working/demonstration level but problems have been encountered in the production process. The source of these problems can be traced to a lack of clarity in strategy concerning some aspects and the absence of commonly accepted methodolgies at present in other areas.

Lack of experience in knowledge elicitation and formulation methodologies, compounded by the lack of published case studies in this area with tangible examples, caused time to be lost during the project. The development and use of a rapid prototyping strategy did not prove as effective as anticipated for this particularly complex, and somewhat controversial, application.

Delays were further compounded by the late realisation of the constraints imposed by using an inappropriate shell. The change to a more sophisticated shell at a later date allowed greater flexibility in knowledge representation but this hampered the researcher by forcing him to learn to programme in a different "language" at a time when testing of the prototype should have been well advanced. The choice of shell is crucial to a successful project but the problem of fitting knowledge to a particular representation will always remain whilst shells are used. The constant flow of new, more sophisticated shells onto the market will provide researchers with continually greater flexibility but the choice of shell wil, of course, become more difficult.

In retrospect the time scheduled for completion of the project (12 man-months) was over-optimistic but the shell choice was a mitigating factor here. If exploration of alternative advice strategies and representations needs to be undertaken then the schedule allowed should be generous.

Despite and because of the preceding comments the project has been successful in that:

i   a working system has been produced
ii   an understanding of the demands of knowledge acquisiton and representation has been developed
iii a scenario has been generated for use in considering future developments.

REFERENCES

(1) NEDO, Faster Building for Industry, 1983, London
(2) Rowlinson, S.M., The Influence of Procurement Form on Project Performance, Proc. of 10th CIB Congress, Sept 1986, Washington
(3) Mobbs, G.N., Industrial Investment - A Case Study in Factory Building, 1976, Slough
(4) Cranfield School of Management, Industrial Decision Making in Britain, Financial Times, 1979, London
(5) NEDO, Construction for Industrial Recovery, 1978, London
(6) NEDO, The United Kingdom Construction Industry, 1982, London
(7) CIRIA, Client Guides SP15, SP29, SP33, 1985, 1983, 1984, CIRIA Publications, London
(8) Attarwala, F.T. & Basden, A., A Methodology for Constructing Expert Systems, R & D Mgt., 1985, 15, 141-149
(9) Jansen, J.J. & Puttgen, H.B., ASDEP, An Expert System for Electric Power Plant Design, IEEE Expert, Spring 1987, 56-66
(10) Hayes-Roth, F., Klahr, P. & Mostow, D.J., Knowledge Acquisition, Knowledge Programming and Knowledge Refinement, in Expert Systems (ed. Klahr & Waterman), 1986, Addison-Wesley
(11) Dreyfus, H. & Dreyfus, S., Why Expert Systems do not Exhibit Expertise, IEEE Expert, Summer 1986, 86-90
(12) Born, R., Introduction to Artificial Intelligence - The Case Against, 1987, Croom-Helm
(13) Langlotz, C.P. & Shortliffe, E.H., Adapting a Consultation System to Critique User Plans, Int J Man-Machine Studies, 1983, 19, 479-496
(14) Brandon, P.S., Expert Systems in Construction Management and Economics, Proc Int Symp on Economics & Mgt., May 1987, Shanghai, 236-246
(15) Allwood, R.J., Report of the Working Group of 1986 on Expert Systems in the Construction and Transport Industries, 1986, Science and Engineering Research Council, Swindon
(16) Allwood, R.J., et al, Report on Evaluation of Expert System Shells for Construction Industry Application, 1985, University of Technology, Loughborough
(17) Higgin, G. & Jessop, N., Communications in the Building Industry, 1965, Tavistock Institute, London
(18) Basden, A., On the Application of Expert Systems, Int J Man-Machine Studies, 1983, 19, 461-477

APPROACHES TO FORTRAN-PROLOG INTERFACING FOR AN EXPERT SYSTEM ENVIRONMENT

B Kumar*, P W H Chung† and B H V Topping*
*Department of Civil Engineering
†Artificial Intelligence Applications Institute
University of Edinburgh, Scotland

An integrated knowledge-based expert system (KBES) for structural design in civil engineering could comprise of modules reponsible for the preliminary design, structural analysis and detailed design. FORTRAN has long been extensively used for the structural analysis programs. On the other hand, PROLOG has emerged as an important language in Artificial Intelligence and has been successfully used for developing KBESs and, thus, becomes an obvious choice for writing systems for preliminary design, which are mainly based on heuristics and approximate analysis. Consequently, a need arises for an interface between FORTRAN and PROLOG in the development of such an integrated system. This paper briefly describes and compares two approaches to the implementation of such an interface in a rule-based system for the design of industrial buildings, INDEX. INDEX is currently under development at the University of Edinburgh. It has a black-board architecture and comprises of ten knowledge modules. It is written in Edinburgh PROLOG and The Edinburgh PROLOG Blackboard Shell syntax. The relevant structural analysis programs are written in FORTRAN 77 and, thus, the need for the interface.

1. Introduction

This paper describes two approaches to the development of an interface between PROLOG and FORTRAN in an expert system environment. These are :

1. The File Approach and

2. The C Interface Approach.

FORTRAN has been predominantly used for writing structural analysis programs for a decade or more. However, engineers have recently been exploring ways to utilise more advanced computing methods such as Artificial Intelligence techniques. In the past, considerable investment has been made in the development of FORTRAN programs and it is unlikely that it would be possible or desirable to rewrite existing programs in Artificial Intelligence languages (e.g. PROLOG, LISP etc.). Structural engineers who wish to retain their investment in FORTRAN programs and at the same time utilise the latest advances in computer software and hardware are faced with the problem of interfacing the various computer languages, graphics and other facilities.

This paper describes a design and implementation of the C interface approach and compares it with the file approach. These approaches are being explored to be used in the development of an expert system for the design of industrial buildings, INDEX. A description of the design and implementation of INDEX may be found elsewhere [3]. INDEX is an integrated expert system, in which the structural analysis programs used are written in FORTRAN 77 and the remainder of the knowledge base comprising of heuristics and other domain rules are written using Edinburgh PROLOG [1] and the Edinburgh PROLOG Blackboard Shell [2] syntax. The shell itself is also written in Edinburgh PROLOG. INDEX is being implemented on a Sun 3/50 workstation using the UNIX operating system.

2. The Environment

INDEX is an expert system for the design of industrial buildings [3]. It has a blackboard architecture and the knowledge base is partitioned into different modules called knowledge modules (KMs) surrounding the central blackboard (see figure 1). One of these KMs, ALTSEL, is responsible for the preliminary design of the building. The input to this module is the initial data given by the user and consists of the grid plan of the building fixed during the architectural planning stage. The estimated loads also have to be input at the same time. A separate module for assessing and advising on the design loads on the building remains to be developed . The horizontal loads are ignored in the preliminary design stage. The outputs from this module are the following :

1. The feasible lateral load resisting frames, e.g, single or multi-span portal frames, truss and columns arrangements etc.

2. An indication of economic frame spacings.

3. Feasible alternatives of the types of purlins and roof system.

4. Alternatives of roof and side claddings.

5. An indication of the most economical lateral load resisting frame alternative out of the feasible ones.

6. A preliminary analysis of all the feasible alternatives of lateral load resisting systems.

7. A preliminary proportioning and sizing of the feasible alternatives.

8. A preliminary relative evaluation of the feasible alternatives.

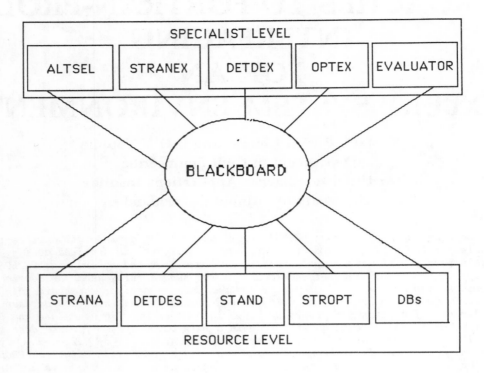

Schematic Model of INDEX

Figure 1

At this stage, another module STRANEX is invoked which decides about the particular analysis routine to be used in different cases. The analysis routines that INDEX may call are :

1. Elastic analysis for trusses,

2. Elastic analysis for rigid–jointed plane frames and

3. Plastic analysis of plane frames.

It is at this stage that one of these programs is invoked. The inputs coming from the ALTSEL module have to be fed directly to the FORTRAN program and, thus, the need for an interface between ALTSEL and the analysis routine. Thus, an interface between the Edinburgh PROLOG and FORTRAN 77 is required (see figure 2).

3. The Interface

Two interfacing approaches were explored as discussed below.

The file approach – this is a simple way of developing an interface. In this approach, the knowledge-based component and FORTRAN communicate via files. Some implementations of PROLOG (e.g., Quintus-PROLOG, Edinburgh PROLOG and C-PROLOG) allow for calling the operating system and executing any system command from PROLOG. This facility is the key to this method. The knowledge-based component stores all the input data for the FORTRAN program in a file. The FORTRAN program is invoked by a system call from PROLOG. Similarly, the FORTRAN program stores its

output on a file which is read from PROLOG. This approach is quite straightforward. However, it does not provide a fully integrated environment.

The C interface approach – with this approach, the communication between PROLOG and FORTRAN is through C functions as the intermediary. Some implementations of PROLOG (e.g., Quintus-PROLOG, Edinburgh PROLOG) allow for loading of pre-compiled object codes. On the other hand, the Berkley Unix implementation of FORTRAN provides for calling pre-compiled FORTRAN function from C and vice-versa. Thus, the strategy adopted for INDEX [3] was to call C from PROLOG and then FORTRAN from C . To accomplish this, both the C and FORTRAN functions are compiled and linked together in one file. This linked file is, then, loaded in Edinburgh PROLOG. Since the compiled FORTRAN and C functions are linked together, both share common data storage (see figure 3). Thus, FORTRAN functions have direct access to any data passed from PROLOG to C. Similarly, any output data from FORTRAN is directly accessed and sent to PROLOG by C.

Pre-compiled codes may be loaded in Edinburgh PROLOG [1] by the load/3 predicate, where 3 stands for the number of its arguments, as given below :

load(ListofPredSpec,ObjectFiles,Libraries).

A simple example for loading pre-compiled C functions is :

load([pred/1=cfunc1, pred/2=cfunc2],'tmp.o','-lm -termcap').

The first argument *ListofPredSpec* is a list of predicate specifications, each of which specifies a PROLOG predicate and its arity that is to be associated with a C

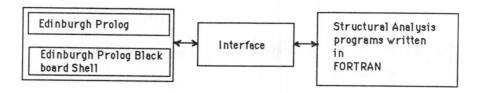

The Environment

Figure 2

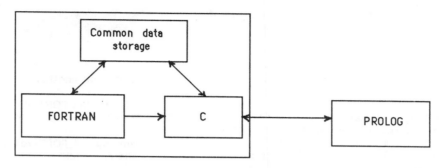

The Interface

Figure 3

function. In the example given above two C functions *cfunc1* and *cfunc2* are to be loaded. These functions are to be called from PROLOG by pred/1 and pred/2 respectively.

In the present version, only simple data types, i.e., integers, floats and atoms, may be passed between C and PROLOG. There are three C functions provided for the C code to access the arguments passed to it from PROLOG. They are :

getint(),getfloat() and getatom()

Another three C functions are provided for the C code to pass back the values to PROLOG. They are :

putint(), putfloat() and putatom()

A brief description of these functions [1] is as follows :

getint(ArgNo, AddrOfInt) – *ArgNo* is a positive integer specifying which PROLOG argument is to be accessed. *AddrOfInt* is the address of a C integer variable. getint(ArgNo,AddrOfInt) assigns the value of the *ArgNo*th argument of the PROLOG call to the *AddrOfInt* variable and returns the value 1. If the corresponding PROLOG argument is not an integer the assignment operation is skipped and the function returns the value 0.

getfloat(ArgNo,AddrOfFloat) - This function is similar to getint(), but is used for accessing floating point numbers rather than integers. *AddrOfFloat* should be the address of a C variable declared as double.

getatom(ArgNo,AddrOfPointerToString) – This function is for accessing a PROLOG atom. The meaning of ArgNo is the same as for getint() and getfloat(). *AddrOfPointerToString* should be the address of a pointer to a string of characters. The function makes the string pointer point to a string of characters representing the PROLOG atom. If the specified

argument is not an atom, the function returns the value 0.

putint(ArgNo,IntValue) – *ArgNo* is a positive integer specifying which argument in PROLOG is to be unified with the integer value *IntValue*. If the unification succeeds the function returns the value 1, otherwise the value 0.

putfloat(ArgNo, FloatValue) – This is similar to putint() except that it is used for floating point numbers.

putatom(ArgNo,PointerToString) – This function is similar to putint() except that the second argument should be a pointer to a string. This function creates a PROLOG atom from the string and unifies it with the specified argument. If the unification succeeds the function returns the value 1, otherwise the value 0.

3.1 Accessing arrays

The communication of simple variables does not prove any problem but accessing arrays requires further consideration. The arrays are represented as lists in PROLOG. One-dimensional arrays are represented as single lists whereas multi-dimensional ones are represented as lists containing sub-lists as shown in figure 4. Each sub-list in figure 4 represents a row of the equivalent C two-dimensional array. The array that is passed back from C is also a list consisting of sub-lists. The methods of accessing these arrays in the two methods of interfacing are described below.

The file approach – The elements of the lists representing the arrays in PROLOG are written to a file which is then read by the FORTRAN program. The FORTRAN program writes its output on a file. The output arrays are then read and formed into lists by PROLOG. Each element of the arrays is passed back to PROLOG one by one and the corresponding list keeps

$$[A] = \begin{bmatrix} A11 & A12 & A13 \\ A21 & A22 & A23 \\ A31 & A32 & A33 \end{bmatrix} \Rightarrow \begin{bmatrix} [A11,A12,A13], [A21,A22,A23], [A31,A32,A33] \end{bmatrix}$$

Representation of Arrays in PROLOG

Figure 4

getting constructed in PROLOG using a simple PROLOG procedure .

The C interface approach – The elements of the lists representing the arrays in PROLOG are passed one by one recursively to FORTRAN via C. Similarly, the elements of the output arrays from FORTRAN are passed back one by one and the corresponding list gets constructed recursively in PROLOG .

Considering the mapping of arrays between C and FORTRAN, the most important requirement is that the dimensions of the arrays have to be altered. This is because FORTRAN 77 arrays are stored in column-major order whereas C arrays are stored in row-major order. Thus, the column dimension of a FORTRAN 77 array will become the row dimension of the equivalent C array and the row dimension of FORTRAN 77 array will become the column dimension of the equivalent C array. For example, an array A(3,2) in FORTRAN will have to be represented as A[2][3] in C and will be the transpose of the actual array required in FORTRAN. Another important point is that the first element of a C array always has a subscript zero whereas FORTRAN 77 array elements always begin with a subscript of one.

3.2 Performance measurement

An ideal performance measurement for our purposes would have been to compare the cpu times taken in running an analysis program written in PROLOG and a similar program written in FORTRAN using the interface. Such a test would have ascertained whether rewriting the analysis program in PROLOG was worthwhile or not. If a PROLOG program ran faster than the FORTRAN one running with either of the two methods of interfacing, it would be worthwhile to rewrite the FORTRAN programs in PROLOG. But, such a decision would mean losing all the investment made in writing FORTRAN programs and making new investments in rewriting the same programs in PROLOG. This is a crucial decision as rewriting the programs in PROLOG would need quite a lot of effort and time, which might not be desirable. It can be very safely said that a PROLOG program to perform the analysis would be slower than an equivalent FORTRAN program. In general, PROLOG is slow in performing numerical operations. Here, an evaluation of the performance of the two approaches is presented by comparing the times in running a FORTRAN structural analysis program in the following different ways:

1. running the FORTRAN program without any interface, i.e., reading the data directly from a file and writing the

output on another file,

2. running the FORTRAN program using the 'C interface approach' and

3. running the FORTRAN program using the 'file approach'.

These tests were carried out using the same set of data. The test structure and loads are given in figure 5. This gives an indication of relative overheads of using the two approaches to interfacing.

The results of these tests are given in table 1. It is clear from these results that the C interface approach is faster than the file approach. It is very marginally slower than the FORTRAN program running by itself without using any interface. On the other hand, the file approach is considerably slower. Since the computing time for analysis is the same in both cases, the time difference between the two approaches is equal to the difference in time taken by each in transferring the arrays and other data between FORTRAN and PROLOG.

To obtain some idea of the time spent in passing and returning arrays of different sizes by each approach, another test was undertaken. The results of these tests are shown in table 2. These results explain the results shown in table 1. Table 2 actually gives an indication of the relative overheads involved in using the two methods of interfacing.

Based on the results of tables 1 and 2, it is clear that the C interface approach is almost three to four times faster than the file approach, on an average. However, for the test problem tried, the difference was only around 25 centiseconds on an average. Thus, it may be concluded that the choice between the two approaches will become crucial only when the number and sizes of the arrays to be used by the FORTRAN program are quite large. For example, if a program uses 100 arrays of 1000 elements each, the difference in time in just passing these arrays would be almost 7 minutes. Although, this difference would not be significant for a program that runs for hours, it is quite considerable. On the other hand, for graphics and other user interface facilities, time is of utmost importance and the obvious choice in that case would be the faster approach even if the time difference is minimal.

3.3 Merits and Disadvantages of both the approaches

The C interface approach – one of the most important limitations of this approach is that the FORTRAN program cannot be used straightaway as it is originally written. Minor modifications have to be made to it in

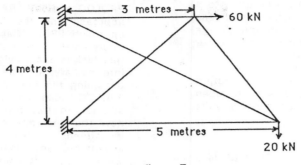

figure 5

Test No.	Test Description	Average cpu time of three runs (in centiseconds)
1.	the FORTRAN program running without any interface	10
2.	the FORTRAN program running using the C interface approach	13
3.	the FORTRAN program running using the file approach interface	35

Table 1

Array size	Average cpu time of three runs (in centiseconds)	
	The C interface approach	The file approach
10 x 10	15	69
25 x 10	38	165
30 x 10	45	205
50 x 10	74	336
100 x 10	146	675

Table 2

order to load them in PROLOG. They are as follows:

1. to change the FORTRAN program into a function/subroutine, which means removing the main program and change it into a function which calls other functions/subroutines and

2. to remove of the input and output statements since it is difficult to open input/output channels in FORTRAN while inside PROLOG.

These changes did not prove too difficult to us since the routines were written by ourselves (Kumar and Topping) only. However, there could be problems on this account while using a commercial package due to the source being inaccessible to the user. This could be seen as a serious limitation of this interface.

In terms of speed, the above-mentioned results clearly show that it is faster than the file approach. Another merit of this approach is that it provides us with a fully integrated environment in the sense that all the components, i.e., PROLOG and FORTRAN, of the expert system are interlinked and the whole system behaves as one single unit.

The file approach – this method does not require any modifications to be made to the FORTRAN program . However, in terms of speed, this approach is considerably slower. Another important disadvantage of this method is that it does not provide a fully integrated environment.

4. Conclusions

Two approaches to interfacing between the Edinburgh PROLOG and FORTRAN 77 were described, viz., the file approach and the C interface approach. In the file approach, PROLOG and FORTRAN communicate through intermediate files whereas in the C interface approach, this task is accomplished by having C functions as the intermediary. It was felt that the main obstacle in designing the interface was accessing arrays because PROLOG does not have an array data structure. A solution to this problem was suggested. In practice, new routines may be written in PROLOG unless the investment in rewriting is likely to be large. The advantages and disadvantages of the two approaches were also discussed. The interface approaches discussed in this paper provide a route for software developers to utilise existing FORTRAN coding in Expert Systems applications without the expense of rewriting FORTRAN codes in PROLOG.

References

(1) Artificial Intelligence Applications Institute, University of Edinburgh, "Edinburgh PROLOG (The New Implementation) User's Manual, Version 1.4", 1986.

(2) Jones, J. and Millington, M, " An Edinburgh PROLOG Blackboard Shell", Department of Artificial Intelligence, University of Edinburgh, 1986.

(3) Kumar, B., Chung, P.W.H., Rae, R.H., Topping, B.H.V., "A Knowledge-Based Approach to Structural Design", presented at Civil-Comp '87.

KNOWLEDGE ELICITATION METHODS : A CASE-STUDY IN STRUCTURAL DESIGN

Paul Wai Hing Chung* and Bimal Kumar†
*Artificial Intelligence Applications Institute
†Department of Civil Engineering
University of Edinburgh, Scotland

This paper first describes a framework for knowledge elicitation, followed by some specific techniques. Each of these methods is designed to elicit a particular type of knowledge. To gain a fuller picture of the issues involved in knowledge elicitation a case study in the civil engineering domain is considered.

1. Introduction

The construction of an expert system is an attempt to embody the knowledge of a particular expert within a computer program. The knowledge used in solving problems must be elicited from the expert so that it can be acquired by the expert system. It is recognised that the elicitation of knowledge from the experts is one of the major bottlenecks in the construction of expert systems. The main reason for this, in many cases, is that experts find it hard to articulate and make explicit the knowledge they possess and use. An important part of a knowledge enginner's job is to help the expert to structure the domain knowledge and to identify and formalize the domain concepts. Although a number of knowledge elicitation methods or techniques do exist (Welbank, 1983), the area is not well understood and few tools exist to mechanise the process.

This paper aims to provide a simple model of knowledge elicitation for those wishing to build an expert system. In the following, we will first describe a framework for knowledge elicitation, followed by some specific techniques. Finally, a case study in building a system for use by civil engineers is used to highlight some of the practical issues.

2. A Framework For Knowledge Elicitation

The framework is based on three generally accepted ideas:

1. there are different types of knowledge

2. there are different knowledge elicitation methods for different types of knowledge

3. the knowledge elicitation process can be divided into sub stages.

There is no doubt that there are different types of knowledge, even in a single domain of expertise. However, it is not clear how knowledge should be classified into different types. "Finding a way to taxonomise knowledge on a principled basis is a difficult and ambitious task that has eluded philosophers for thousands of years" (Gammack and Young, 1985). For the practical purpose of building

expert systems, knowledge can be conveniently divided into three types: facts, conceptual structures and rules. Facts are simply a glossary of terms and a list of domain entities. In an engineering domain, this type of knowledge may be a collection of engineering concepts and the names of the components of a particular structure or plant. The second type of knowledge, conceptual structures, decribes the relationships between identified concepts and components. Finally, rules are the reasoning part of the domain knowledge. Facts and conceptual structures are reasonably static and are easier to elicit than rules. Figure 1 illustrates a simple but a natural sequence of knowledge elicitation process.

In each part of the cycle, a suitable elicitation technique should be used. Some studies have been carried out to match techniques with types of knowledge (for example see Gammack and Young, 1985; Welbank, 1987). In the next section, for each type of knowledge, a knowledge elicitation technique that has been identified as particularly suitable has been described.

3. Techniques

There are two classes of techniques for knowledge elicitation. The first class is psychological technique which involves some kind of interaction between the knowledge engineer (KE) and the domain expert (DE). The second class is machine induction, in which the computer induces rules from examples automatically. For a domain like structural design, machine induction is inadequate. Bloomfield (1987) developed a set of criteria for selecting domains suitable for the elicitation of knowledge by machine induction. One such criterion is that "any chosen doamin must contain sufficient examples that it is possible to construct a training set which constitutes a comprehensive encapsulation of expertise in that domain". Structural design expertise cannot be completely encapsulated in examples. Hence, only psychological techniques are considered.

3.1 Interviews

Direct interviewing is the technique most familiar to KEs and DEs. It is good to start the knowledge elicitation process using a technique that the DE feels comfortable with. An interview may range from an informal chat to a highly structured discussion. Nancy Johnson has developed some interesting openers for an interview

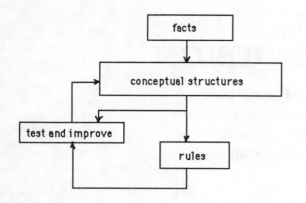

Figure 1

Source	Number of rules
Design Engineer	35
Literature	53
Other Sources	22

Figure 3

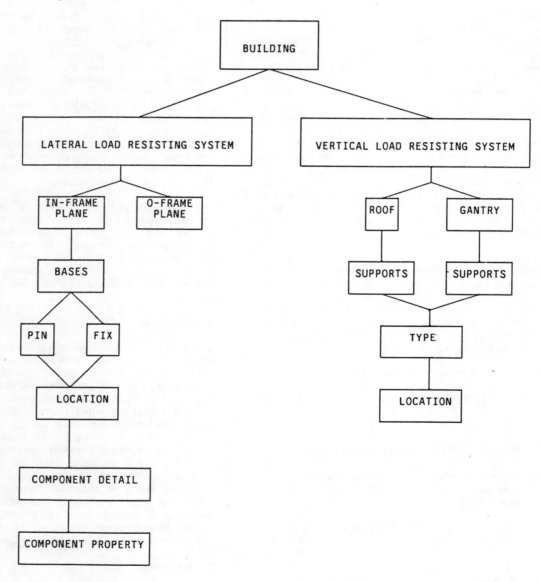

Figure 2

– if you had a good new graduate just starting to work for you what would you expect him to have learnt after six months ?

– You find a book on your application area which turns out to be the book you wish you had started in the field. What chapter headings are in it ?

Using this technique, a lot of information about the terminology and the main components of the domain can be generated in a relatively straightforward way. The problem is how to probe further so that ideas may be pursued to a greater depth. To ensure that an interview is productive, the KE should have a set of good questions prepared beforehand to help him direct the discussion. Instead of just open questions he needs to have some clear and specific ones. The DE could also be asked to prepare and deliver an introductory lecture.

3.2 Concept Sorting

Experts use a specialist knowledge to solve problems; they are likely to have a global perspective on how a domain is organised. Concept sorting is appropriate where there is a large set of concepts which need to be organised into a manageable form. The basic procedure is similar to the categorical knowledge elicitation technnique described by Regan (1987):

1. collect a set of concepts in the domain. This can be obtained from the literature or from an introductory talk or from the DE;

2. write each concept on a small card;

3. ask DE to sort the cards into groups;

4. ask DE to label each group;

5. discuss with DE about each group to find out its characteristics;

6. ask DE to specify the relationship between the groups and to organise them into a hierarchy.

3.3 Protocol analysis

In this technique, the DE's behaviour is recorded (either video or audio) as they work through a problem or task, and the protocol is transcribed and analysed. In this way, the KE is given not only the answer to the problem but also the information about the problem solving process itself. In practice this technique is found to be very helpful. Though DEs may have difficulty in stating the general rules that they use, they can ussually identify the specific rules that they are applying. However, it is easy for familiar ideas to be taken for granted, so they need to be kept aware of any tendencies towards omitting 'trivial' details. For this technique to be effective a representative set of problems has to be chosen, otherwise there could be serious errors of ommission.

There are three different ways of generating protocols:

– think-aloud protocols – the DE thinks aloud during the solving of a problem;

– retrospective verbalization – the DE completely solves a problem before reporting how it was solved;

– discussion protocols – a small number of DEs discuss with one another as they attempt to solve a problem.

These variations each have their own advantages and disadvantages. An important problem with think-aloud protocols is that the reporting may interfere with the DE's task performance. Related to this is any need to conform to real time constraints. For example, solving a maths problem allows the mathematician to stop and ponder. However, an operator dealing with an emergency may require immediate responses. These criteria may help when having to decide between think-aloud protocols and retrospective verbalization.

Expert system projects are often based on collboration with a single DE. In fact most of the literature would recommend this (for example see Hayes-Roth et al 1983). However, discussion protocols are helpful because they provide different perspectives on how a problem may be solved by clarifying alternatives and resolving conflicts. The problem here is that of managing the discussion. Avoiding the problem, the strategy that Mittal and Dym (1985) adopted was to interview one DE at a time. Although this technique worked for them, it provides very little opportunity for the DEs to interact with one another and to discuss issues.

A potentially useful computer tool for collaborative problem-solving in face-to-face meetings is Colab, which has been created at Xerox Parc (Stefik et al, 1986). This project advocates the use of computers rather than a passive medium like chalkboards in meetings. The idea is that in the meeting room each person has a keyboard and mouse on his table and there is a very large screen in the front of the room. Each person can retrieve information from the computer and can easily write and draw to the screen by using the keyboard and mouse in front of him. In this mode of working a meeting can be dynamic and interactive, and at the same time all the text and sketches that have been generated in the meeting are automatically stored on the computer. The abundance of information is conveniently accessible for analysis when needed.

3.4 Rapid Prototyping

The most obvious technique for testing and improving an expert system is rapid prototyping. The DE is confronted with the behaviour of an unfinished version of the system which is modified in the light of his and her comments. Each iteration brings the behaviour of the system closer to completion although, since it is often carried out without a clearly defined notion of completion, it is perhaps better thought of as iteration towards adequate achievement.

3.5 Summary

These are just some of the techniques that have been identified as useful. They should be viewed as complemetary rather than competitive with one another because different techniques can be used to capture different types of knowledge more effectively. Interviews are good for gaining an overall view of the domain; concept sorting is good for structuring the domain; and protocol analysis is good for collecting rules. The main point is that the KE needs to be aware that there are different techniques that can be applied. Their usefulness also depends very much on individual KEs at present; factors such as KE's knowledge of the problem domain and how well they get on with the DE matter a lot.

From the description of different techniques, it should also be clear that feedback plays a very important role in knowledge elicitation. It is highly unlikely that a DE can impart all relevant knowledge at one meeting even if the domain is extremely simple. The question is then *What form of feedback should be provided?* An obvious but important comment is that what is fed back should be familiar to the DE so it can easily be understood and commented upon.

4. Case Study

This case study shows, in a limited way, the relevance of these different techniques in practice and also shows how a DE's attitude was changed through useful feedback and steady progress.

4.1 Project Description

The KE was a Ph.D. student whose project was to design and implement a knowledge-based system for designing industrial buildings. This system would take a design specification and automatically generate a design for the structures for the building (Kumar et al, 1987).

The process of designing industrial buildings may be divided into three stages:

1. Preliminary Design: functional requirements and constraints are synthesised into a preliminary concept. This involves selecting a potential structural configuration which satisfies layout and spatial constraints and carrying out an approximate analysis evaluating its response.

2. Detailed Design: having chosen a structural configuration, it must be detailed by

   a. performing a structural analysis;

   b. proportioning the structutal members;

   c. checking applicable design constraints.

3. Preparation of Design Documents: once a suitable design has been formulated it has to be properly documented.

This project was limited to only the first two stages.

The KE was in a very advantageous position; not only did he know the basic terminology of structural design, he had a Bachelor's and a Master's degree in civil engineering himself. To prepare himself he read literature related to artificial intelligence in civil engineering, to expert systems in general and to knowledge representation. He also developed a rule based system for checking whether designs conformed to the British standards. For this task the expert knowledge was contained in the British Standard Code, so (virtually) all he had needed to do was to translate the relevant clauses into rule form. Armed with this knowledge and experience he then felt confident to meet with DEs.

4.2 Meeting the Experts

The KE contacted a consultancy company which specializes in designing industrial buildings. To date, four meetings have taken place, with each lasting approximately three hours. The following is a short commentary on what happened during these four meetings.

4.2.1 First Meeting

At this meeting the KE met the DE, a design engineer with many years of experience. The DE knew that he had expertise and was sceptical that a computer could perform the same function. So, throughout this meeting, the KE tried to convince the DE by describing to him how expert systems work and showing him the listing and runs of the design checker. The DE remained unconvinced. He had two basic doubts:

1. How could a computer reason except through obeying instructions?

2. Every design is different; how could a single set of rules apply to all designs?

The KE left the meeting frustrated and discouraged. Nonetheless, they agreed to have a second meeting two weeks later.

4.2.2 Second Meeting

At this meeting, there were three DEs: the previous design engineer, another design engineer and an expert in computer aided design. The first part of the meeting was very much the same as the previous one with the KE trying to convince the DEs that expert system technology was workable.

However, this time the KE had a copy of a diagram with him that illustrated a hierarchical abstraction of the structure of a building. The diagram (see figure 2) is a simplified version of another diagram that the KE had found in the literature. The original abstraction diagram was developed by Sriram (1986) for his work on a knowledge-based system for designing buildings. He showed this to the DEs who immediately identified that this reflected how they carried out design. In other words, the diagram helped the DEs to conceptualise their own thinking preoceses and relate them to those of an expert system.

Some time later the KE was left with the second design engineer to work through a design problem that he had recently solved. The DE was quite happy to explain how he had made certain decisions when he was asked the question *"Why?"*. The DE also pointed out some literature that practicing engineers read.

From the informal protocol collected the KE was able to produce ten rules. More importantly, the KE realised that the preliminary design could be broken down into four sub-stages:

1. Preliminary synthesis;

2. preliminary analysis;

3. preliminary design;

4. preliminary evaluation.

With this decomposition in mind, the KE was able to identify and glean more rules from the literature that he had read. The KE then built a prototype that took a specification as input and produced alternative feasible structural configurations as output, alongwith a recommendation of which of these alternatives was most favourable for further analysis and detailed design.

4.2.3 Third Meeting

This meeting took place a month after the previous one. When the DE saw the runs and rules of the system, he was very surprised by the progress that had been made. He spent most of the time in this session commenting on the rules.

After this session the KE was able to refine his rule-set and try the system on other problems that he had collected from literature.

4.2.4 Fourth Meeting

At this meeting the DE introduced three new problems and described to the KE how he had solved them.

To date, the knowledge-base already has over a hundred rules. The table in figure 3 gives a break down of the sources of the rules.

4.3 Discussion and Conclusion

In this case study the KE was in a rather fortunate position because he was already familiar with the domain. He did not have to go through the initial phase of gathering the general information about the domain by interviewing the DEs. Our estimate is that this initial phase would take at least three to six months. However, he had the problem of trying to gain the co-operation of the DEs. The conventional wisdom in knowledge elicitation is that the KE should choose for himself a willing informant. This sound advice could not be heeded in this case. The KE did not have many choices, due to geographical and other constraints. In tackling the problem of gaining the DE's co-operation he made the mistake of trying to gain their confidence by explaining to them how expert systems work. It seems that DEs are unlikely to convinced by this approach. Instead, the KE should concentrate on helping them to reflect on their own thinking processes. In this case the abstraction diagram helped a great deal beacuse it helped them to conceptualize their own thinking processes. This is a good example of how one KE had benefitted directly from the work of another KE. The process of knowledge elicitation begins well before the KE meets the DE. All information gathered from other sources, such as reading, should be retained as potentially valuable.

Although a KE might not always be able to find or generate a relevant diagram by himself, he should be able to produce one with the assistance of the DE. The concept sorting procedure (described in section 3.2) is a good bottom-up technique to use. Any diagram during the knowledge elicitation phase can form useful documentation of the system.

Protocol analysis, or more precisely, studying case histories, was found to be a verry useful way of generating rules. However, it is interesting to note that only a third of the rules were gleaned directly from the DE (see figure 3). Following through the information provided by the DE as to where to look for further or more detailed information yielded much dividend.

The KE found decomposing the problem, especially the preliminary design part into sub-problems at an early stage was an extremely important step in formalising the domain knowledge. Once the problem was decomposed it not only helped the DE to recall and provide the relevant pieces of information it also helped the KE to pick out relevant material from other sources. From the system construction point of view it was also very helpful because the knowledge base could then be divided into smaller modules making them easier to maintain.

The DE was surprised and impressed by the result of prototyping. It is definitely a very useful way for getting feedback from the DE. In this case it was a shame that due to geographical constraints the DE did not see the prototype running but could only comment on the output of the program.

When using prototyping as a technique for getting feedback the KE found it necessary to guard against letting the documentation slip. It is easy to get into the habit of making quick changes to the system without keeping a record of the changes made, thus making the system difficult to modify and maintain in the future.

Acknowledgments

The work described in this paper is part of a collaborative project being undertaken by the Department of Civil Engineering and Artificial Intelligence Applications Institute, University of Edinburgh. Paul Chung is supported by SERC Grant number SO/824/86. Bimal Kumar is supported by an Edinburgh University Postgraduate Studentship. Diana Bental and Robert Rae provided helpful comments on a draft of this paper.

References

Bloomfield, B.P. (1986) *Capturing Expertise by Rule Induction.* The Knowledge Engineering Review, Vol 1, No. 4.

Gammack, J.G. and Young, R.M. (1985) *Psychology Techniques for Eliciting Expert Knowledge.* In **Research and Development in Expert Systems**, Bramer, M.A. (Ed.). Cambridge University Press.

Hayes-Roth, F., Waterman, D.A. and Lenat, D.B. (Eds.) (1983) *Building Expert Systems*, Addison Wesley.

Kumar, B., Chung, P.W.H., Rae, R.H. and Topping, B.H.V. (1987) *A Knowledge-Based Approach to Structural Design in Civil Engineering*, to be published.

Mittal, S. and Dym, C.L. (1985) *Knowledge aquisition from Multiple Experts* , AI Magazine, pp 32-36, Summer 1985.

Regan, J.E. (1987) *A Technique for Eliciting Categorical Knowledge for an Expert System.* Paper submitted to AAAI-87.

Sriram, D. (1986) *Destiny: A Model for Integrated Structural Design.* Proceedings of CAD 86.

Stefik, M., Foster, G., Bobrow, D.G., Kahn, K.M., Lanning, S. and Suchman, L. A. (1986) *Beyond the Chalkboard: Using Computers to Support Collaboration and Problem Solving in Meetings.* Paper submitted to CACM.

Welbank, M.A. (1983) *A Review of Knowledge Acquisition Techniques for Expert Systems.* British Telecom Research, Martlesham Heath.

Welbank, M.A. (1987) *Perspectives on Knowledge Acquisition.* Proceedings of Workshop on Knowledge Acquisition for Engineering Applications. Rutherford Appleton Laboratory Report.

II CONSTRUCTION PLANNING, MANAGEMENT AND CONTROL

CAN EXPERT SYSTEMS HELP THE CONSTRUCTION INDUSTRY?

Denis M Wager, BSc, MCIOB, FFB

Management Consultant with the Construction Industry Computing Association, Cambridge, England

Intelligent knowledge based systems (IKBS) will play an increasing part in our computer programs in the future. The knowledge bases will in many cases contain knowledge previously only available to the specialist domain expert. Such systems will have considerable impact on the construction industry particularly on the relationship between the professionals within the industry.

This paper briefly describes how intelligent knowledge based systems or expert systems differ from other techniques and looks at some of the research and development work now being undertaken that could affect the construction industry.

It is suggested that future expert systems will be integrated to form parts of suites of computer programs rather than huge stand alone 'experts', and that development should be carried out as joint ventures between industry and the Universities and Polytechnics

Why Expert?

What do we actually mean by the phrase Expert System. It is a rather unfortunate and misleading title that has been given to a type of computing or programming technique where heiristic, rule of thumb or expert knowledge is held in the computer system in such a way that it can be accessed to give advice and information much in the way that experts would. It is not, however, 'any' computer system which may have expert data built into it within the code structure of a traditional Von Newmann type programme language. The more accurate title for an expert system is intelligent knowledge based system.

The structure of IKBS

The diagram (figure 1) indicates that intelligent knowledge based systems have three main sections, the knowledge manager, the knowledge base and the situation model.

The central core of the system is the knowledge manager which controls the interface with the user together with the inference mechanism which compares the user problems with knowledge information stored in the system's knowledge base.

As the name intelligent knowledge based system implies an important part of such a system is the knowledge base. This contains knowledge acquired from someone with extensive experience and wide knowledge about a certain subject, we tend to call such people experts. The knowledge base is part of the system which is quite separate from the knowledge manager and the inference engine. When a user consults a system a model of the consultation is built up as it progresses, this is called the situation model.

The relevant knowledge is kept within the situation model and on completion of the consultation the system can arrive at some conclusion, even if this may be that it is unable to help, and can also say how and why it arrived at the conclusion.

The History of IKBS in Construction

Interest in IKBS has increased rapidly over the last few years, but one of the first publications prepared with direct reference to the construction industry was a report entitled 'Expert Systems: Their Impact on the Construction Industry" by John Lansdown. In 1980 the RIBA Conference Fund agreed to award a Fellowship for him to study the subject, and in 1982 the report was published together with an expert system shell program.

The CICA arranged a series of meetings, the first being in 1983 where 'experts' were invited to develop the Lansdown shell system by adding their own knowledge. Although these were basic systems they did show the concepts of knowledge based systems. From this ad-hoc group of people the CICA Expert System Special Interest Group was formed which meets at intervals to look at various apects of IKBS.

Other areas of construction research have been started, mainly at academic centres, some in association with industry, they include the Department of Civil Engineering at the University of Technology, Loughborough; the Department of Construction Management at the University of Reading; the Knowledge-based System Centre, part of the Polytechnic of the South Bank; the Building Research Station, Garston, Watford; BSRIA, the Building Services Research and Information Association; and the University of Salford together with the RICS.

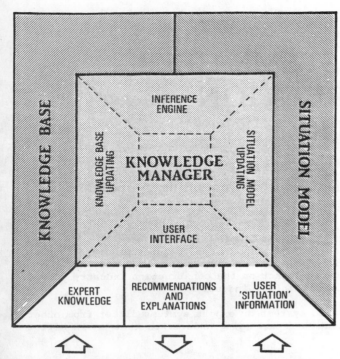

KNOWLEDGE BASE

INFERENCE ENGINE

KNOWLEDGE BASE UPDATING

KNOWLEDGE MANAGER

SITUATION MODEL UPDATING

SITUATION MODEL

USER INTERFACE

EXPERT KNOWLEDGE

RECOMMENDATIONS AND EXPLANATIONS

USER 'SITUATION' INFORMATION

Figure 1 - A diagram showing the structure of an Intelligent Knowledge-based System.

Overseas research is being carried out at the Construction Engineering Research Laboratory at Champaign, Illinois, USA; the University of Sidney, Australia; Department of Civil Engineering, University of Stanford, and the University of Colorado.

The subjects being considered by the researchers include quality control, dampness in buildings, buildings security, buildings maintenance, regulations and codes of practice, safety practices, selection of plant and equipment such as types of earth-moving equipment, contractural claims analysis, scheduling, project management and long term planning, evaluation of alternative construction methods at an early design stage, cost planning, and the selection of air conditioning systems.

Potential Expert Systems

You can see that the choice of subjects is vast and wide ranging. In a recent report prepared by the CICA in association with the University of Loughborough it was pointed out that any area where there is some specialist expertise in a particular subject such expertise could be the basis of the whole or part of the knowledge base. In the long term there will be a large number of different knowledge based applications and there are many potential domain areas for such systems.

However the expert system is not a new method of computing looking for applications. It is another tool for those developing computer programs to use in order to carry out specific tasks more efficiently, to include rule of thumb knowledge or heuristics, and perhaps uncertainty or probability associated with a problem.

No systems are yet commercially available or in use in the construction industry, in fact very few are being used in other industries, even in the well publicised area of medical diagnosis where most of the early research work was done it has had little or no impact on the medical profession.

..and the Future

Future development of expert systems is not seen as producing large stand alone 'experts' in one domain area but more a move towards the integration of knowledge based techniques with other more conventional programme methods, linking with packages such as databases, financial modelling, word processing etc.. Another way of implementing such a system is as a front end or back end to more sophisticated and perhaps complicated suites of programs. The SACON system was an early system of this type being the front end to MARC the finite element analysis program. Some research being carried out today by W S Atkins in association with the Building Research Station is a buildings security system where the expert system monitors input from many sensors throughout a building and only alerting security staff when the combination of information indicates that is a security risk is high.

Intelligent knowledge based systems can and will help the construction industry although considerable research and development work is necessary. This research can be effectivly undertaken with the joint participation of both industry and academia to ensure that any systems are well founded, they use the expertise available in our Universities and Polytechnics, the skills of experts in industry, and that the experts understand their potential for the future.

Bibliography

ALLWOOD RS, STEWART D S, HINDE C, and NEGUS B
    Evaluations of Expert System Shells for
    Construction Industry Applications,
    Loughborough University of Technology, 1985

AUSTEN A D & NEALE R H (eds) -
    Managing Construction Projects.
    International Labour Office, Geneva 1985

BJORK B-C - Computers in the British Construction
    Industry. Technical Research Centre of
    Finland,   1985

BRANDON P S - Computer: Friend or Foe?
    Portsmouth Polytechnic, Department of
    Surveying 1984

D'AGAPEYEFF A - Expert Systems Fifth Generation
    and UK Suppliers. NCC publication 1983

DIEKMANN J E and KRUPPENBACHER T A -
    Claims Analysis and Computer Reasoning.
    ASCE Journal of Construction Engineering and
    Management,pp 391-408, December 1984

DYM, CLIVE L - New approaches to Computer Aided
    Engineering. Palo Alto Research Centre 1984

FURUSAKA S and GRAY C - A model for the selection
    of the optimum crane for construction sites.
    Construction Management and Economics
    pp 159-176   1984

Bibliography (Continued)

GERO J and COYNE R - The place of Expert Systems
      in Architecture
      Proceedings of the sixth international
      conference and exhibition on computers in
      design engineering pp 522-528   1984

GOODALL A - The Guide to Expert Systems
      Learned Information (Europe) Ltd, 1985

GRAY C and LITTLE J - The Use of Artificial
      Intelligence (AI) Computing to Evaluate
      Alternative Design/Construction Strategies
      During Design Development. A paper,
      University of Reading, 1985

HAMILTON G - Expert Systems in Building Services.
      A paper for the CICA Construction Expert
      Conference, 1985

LANSDOWN J - Expert Systems: Their Impact on the
      Construction Industry.
      RIBA Conference Fund 1982

RUTLAND P - The Business of Getting Business.
      Building Technology & Management,
      Vol 23 No 2,   1985

SHAW M R - Expert Systems - An Objective View. A
      paper at Computers in Building and Services
      Design Conference, University of Nottingham,
      April 1985

SHAW M R - Research Report - Expert Systems
      Building Services Journal, May 1985

STEFIK M J - The Organisation of Expert Systems, a
      Tutorial. Artificial Intelligence 18, 1982

TAFFS D - Expert or Knowledge-based Systems:
      Consequences for the Industry.
      ICE Computer Conference 1984

TRIMBLE G - Practical Aspects of Expert Systems in
      Construction: Report on visit to UK by
      Mr. Frank Kearney to discuss practical
      aspects of expert systems in construction.
      Loughborough University of Technology, 1985

TRIMBLE G - Expert Systems in Practice: The User's
      Perspective in Relation to Building and
      Construction Management. A paper, 1985

WAGER D M - Expert Systems for the Construction
      Industry.   1984
      Construction Industry Computing Association.

WAGER D M - The Future of Sxpert Systems in
      Construction Management   1985
      Construction Industry Computing Association.

THE INTEGRATION OF AN EXPERT SYSTEM INTO THE CONSTRUCTION PLANNING PROCESS

D W Wijesundera and Dr F C Harris,
Department of Civil Engineering
University of Technology, Loughborough

An expert system is a computer program designed to simulate a consultation between an expert of a particular field and the non-expert. Typically, the non-expert is the end user and the computer model the expert.

The technique which is at its early stages of development, has successfully demonstrated the possibility of carrying out a realistic consultation between the user and the expert for selecting plant for high rise construction.

The standard achieved by the system as developed so far falls short of some of our earlier expectations and problems relating to uncertainty remain for further investigation. This paper describes the process of knowledge acquisition and its representation in a computer model in a form suitable to aid plant selection for the construction planning process.

INTRODUCTION

The concept of expert systems was first introduced to the authors after visits by Professor Geoffrey Trimble to institutions in the U.K. and U.S.A. Subsequently a research grant was awarded by the Science and Engineering Research Council (Ref. 1) to explore the potential of an expert system for use in selecting materials handling equipment for high rise construction. This work is now at an advanced stage and is described in this paper.

Expert systems have been developed for several applications, most notably in medical diagnosis, but as far as the authors are aware, this concept is unfamiliar to construction industry practitioners. Indeed, this is not surprising as the field is dominated by computer specialists, with the literature concentrating on computer aspects rather than on applications. However, after overcoming the jargon, it became clear that expert systems had potential and progress was made in the direction of a specific application.

As an initial step the differences between conventional knowledge programs and existing expert systems were explored, revealing that expert systems came in two parts, the knowledge base and the actual computer program called the shell (Fig. 1). Quite sophisticated shells are now commercially available and so it seemed more prudent to purchase rather than develop our own shell.

HOW DO EXPERT SYSTEMS WORK?

In its basic form an expert system consists of a knowledge base structured logically and stored in a computer. This knowledge can be accessed by the computer program known as the shell posing a series of questions to be answered by the user typically in the format Yes, No or Don't know.

The program (shell) then locates the applicable rules and produces a decision giving likely solutions to the problem in hand. However, the most recent shells offer more advanced facilities such as:

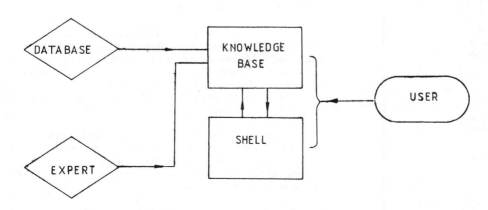

Fig 1

(a) Handling of uncertainty of fuzzy logic.
    Whereby the user answers a question on a
    scale from +5 to -5.

(b) Provide numeric answers to questions.
    (e.g. What is the maximum load to be
    transported? = 02 etc).

(c) Access to external information.
    (e.g. data bases)

As an aid to clarity and understanding of the
logical relationships the knowledge may be
represented in the form of a "decision tree" prior
to computer coding as shown in the example given
in Figure 2.

In a comprehensive shell program there are many
options available at each stage of operation. The
most useful among these being:

(i)   the explanation facility

(ii)   the question volunteer level

(iii)   the reporting facility.

The above facilities are shown in Figure 3.

(i) The explanation facility gives the user the
reasons behind the present analysis and why a
particular question is asked and its significance
to the hypothesis pursued at the time. To the

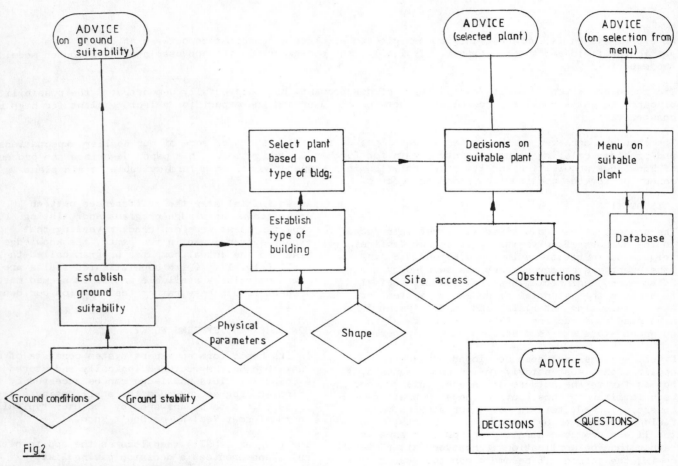

Fig 2

THE OBJECTIVE OF THE RESEARCH

On the basis of the above principles, research was
undertaken with the aim of devising a means of
selecting items of equipment suitable for
executing the materials handling part of the
construction of a concrete framed building. The
mode of advice being that captured from the
experts well experienced in doing this in real
situations. The technique was directed towards
allowing the user to work through the process
starting from a base of little knowledge to arrive
at the best choice for a particular piece of
equipment, weighed against all the objectives.

THE MODE OF OPERATION BY THE USER

The operation of the knowledge base is quite
similar to operating any other computer program.
The computer presents a menu or questions and the
user responds with suitable answers, the type of
answers expected from the user being indicated
in the text of the question.

novice this is a useful teaching facility; to the
experienced user and the developer it provides a
facility to debug the model.

(ii) It is possible for the user to answer only
the questions thought relevant to capture the
problem. The user can call up these questions and
volunteer information, but the model will also
decide whether the questions answered are sufficient
to make a valid decision, if not it will as further
questions in order to solve the problem.

(iii) When the problem has been fully evaluated
the user generally needs to see the result in
varying levels of detail depending on the
information required. For example level 1 could
include only the decisions and level 2 the
reasoning process as well. It is pointed out
however that all these facilities have to be built
in by the designer as clearly the supply of
knowledge is not self generated.

......Welcome to CONPLANT......

The expert system for plant selection in multi storey construction

Can you tell me whether you are familiary with CONPLANT

(Y..!..N or an option) Y

You seem to have used CONPLANT before. Remember the help facility can be invoked by pressing 'h' if you get stuck.

We shall now start the consultation on plant selection

I am now trying to find the suitability of the ground to take the loading of equipment. The questions presented to you are intended to find out:

     - the internal structure of the soil
     - external factors affecting the soil....

(I am currently trying to find out the ground conditions in relation to its ...... soil properties

The ground conditions of the site have to be investigated to find out if the ground can take the loading of heavy equipment.
     If you are in an office and have not visited the site it may be difficult to answer this question. Try to get details of the soil investigation which might help you to answer this question.
     Does the ground consist of:
          1) - soil or
          2) - thin soil bed overlaying rock bed
     enter a number and remember that an answer '!' shall be taken as unknown

(1..2, ! if not known or an option) 1

(I am currently trying to find out the ground conditions in relation to its ...... soil properties

The soil bed can be of four types, and the characteristics of each layer will affect the foundations required for plant. Can you tell me the soil description of your site. A soil classification chart is provided with this question.
     Enter your choice:
          1) gravel
          2) sand
          3) silt
          4) clay
Do you want to see more (Y,N) ? N

(1..4, ! if not know or an option) 1

(I am currently trying to find out the ground conditions in relation to its ...... soil properties

When a site is located in built up areas it is quite common to have open excavations protected and unprotected which may have been unforeseen during feasibility studies. It is important for me to check on this before advising on plant to be used. Can you tell me whether there are such open excavations outside the site boundary.
     Answer:
          -5 if there are unprotected excavations
          -3 if there are partially protected excavations
           0 if you are uncertain
          +3 if there are excavations but protected
          +5 if there are no excavations around site.

(-5..0..5 or an option) 3

Now I have completed the questions on ground conditions. Do you wish to see a sub-report or simply carry on with the consultation.
     Please enter your choice:
          1 - to see the report
          2 - to carry on with the consultation
(1..2 or an option) 1

The report is:-
     The evaluation of the ground condition is now complete and my assessment is that ....

     The ground should be able to take the load of heavy plant.

Figure 3

STARTING TO DESIGN AN EXPERT SYSTEM FOR PLANT SELECTION

On commencing design of an expert system for materials handling obtaining a good understanding of the way decisions are made in a contractor's organisation is important. For example, in the planning office there will commonly be a team of engineers with different areas of specialisation. Each member usually offers suggestions on items of plant based on rules of thumb with the final decision being taken by the chief planner who weights them into order. These weightings largely depend on previous experience, economic factors and physical properties of the job in question. This arduous process takes place each and every time a plant selection has to be carried out in the planning office or elsewhere and must be captured in the Expert System.

An illustration of this procedure is given in Table 1 which shows how knowledge extracted from an expert can be presented in the form of general rules as the first step and later converted to more precise rules. For an example the following rule can be formed from the table. If the structure is a conventional R.C. frame and if the shape is long and narrow or square with a large floor area then a tower crane with a 40-50 metres long boom travelling on track is appropriate. Also a mobile crane with a fly jib is suitable if there are less than 3 floors and area is small enough for the crane to reach over.

Classification	Explanation	Tower Crane Type	Mobile Crane Type
Conventional r/c frame or a mixture of r/c and p/c	Long and narrow structure or a square structure with a large floor area. No access to the centre.	Tower crane commonly with radius (40 to 50) metres A travelling T/C on tracks or several T/Cs.	Mobile crane possibly with a fly jib capability to reach over building. Access roads may be needed at each side of building.
	As above but with access to the centre possible.	A large radius T/C (dependent on the dimensions of bldg) at the centre could provide reach required.	
Tall building with r/c core (slip formed) and r/c or steel frame r/c floor.	Shape generally irrelevant as the crane positioned inside core.	T/C may be used for slip-formed core and the floor or only for the construction of the floor. Note: support of T/C to be considered if free standing height is exceeded, e.g. tied-in T/C or climbing T/C	Height usually rules out the possibility of of using mobile cranes.
Physical obstructions	Other buildings in the vicinity. Overhead lines, oversailing other property and client-imposed restrictions.	Options: Several small radius T/Cs Luffing jib T/C Articulated jib T/C Use of self erecting T/C where the jib can be lowered at night.	Mobile cranes usually avoided.
	Ground conditions and levels.	Heavy crane on poor ground will require expensive foundations. Sloping ground may preclude the use of travelling T/Cs.	Adequate foundations required for crane stabilising pads.
	Proximity of the crane foundations to other buildings & services.	Surcharging of retaining wall, foundations near open excavations & underground services may need careful examination prior to erecting of T/C	
	Access for erection and dismantling	Erection & dismantling of large radius T/Cs demands the use of a 100 - 200T mobile crane. These are very expensive to hire and in certain circumstances public roads may also have to be closed.	Generally not t problem for mobile cranes.

Period of use	Only required for a short period or intermittent use only.	Conventional T/C not normally suitable for short durations due to the cost of foundations, erection and dismantling. Self erecting saddle back T/C suitable.	Lorry mounted crane with a strut jib or tower & luffing jib configuration.
Safe working load	Radius & load to be determined.	T/C are normally used as general purpose machines for lifting formwork, concrete reinforcement, etc.	Mobile cranes similar duties tower cranes but are available with much higher capacities. Travelling under load usually avoided. Outreach poor.
	Height	Free standing height is dependent on the type of base section of the tower, wind effects etc. 1. Strengthen sections to take the height. 2. Tie to the building under construction. Care has to be taken to ensure that the structure can withstand the tie forces.	Mobile cranes limited by relatively short jib length.

Table 1

Extract of knowledge assembled from interviews with practitioners.

THE KNOWLEDGE BASE

The first attempt at producing a model was undertaken as a student project (Ref. 2) using only knowledge and experience available inhouse. While the principles of assembling knowledge and applying it to a shell program were quickly understood the following problems became evident.

(1) How to approach experts?

(2) How to acquire the knowledge?

(3) How to encode the knowledge?

Equipped with an Apricot computer (complete with Sirius/Victor 9000) two construction companies were approached and the trial model on materials handling demonstrated to personnel in the planning and computer departments. The immediate response led to further cooperation and actual knowledge acquisition.

THE APPROACH TO KNOWLEDGE ACQUISITION

The best results in gathering knowlege are generally obtained by building up a good relationship between the model builder (i.e. knowledge miner) and the expert. However, this will vary from person to person and may involve several meetings before suspicion of the interviewer's intentions have been overcome. Eventually a free exchange of information will evolve. The following methods were attempted:

1. Informal conversations

2. Questionnaires

3. Examples

Conversations were always recorded with a micro recorder, while the analysis and rules formulation were carried out carefully back at base.

Informal conversations

The initial approach between the company man and the model builder was to decide on an item of plant for a particular situation and then cover all reasons as to how and why the decision would be acceptable. Unfortunately, often this method considered only the facts in favour of the decision. However, from the recording of the conversation it was possible to select information to formulate questions to ask the experts as to what actions would have been taken if the facts were against the decisions being made. This gave alternative decisions the expert might have taken. A typical example to demonstrate this point would be as follows:

Rule 1

IF soil is sand or gravel

AND no open excavations are present around site THEN the soil is suitable for heavy plant.

The above are facts in favour of using heavy plant but if the soil is clay or silt, then clearly it becomes necessary to look at alternatives, i.e. heavy plant cannot be used without additional foundations.

Questionnaire

Approaching the expert with a set of questions was soon realised as unsuitable because the expert is restricted to answering questions within the area opened to him by a non-expert. Hence, it was decided that in general the procedure for forwarding questionnaires should be ruled out.

Examples method

Using examples for acquiring knowledge was the next option available. This method has been tried previously by analysing data statistically such as linear regression analysis and forming rule generators. However, such systems require the user to choose variables very carefully. For instance in a situation where concrete is to be poured the variables might be volume, temperature, demand, location, mixture and aggregate condition. If there are variables such as day, date, etc. whcih are not important then the rule generator may produce a silly rule such as "Don't pour concrete on Thursdays". (Ref. 3).

SHELLS

Our experience showed that the method of structuring the knowledge base was different depending upon the shell program. (Ref. 4). Nevertheless, the following facilities were generally required of the shell.

1. Able to handle rules of the YES/NO type (boolean logic) and those involving uncertainty.

2. Explanation facility

3. Text manipulation

4. Able to carry out calculations

5. Handle string variables such as plant names

6. Exit facility to data-bases, graphics and planning packages.

With a budget of £1,500 the SAVOIR shell was chosen to satisfactorily handle these aspects.

Uncertainty

The features of uncertainty may be dealt with as demonstrated in the following examples:

(Question)
Is the bearing capacity of the soil suitable for a tower crane base.
Answer   −5 −   definitely not suitable
       0 −   do not know
    +5 −   definitely suitable.

The reply to this can be +5 in which case no improvements need to be carried out to the existing ground, while at the other extreme, a −5 reply requires that a concrete foundation must be constructed and for any reply inbetween the type of foundation will vary from a pile foundation or concrete foundation to railway sleepers on the surface to distribute the load.

Explanation facility

A text explanation facility is a very helpful debugging device for the developer of the knowledge base and is absolutely essential to the user. It is important to know why the system has suggested a particular solution to the problem, and the reasoning behind it. The explanation facility traces along the knowledge tree from the decision to first question asked and displays why this path has been taken.

Text manipulation

Text manipulation is a feature to help the model builder in formatting questions so that they are easily understood by the user. For example sentences such as:
"Is it true that materials are to be transported?"

answer YES/NO
may be presented as

"Are materials to be transported?"
or

"Do you intend to transport materials?"
answer YES/NO

Exit facility

The consultation often only results in the recommendation of a broad category of equipment. The precise model or type would be determined from further calculations. These can be carried out externally and linked to a database of stored equipment items for the final selection. Programs coded in Pascal (since Savoir is written in Pascal) was linked to the shell to achieve such a facility. Furthermore, graphics can be used for presenting problems to the computer. For example, the actual shape of site, location of plant yard, batch plant and other material storage can be indicated on a graphics screen based on co-ordinates and also linked to the external program.

THE MODEL (Figures 2 & 3)

The model begins by requesting replies to questions on the ground and soil conditions to be encountered on site, followed by questions on the presence of open excavations near the foundations of the structure etc. A table of soil properties and characteristics is presented to the user as an aid in deciding on the suitability of the soil to support various forms of heavy plant. Depending on the replies relevant advice is given on the required measures to be taken to improve the ground conditions. Subsequently the model proceeds to ask questions on the physical parameters of the structure, such as shape, size and height etc. These parameters limit or eliminate the use of certain types of equipment. With the options now narrowed answers are requested to questions on site access and obstructions. At the end of this session the model suggests suitable categories of plant for materials handling.

The user is now offered further consultation on each suggested category aimed at advising on a specific recommendation, for example type of tower crane. This is achieved by linking an external data bank of equipment data to the shell. Questions relating to crane operating radius, load and location relative to the structure such as outside the frame or in the lift shaft, enable the load moment values to be calculated and subsequently matched to a particular crane or manufactured type.

The user is then given the option of varying the input information to obtain an alternative solution.

PROBLEMS ENCOUNTERED IN KNOWLEDGE REPRESENTATION AND ENCODEMENT

The consultation revealed that an expert did not normally start the thinking process by always asking the same initial question and proceeding with a fixed series of further questions. This caused considerable problems in formulating the hierarchy of the decision tree. Furthermore, only the structured part of the expert's knowledge could be utilised. For example "in the process of selecting hoists for a building, there appeared to be no fixed rule in determining the number of hoists required, but at least there were rules of thumb that planners followed for part of the decision, such as 'a hoist for every 500 sq.m of floor area'. The other factors affecting the decision were typically:

a. Shape of building
b. Type of material to be used
c. Frequency of the material requirement
d. Size of hoist available
e. Number of floors in the building
f. Other backup plant available
g. use of landing platforms
h. Experience of the planner

No definite rules governing the weighting of each of these variables could be ascertained. The final decision being an unknown combination of each variable depending on the persons making the decision and their past experiences. The present model thereofre only achieved partial simulation. This aspect was further complicated by the way the experts tended to express uncertainty, giving replies such as "sort of" and "likely" to mean different things to different people. Knowledge acquired in this form was almost impossible to quantify accurately, and only "rules of thumb" could be formulated.

THE EXPERT SYSTEM AND THE PLANNING PROCESS

Normal planning methods require preparation of a detailed program of construction operations with the resources balanced to produce minimum cost. The engineer decides on the construction methods and suggests different items of plant, the final choice being tempered by considerations on flow of work, and economic factors. Thus a particular activity may be allocated less than ideal equipment if such plant is already available and produces a cheap solution. Expert systems which recommend only the most appropriate items of equipment may thus have to be over-ruled when integrated into the total project plan. It would therefore appear that for materials handling plant selection expert systems provide only a part solution. They could nevertheless at least contribute to that part of decision making which has hitherto been subjective and not easily determined by calculation.

CONCLUSIONS

While the potential of the technique for capturing knowledge in a readily usable form has been encouraging, the complexities of rule encodement required of the computer programs would presently limit the applications to well defined knowledge areas. Unfortunately the selection of construction equipment being largely based on uncertain and intuitive knowledge allowed only broad rules of thumb to be formulated'. Further development of this particular application is therefore unlikely to gain authentic support, until more output data and production information appertaining to plant and labour resources has been evaluated and more generally applied by practitioners in their planning and estimating processes.

REFERENCES

1. S.E.R.C. Research grant GR/C/90638. An Expert system for materials handling and construction methods for building projects, Department of Civil Engineering, Loughborough University of Technology, 1984/85.

2. Wijesundera D.A., Expert Systems for multi-storey construction, MSc project report, Department of Civil Engineering, Loughborough University of Technology, 1984.

3. Kearney, F., seminar on expert systems presented in the Department of Civil Engineering, Loughborough University of Technology, November 1984.

4. Allwood, R.J., Stewart, D.J., Hinde, C, and Negus, B, Evaluation of expert system shells for construction industry applications, Final report, Department of Civil Engineering, Loughborough University of Technology, 1984/85.

5. Micro-Expert, ISIS Ltd., Oakdene Road, Redhill, Surrey.

6. Savoir, ISI Ltd, Oakdene Road, Redhill, Surrey.

AN EXPERT SYSTEM
FOR
CLAIM ANALYSIS

Sabah Al-Kass, BSc, MSc, MCIOB, MIED, MASCE and
Frank Harris, BSc, MSc, PhD, CEng, MICE, MCIOB
Department of Civil Engineering, University of Technology, Loughborough

Knowledge based models (expert systems) provide an interesting new tool for decision making for construction related problems. This paper describes the nature of such systems with reference to an application for claims analysis under the international conditions of contract. Knowledge and experiences accumulated from construction contract disputes have been captured and stored in a computer in the form of an Expert System. The user obtains advice in a manner similar to consultation with a professional practitioner.

INTRODUCTION

Experts usually record their knowledge in books, papers, articles, reports, and similar mediums. Unfortunately the material thereafter tends to become diffuse and also difficult to assimilate for the inexperienced reader. An expert system attempts to assemble and structure such knowledge in a manner that facilitates a user to steer a step by step course in learning and so solve problems which are largely judgement dependent.

To capture an expert's knowledge is time consuming, laborious and complex, but when successfully achieved and superimposed onto a well designed computer program an expert system can simulate a consultation as though the computer is the tutor and the user a pupil. To demonstrate this concept this paper describes a model concerning contract claims, contract disputes resolution being an area where the parties involved often require legal advice, all too often not sought because of expense or inaccessibility. The prototype computer program aims at giving assistance in deciding when and how to pursue a claim with particular relevance to the international conditions of contract. The procedures for basing, and formulating the claim are contained in a carefully arranged set of knowledge manipulated by the program in response to questions and answers provided by the user. The output of the consultation is directed towards minimising, if not preventing, a dispute arising.

EXPERT SYSTEMS

Expert systems manipulate knowledge rather than data, and also provide the opportunity for the user to make alternations, for example correct a mistake or add new rules into the knowledge base. In contrast locating, correcting, and testing a change in a conventional program is a time consuming process. To arrive at the expert system the following components and actions are required:

1) A knowledge engineer to obtain and store the knowledge in a form capable of simulating human reasoning. The knowledge engineer could be the expert.
2) A knowledge base, containing a collection of facts and rules on a specific subject or domain, the domain for this system being claims management.
3) A shell, or computer program, to direct the knowledge base according to a set of rules.
4) A user to provide replies to questions asked by the system.
5) A means of communicating with the system, i.e. a computer.

The essence of the system lies in the ability of the system to refer to the knowledge base. Examples of Expert System models developed for the construction industry include automated schedule update (1), claim analysis and computer reasoning (2,3), materials handling (4).

DESIGNING AN EXPERT SYSTEM

The knowledge engineer is fundamental to the process of model design. With respect to claims expertise this person should have a good understanding of managing construction contracts and some knowledge of legal matters, otherwise a lack of respect on the part of the expert providing knowledge for the domain may hinder the prospects for developing a good relationship. A sound knowledge of the system shell is also important, but paramount is the ability to interpret the expert's advice into rules, to order these into a logical pattern, and to explain the reasoning behind decisions subsequently made by the system. Figure (1) illustrates the procedures involved.

CLAIMS

The claims are "demands for something due", more specifically for a civil engineering contract, Worby (5), suggests that a claim is :"A request, supported by full details and particulars, for

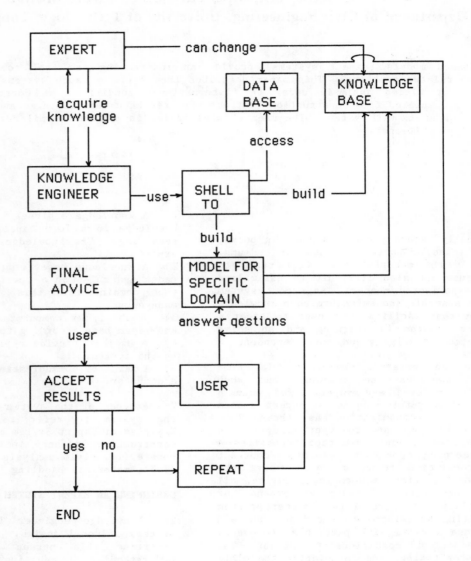

(Fig I)
Relationship in an Expert System

something that one party believes it is entitled to (usually time or money or both), by virtue of a term or terms in a valid contract with another party but for which there is as yet no agreement". An Expert System can help in deciding on the validity of this entitlement by establishing the legal basis namely:

CONTRACTUAL claim - falls within specific clauses embodied in the contract, typically ground conditions and variations.

Ex-contractual claim - has no specific grounds within the contract but results from breach of contract, typically extra work incurred as a result of defective material supplied by the client.

Ex-gratia claim - no ground exists in the contract or common law, but the contractor believes that there is moral basis, e.g. additional costs incurred as a result of rapidly increased prices.

As far as construction contractors and their clients are concerned the kinds of situation coming under the above headings are generally concerned with:

1. Alteration, addition, omission.
2. Unforeseen physical conditions.
3. Supply of information and drawings.
4. Variations.
5. Delays and disruptions caused by the above.

The model CLAIMS EXPERT

Claims_Expert is capable of identifying various potential entitlement issues from given facts, and provides guidelines for preparing the documentation and procedures necessary to pursue the case. A likely prediction of the outcome is also presented (i.e. entitlement or not), together with an explanation of the reasoning.

The mode of the operation consists of a series of questions linked by (IF_THEN) logic, the logic tree being a set of rules arranged to reflect the reasoning of the expert practitioner. Figures (2 & 2a) show a particular route for a small section of the knowledge base dealing with ground problems. The consultation begins by the user providing responses to the questions in the form of YES, NO, DO NOT KNOW. The applicable rules are located and further questions posed, ultimately leading to a particular decision or course of action to take on the problem in hand. For example in the model the following rules would have to be satisfied when deciding on entitlement to a claim:

IF   The ground conditions are different from those expected,

AND   Delays and disruptions have occurred as a result,

AND   Reasonable soil investigations could not have prevented the situation,

AND   The contractor is not responsible for the site investigations,

AND   Written notice has been given to the Engineer raising the matter.

Other aspects and contract clauses or conditions are dealt with in a similar but specific manner.

At any stage in this process the user can call for explanations and the path of reasoning adopted. Furthermore, guidance on standard information, record-keeping, cost estimate preparation etc. needed for presentation of the case may be requested. A facility of this kind was found very helpful for users relatively inexperienced in presenting appropriate claims documentation. Figure (3) illustrates a typical section of diagnosis procedure between the user and the computer.

CONCLUSION

The model although developed using past examples and advice from experienced managers and legal experts is still undergoing detailed evaluation with respect to its ability to correctly identify complex legal issues. The procedures for the presentation of claims however seem satisfactory and provide useful guidelines for most cases arising on typical construction projects. By way of concluding remarks, results of trials with users indicate that the concept provides a disciplined method of transferring knowledge and expertise especially to young and untrained construction engineers. Indeed the next phase of research is attempting to ascertain how well the model performs on carefully chosen samples of users with various levels of expertise of the subject. Finally, to overcome the problem of different experts having different ideas, the system could have more than one knowledge base, but it must be emphasised that expert systems are strictly limited by the knowledge stored and are therefore only applicable to the specific domain, whereas the expert is normally much more versatile.

REFERENCES AND BIBLIOGRAPHY

1. Levitt, R.E. And Kunz, J.C.
   "Using knowledge of construction and project management for automated schedule updating". Project Management Journal, September 1985.
2. Deikman, J.D. and Kruppenbacher, T.A.
   "Claim analysis and computer reasoning". ASCE Journal of Construction Engineering and Management, 1984.
3. Cobbi, J.E. and Deikman, J.D.
   "A claim analysis expert system". Project Management Journal, June 1986.
4. Wijesundera, D.W. and Harris, F.C.
   "The integration of an expert system in construction planning process". Proceedings of Second International Conference on Civil and Structural Computing, CIVIL-COMP, 1985.
5. Worby, G., Tyler, A.H. and Harris, F.C.
   "Management of Claims". Building Technology and Management, July 1985.
6. Jones, G.P.
   "A new approach to the International Civil Engineering Contracts". Construction Press, 1979.
7. Abrahamson, M.W.
   "Engineering law and I.C.E. contracts". Applied Science Publisher.
8. Lansdown, J.
   "Expert Systems: Their impact on the construction industry", Report RIBA Conference Fund, 1984.

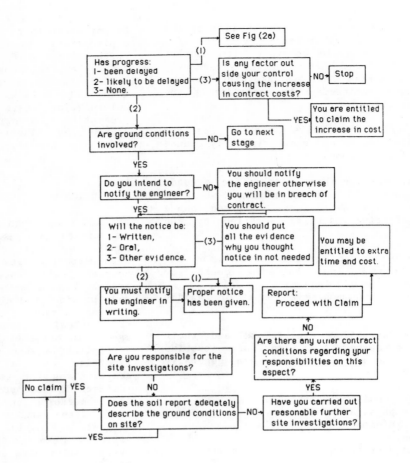

Fig (2)
Knowledge base route for ground conditions
where the progress is likely to be delayed

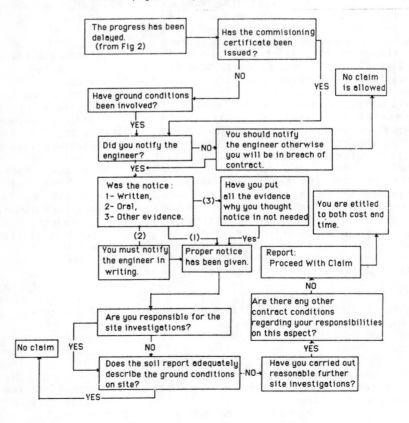

Fig (2a)
Knowledge base route for ground conditions
where the progress has been delayed

W e l c o m e   t o   CLAIMS_EXPERT.

        .... a demonstration Expert System knowledgeable on the subject of
claims analysis under the international conditions of contract.

            Have you used CLAIMS_EXPERT before ?

(Y..!..N or an option) Y

  Has construction progress:

  1- been delayed? or,
  2- likely to be delayed ?
  (1..2, ! if not known or an option) 2

  >>
  Is the delay due to one of the following:

  1- Failure by the engineer to supply drawings
     or instructions.
  2- Ground conditions or obstructions.
  3- Incorrect informations supplied by the engineer.
  4- Variations.
  5- Discovery of old foundations, etc.
  6- Act of war.
  7- Work carried out under engineer'sinstructions
     but not included in the contract.
  8- Other reasons.

  (1..8, ! if not known or an option) 2

  Do you intend to notify the engineer?

  For more explanation please type A.

  (Y..!..N or an option) A

  **
  Failure to give notice immediately may prevent
  the engineer from exercising his power and
  authorities under the contract conditions
  (i.e. to vary or omit work). **

Do you intend to notify the engineer?

For more explanation please type A.

(Y..!..N or an option)   Y

What form of notice will be?:

1- Written,
2- Oral,
3- Other events surrounding the not.

For explanations please type A.

(1..3, ! if not known or an option)   A

**   If you choose other than written notice, then
   you should notify the engineer in writing
   IMMEDIATELY. Failure to do so may prevent
   the engineer from exercising his power and
   authorities under the contract conditions
   (i.e. to vary or omit work). **

What form of notice will be?:

1- Written,
2- Oral,
3- Other events surrounding the not.

For explanations please type A.

(1..3, ! if not known or an option)   1

>>
Does the problem involve unforeseen
physical ground conditions or unexpected
obstructions?

(Y..!..N or an option)   Y

>> Are you responsible for the site
investigations?

(Y..!..N or an option)   N

>> Did any of the following aspects affect
your pretender site investigations:

1- Access to the site was denied.
2- Inadequate time was allowed.
3- Non.

For explanation please type A.

(1..3, ! if not known or an option)   A

** Even if you are not responsible for site investigations
   you should do your own ON site inspections before
   submitting your tender. **

```
>>  Did any of the following aspects affect
your pretender site investigations:

1- Access to the site was denied.
2- Inadequate time was allowed.
3- Non.

For explanation please type A.

(i..3, ! if not known  or an option)  3




>>  Does the soil report adequately describe the
ground conditions on site?

(Y..!..N or an option)   Y




>>  Are there any extra conditions in the
contract requiring your responsibilities
on ground conditions?

(Y..!..N or an option)   N




>>  Do you believe that such conditions
could not have been foreseen by
experienced contractors?

(Y..!..N or an option)   Y




>>  Does the engineer believe that such
conditions could have been foreseen
by experienced contractor?

(Y..!..N or an option)   N




DECISION :

Proceed with claim.
Under the international conditions of contract
you may be entitled to extra time and cost.




>>  Do you want to:

1- See the reasons for the decision made.
2- Restart the consultation.
3- End the consultation.

(1..3, ! if not known  or an option)  1
```

```
The RULES BEHIEND THE DECISION BASED
ON YOUR RESPONSES ARE AS FOLLOWS:
----------------------------------


The progress HAS BEEN DISRUPTED.
WRITTEN notice has been given.
UNFORESEEN PHYSICAL CONDITIONS are involved
The contractor is NOT RESPONSIBLE for site investigations
The conditions COULD NOT have been foreseen by
an experienced contractor.
The engineer AGREES that the conditions COULD NOT
have been foreseen by an experienced contractor.



>>  Do you want to:

1- See the reasons for the decision made.
2- Restart the consultation.
3- End the consultation.

(1..3, ! if not known  or an option)  3



THANK YOU - THAT IS THE END OF THE CONSULTATION.
```

Figure 3
**Typical section of diagnosis procedure between the user and
the computer**

CRANES – A RULE-BASED ASSISTANT WITH GRAPHICS FOR CONSTRUCTION PLANNING ENGINEERS

C N Cooper,

Department of Civil Engineering, University of Technology, Loughborough

SYNOPSIS

The CRANES rule-based system for selection of tower cranes for multi-storey construction sites is described. The system incorporates a procedural graphics module which allows the user to suggest locations for tower cranes on a graphic display. The geometric and lifting requirements thus specified are then checked against a data-base of available machines. Knowledge about the production capabilities of tower cranes enables the system to compare the productivity requirements and spatial coverage requirements for a given contract. The user is then advised how he might amend his choice of cranes in order to maximise crane utilisation.

The system has been developed as part of a programme of research into techniques of knowledge acquisition for construction industry applications. The methods used are described.

CRANES is currently written for the Savoir expert system shell and mounted on an IBM PC XT. The advantages and disadvantages of Savoir for this application are discussed.

INTRODUCTION

Knowledge-based systems, popularly referred to as expert systems, are a computer technology developed over the last twenty years. This technology is being developed in a wide range of industries, and a number of knowledge-based systems are now in every day use. In the United States 400 copies of the PumpPro expert system on faults in centrifugal pumps have been distributed and systems relating to welding procedures and defects are also in use (Ref. 1).

Typically a knowledge-based system embodies the expertise of one or more human experts. The Department of Civil Engineering at Loughborough University has been researching potential applications of knowledge-based systems in the construction industry for some years. One of our prime areas of interest at present is the process of acquiring from the domain experts the knowledge which is to be embodied in the system. Many workers have reported that this is a particular area of difficulty in system development (Ref. 2).

The system described in this paper is one of five so far developed in the course of our research programme into knowledge acquisition techniques. The domains covered by these systems are summarised as follows:

BREDAMP – diagnosis of the cause of dampness in buildings
BIDDER – decision of a design and construct contractor on whether to bid for a project
MATSEL – material selection for boiler pressure parts
NETWORK – diagnosis of faults in a national computer network

CRANES – selection of tower cranes for multi-storey construction sites.

BACKGROUND

Selection of the type, number and location of cranes to be used on a multi-storey construction site is in many ways the central decision in the planning of the construction operation. The decisions taken are complex and the wrong choice is likely to have serious consequences and produce uneconomic construction (Ref. 3).

The selection of cranes and other materials handling equipment to be used on a construction project is generally carried out by highly experienced engineers in the planning department of a contracting organisation. The expertise held within such a planning department will continually be eroded as the more experienced engineers retire or leave the company and there will be a constant requirement to train and supervise less experienced engineers new to the department. A successful expert system could capture the expertise of senior engineers prior to their retirement thus enabling some of this experience to be used and learnt by trainees.

In 1985 the CONPLANT system was developed in the Department of Civil Engineering at Loughborough University (Ref. 4). CONPLANT advised on the selection of items of plant for handling materials during the construction of a concrete framed building. The authors of CONPLANT reported that this early system was limited by a lack of production information appertaining to plant and labour on construction sites. They also recognised that assumptions of "square", "rectangular" or "circular" buildings made in CONPLANT were inadequate for the real world and that a graphics facility was required.

47

CONPLANT was subsequently demonstrated to planning engineers from Wimpey Construction UK Ltd who reiterated the need for graphics and who also clearly had a different approach to crane selection from the domain experts interviewed during the development of CONPLANT.

One of the earlier but key findings of research into expert system development at Loughborough is that systems are far more likely to be successful if they are commissioned by a clearly defined client (Ref. 5). The interest shown by Wimpey Construction UK Ltd in seeing further development of the CONPLANT work provided a pseudo client-led environment and it was therefore decided to undertake further work in the domain of materials handling equipment. The ultimate objective was to develop a system which could be used as a training aid for junior engineers in a construction planning department.

THE DEVELOPMENT OF CRANES

Domain experts employed by Wimpey Construction UK Ltd were to provide all the knowledge for the CRANES system, but Wimpey was not among the organisations who had contributed to CONPLANT. The decision was therefore taken to construct a completely new knowledge-base for CRANES which would be specific to Wimpey expertise.

Knowledge acquisition sessions were very productive and it soon became clear that structuring and representation of the knowledge would be a major problem. The sub-domain of selection of tower cranes for multi-storey construction sites was therefore chosen in order to provide a more limited domain on which to concentrate initial development.

The Savoir knowledge-based system shell was chosen for representation of the crane selection knowledge. Adoption of this shell was the result of a comparative evaluation of expert system shells for construction industry applications previously carried out in the Department of Civil Engineering at Loughborough (Ref. 6). Specific features which led to the adoption of Savoir included availability on an IBM Personal Computer and the ability to interface with procedures written in the Pascal programming language.

The experts interviewed adopted two main criteria for deciding on the number of cranes required as follows:

(i) all parts of the building and material off-loading areas must be overswung by one or more cranes and all loads must be capable of being lifted by one or other of the cranes installed.

(ii) the combination of cranes selected must be capable of lifting materials at a rate that will match the planned speed of construction.

These requirements are processed in separate modules of the CRANES system which will be referred to as the graphics module and the hook-time module respectively.

When commencing a consultation a novice user is offered the opportunity of accessing a preliminary consultation module. Questions are asked about the form of construction, the height of the structure and the total contract period available. The system then advises whether tower cranes are likely to be appropriate in this application (or whether mobile or crawler cranes could be considered). The user is also given advice as to how the total contract period should be allocated between construction of foundations, construction of the superstructure and installation of finishings and fittings.

A novice user will then enter either the graphics module or the hook time module. A more experienced user might enter one of these modules directly at the start of the consultation.

THE GRAPHICS MODULE

An interactive graphic display was required to enable a user to select and amend combinations of cranes which would cover the building plan, material storage areas and material off-loading areas. Graphic facilities have not so far been widely used in knowledge-based systems. A system which checks and criticises the design of brick cladding uses a data file created by a CAD system as input to a rule-base (Ref. 7). In Australia a window-frame water penetration expert system uses prolog generated graphic displays (Ref. 8).

The graphics module of CRANES is mainly a procedural programme written in Prospero Pascal with the Prospect graphics toolkit and the GSX graphics operating system extension used to create graphic displays. The pascal code is compiled with the Savoir expert system shell so that data can be directly transferred between the procedural graphics routines and the Savoir rule-base.

In order to use CRANES on a new project a user would digitise the building plan and site boundaries. Wimpey already digitise a general arrangement drawing as part of the routine planning process. The building layout would be represented as a series of polygons each with a defined constant height. In addition the site would be divided into zones on the basis of the maximum crane load in each zone. For example in one zone the maximum load might be a two tonne concrete skip, whereas in another an item of air-conditioning plant of, say, three tonnes might be required. The area covered by load zones would include material off-loading and storage areas as well as the building plan.

During a consultation with CRANES the user is asked to specify crane centres on a display of the building plan, and to define the crane jib lengths required. The system uses the digitised load zone information to determine the minimum lifting requirements of each crane as it is defined. A search is then made of a data-base of available tower cranes to determine whether the size and lifting requirements the user has requested can be satisfied. If these requirements cannot be satisfied then the user must adjust the location or jib length of the crane he has selected. He is prompted to continue adding cranes to the layout plan until all the load zones are covered.

When programme control returns to the rule-base from the graphics module a variety of information is transferred. This includes the number of cranes selected, the location, jib-type and jib-length of each crane, whether a crane has been located inside or outside a structure and the highest point on the building which each crane overswings. On the basis of these data CRANES uses rules to calculate mast heights for the cranes selected using appropriate criteria to avoid jib-jib or jib-mast collision situations where cranes overlap. If the configuration is such that crane collisions cannot be avoided then the user is advised of the problem and returned to the graphic display so that he can amend his choice accordingly.

THE HOOK TIME MODULE

The combination of cranes selected for a project must not only be physically capable of lifting all the loads required for construction but must also be capable of lifting materials at a rate sufficient to match the speed of construction. This criterion is checked by calculating the "hook time" required for the structure i.e. the total number of hours of crane time required to perform all the materials handling tasks during construction. The use of this criterion has been referred to previously in the literature (Ref. 3). From a knowledge of the hook time requirement and the available construction period the minimum number of cranes required can be calculated. This value is generally not an integer.

Within the hook time module the user is prompted for the following information:

(i)   quantities and unit lifting rates for the main construction materials;
(ii)   construction period (which may be known from the preliminary questions);
(iii)   length of working week;
(iv)   crane efficiency;
(v)   likely percentage down-time due to bad weather.

Many expert system shells allow the user to request system options at any point during the consultation. The CRANES system makes extensive use of the following Savoir options:

A - amplification (requests system advice to help in answering the current question).
E - explanation (i.e. why is the system asking the current question?).

Much of the expertise embodied in the hook time module is made available to the user via the amplification option. The user can use this option to request advice on typical values for unit lifting rates of materials, crane efficiency, length of working week etc. and also advice on factors which could lead to a different value being adopted. For example if the user wishes to add a hook time allowance for placing concrete to horizontal slabs then he will be prompted for the rate of placing he wishes to assume. Use of the amplification option results in a display of suggested placing rates for floor slabs of different thicknesses. The user is free to adopt one of these values, or to enter his own value if he has sufficient experience to do so. The consultation is structured so that any number of elements of the structure can be considered separately and allocated different placing or

lifting rates. The expert knowledge of appropriate unit hook time allowances for different materials which is embodied in these hook time texts is extensive and represents one of the main strengths of the system. Considerable knowledge acquisition effort was expended in order to assemble the information presented.

All the suggested values incorporated in the amplification text were provided by expert planning engineers. This essentially represented rule of thumb knowledge although some of the values had originally been based on work study analyses. For example the hook time allowances for in-situ concrete were based on placing rates achieved by concrete gangs. Here it was implicitly assumed that a crane would be dedicated to a pour for the duration of that pour, and hence its rate of working would be constrained by the rate of placing.

An interesting feature of the knowledge elicited was that no explicit allowance was made for the time required to move loads vertically. On a tall structure it would appear that the productivity of cranes would be reduced by an increased average vertical travel of materials. In practice some items such as re-usable forms would be progressively moved up the structure one floor at a time so that overall structure height would be unimportant. The rate of movement of concrete would be limited by the placing rate rather than the speed of operation of the crane. Similarly the rate of movement of precast cladding units would generally be limited by the time taken to fix each unit in place. In the case of other materials experience had apparently shown that improvements in working efficiency as construction progressed counteracted the increased vertical component of lifting to such an extent that practitioners ignored the influence of structure height on the hook time calculation.

For large in-situ concrete elements of the structure, notably slabs, placing can either be by crane and concrete skip or by pumping. The goals of the hook time module are therefore two crane hook requirement values, one calculated on the basis that all materials are moved by crane and the second calculated on the assumption that wherever possible concrete will be pumped.

OPERATION OF CRANES

A central objective of the system is to check that the crane requirements determined from the graphics module (using site coverage criteria) are compatible with those determined from the hook time module (using crane productivity criteria). For example the user might have selected two cranes to cover the site whereas only one would be sufficient to move the necessary materials within the construction period. The basic assumption behind the method of working of the domain experts, at least in the early stages of crane selection, is that the number of tower cranes installed should be kept to a minimum. The user is therefore advised of ways by which he can both keep the number of cranes required to a minimum and maximise the use of the machines installed.

A transcript of this final stage of a consultation is shown in Figure 1. The example shown is a steel framed structure and the user is advised that the steel frame is likely to rise ahead of floor construction making placing of concrete floor slabs by skip difficult. The floor slabs should therefore be placed by pumping. If this is done then one crane should be sufficient to perform all duties but two have been selected to cover the building plan. In the light of this the system advises that the user should either try and use one crane only, or failing this he should install two cranes but maximise the use of them. Hence the system suggests that he could re-enter the graphics module and try:

(i)   using a single static tower crane with a longer jib;
(ii)   using a travelling tower crane.

Alternatively he could re-enter the hook time module and try:
(i)   reducing the construction period;
(ii)   installing one crane for only part of the construction period.

In the example shown in Figure 1 the user chooses the former option and succeeds in covering the site using a single large tower crane.

CRANES has been developed as a helpful assistant to the user. Hence the objective is to highlight weak features of the user's crane selection and to advise him of the alternative methods by which he could improve this choice. The user is always free to ignore the advice given by the system if he knows of important criteria that CRANES does not address. This approach seems to have a wide application, particularly to engineering tasks where decisions are often subjective and unusual solutions may have to be adopted to satisfy unusual criteria.

CRANES therefore relies on the user to generate solutions (i.e. crane layouts) which are then criticised by the system. This approach is very similar to that used by the brickwork expert BERT (Ref. 7). The goals of the system are errors or weaknesses in the user's solution. Such an approach relies on the programmer being able to identify all the possible faults in advance. In the case of the section of CRANES just described nineteen different advice scenarios were identified.

This form of system seems to be a more realistic objective than one which automatically generates "correct" solutions. The design of CRANES recognises that there is more than one acceptable solution, and that decisions required in order to generate a solution may be subjective and coloured by factors which the system has not been coded to take into account.

KNOWLEDGE ACQUISITION

Knowledge acquisition was carried out using interview techniques and iterative prototyping. In general two knowledge engineers were present for each session. Hand-written notes were taken and these were later transcribed in detail. Although these notes appeared to provide a fairly complete record of the interview sessions our more recent use of tape recording in a different domain has led the author to believe that taping of meetings is necessary in order to obtain a full transcript. Transcription of a detailed record of the knowledge acquired, whether from rough notes or from a tape recording, is always a very time-consuming process.

The domain experts were all experienced engineers from the Building Planning Department of Wimpey Construction UK Ltd. In the early stages of knowledge elicitation up to six experts were successfully used for "brain-storming" sessions. However as interviews became more focussed it was not possible to simultaneously involve such a large number of participants. Hence later sessions were conducted with only the two most senior experts present.

So far some 20 hours of knowledge acquisition has been carried out over eight sessions. The author believes it would have been better to have used a larger number of sessions of between one and two hours duration. If sessions are longer than two hours then concentration on both sides starts to wane.

The interview techniques adopted can be classified as follows:
(i)   Unstructured interviews - experts are asked to describe all their knowledge of the domain of interest. The emphasis is on getting an overview of the whole domain.
(ii)   Structured or focussed interviews - experts are asked to describe all their knowledge of small preselected areas. The emphasis is on trying to achieve complete knowledge of a specific preselected area.
(iii) Case-histories - experts are asked to describe real-world examples which they have encountered in the past.
(iv)   Self-reporting - experts are asked to undertake real world examples which they have not seen previously and to describe their thought processes as they undertake these examples.

Iterative prototyping involves the development of a knowledge-base at an early stage during knowledge elicitation and the demonstration of this to the domain experts. Inevitably there will be criticism of the prototype which will lead to it being improved or rewritten in a different form. The basis of this technique is that it is easier for a domain expert to say how the approach of an existing system is incorrect than to state what the correct approach should be in isolation.

*   *   *

Two unstructured interview sessions were carried out at the start of knowledge elicitation to allow the knowledge engineers to get an overview of the domain. Subsequent sessions were mainly structured interviews with prototyping of the first element of the system taking place at the fourth interview. Elicitation of case histories was found to be very valuable as this technique allowed the knowledge engineers to see the approach taken in practice and also revealed some knowledge not elicited by the other techniques. A brief self-reporting session was also carried out. This is good practice in any domain since it serves as a check that the domain experts are describing how they approach a task in practice rather than how they think it ought to be approached.

Demonstration of prototype systems was valuable in that criticism of the prototype always revealed new knowledge. The prototype also served to correct misconceptions about the nature of the system being developed, particularly on the part of the domain experts. Early versions of the prototype merely incorporated small elements of the system - such as a graphic display or part of the hook time calculation. The experts became noticeably more enthusiastic when they saw a later prototype which provided the user with advice in the form of suggested methods for improving his crane selection. In the light of this experience the author would recommend that a prototype system should be developed and demonstrated at a fairly early stage. However for the best response the first demonstration should not take place until the system can give a piece of recognisable and plausible advice.

SUITABILITY OF REPRESENTATION

Up to the present the Department of Civil Engineering at Loughborough has used commercial shell products for the development of expert systems since we believe that at the present time these are more appropriate to the construction industry than the development of inference engines in-house. Savoir enabled us to develop the graphical routines and data-base handling facility for CRANES in procedural Pascal code. It is essential for shells which are to be used in real-world applications to permit direct links to existing or specially developed procedural routines.

Savoir also provided an attractive user interface (a colour window display format) and a variety of user options. The amplification option was essential to this particular system, and an explanation facility is an important feature of all knowledge-based systems. The explanation text in Savoir has to be written by the programmer, whereas the author believes that an automated explanation facility which displays the text of rules within the system should be used. Development of explanation text by the programmer is time-consuming, and there is a risk of explanations becoming out-of-step with the actual logic of the system due to coding errors or a failure to amend the explanation text when rules are changed. Admittedly some rules can appear obscure if displayed directly, and an ideal system would provide an automated display of the rule in use plus a facility for adding additional explanatory comments where necessary.

Knowledge-based systems are usually highly inter-active and should exhibit a high degree of user-friendliness. Because of this they are heavily reliant on a text-based dialogue with the user. The text handling and formatting facilities built into a shell such as Savoir enable a programmer to develop this text very rapidly.

The iterative nature of the crane selection procedure involves repeated looping through the graphics and hook time modules. Loops can be created in Savoir using demons, with "made" variables as loop counters if required (a demon is a command which is executed immediately the trigger condition which qualifies it is satisfied). Care is required to ensure that the

firing of the demons controlling the loop produces the desired effect. If a number of operations are to be carried out by a single demon (i.e. displaying text, clearing previous results, calling a Pascal routine, incrementing a loop counter) then the hierarchy of operations used by Savoir may lead to an outcome not anticipated by the programmer.

Provision of an accumulator for the total' hook time required the provision of a nested loop. This feature was particularly difficult to provide due to the vagaries of demon control.

The most serious problems of representation were encountered when rules were required to determine the mast heights of a number of overlapping tower cranes. The experts suggested a hierarchy of criteria for deciding the relative heights of overlapping cranes which can be summarised as follows:
(i) cranes with luffing jibs must always be the tallest to avoid jib-jib collision when the luffing jib is raised;
(ii) if two crane masts are at a separation which is less than the jib length of one crane, then the crane with the longer jib must be tallest to avoid jib-mast collision. (Note - if both jibs were longer than the distance of separation of the masts then the user would have been instructed to amend his crane selection at a previous stage).
(iii) the crane with the greater load carrying capacity should be the taller;
(iv) the crane with the longer jib should be the taller.

General rules were required which could be applied irrespective of the number of cranes selected by the user. Savoir did not provide a means of representing such rules, and required different rule sets to be written for cases involving one, two, three cranes etc. Only the cases of one and two cranes have been coded. Even the case of two cranes is difficult because the hierarchical nature of the above criteria is tortuous to represent in Savoir (i.e.if (i) or (ii) does not apply then use (iii), if (iii) is not applicable then use (iv)).

Further work is to be carried out to investigate other representations of the overlapping crane problem.

CRANES currently comprises 90 rules and 100 demons, and incorporates 1000 lines of Pascal in the graphics module. Response time is generally good on the IBM PC XT on which the system is mounted but slows at a couple of key points in the consultation. There is no problem with response time on an IBM PC AT.

SPEED OF DEVELOPMENT

Knowledge acquisition sessions produced a wealth of information about crane selection and the system at present only addresses a small proportion of this. Difficulty was experienced in structuring this information and in deciding "where to start". Once coding had commenced delays were experienced at times due to the difficulties of knowledge representation and demon control described in the previous section.

Some of the features which slowed development

have previously been recognised by other authors. It has been suggested that problems which take a few hours to solve represent good candidates for knowledge-based systems (Ref. 9). Our BREDAMP and NETWORK systems model tasks which would probably require less than an hour of an expert's time to resolve and these domains proved very amenable to expert system development. A building planning engineer might spend about three days selecting appropriate cranes for a multi-storey building contract and this time span is reflected in the wealth and complexity of the knowledge encountered in this domain.

Some other features have made this domain more difficult than others that the author has attempted:
(i) use of spatial reasoning;
(ii) use of iterative processes.
This again agrees with the findings of other authors (Ref. 2).

CONCLUSIONS

The developments described in this paper have considerably advanced the work previously done at Loughborough in the domain of selection of materials handling equipment for multi-storey construction sites. In particular a graphics facility has been provided and knowledge about the production rates of cranes has been incorporated.

The CRANES system has been implemented on an IBM PC XT using the Savoir expert system shell. Savoir provided an interface to procedural routines, a good user interface, good text handling facilities and user options including amplification and explanation facilities. The amplification option was of great importance to the system developed.

The iterative nature of the crane selection process necessitated the provision of loops in the rule-base. Some problems were experienced in implementing these, particularly where a nested loop was required. The simple production rule representation of Savoir was inappropriate for reasoning about relationships between a variable number of cranes.

The system acts as an adviser, suggesting values for input data and allowing the user to choose his own crane locations. The system criticises the crane selection which the user suggests, but he is free to accept or reject this advice.

Knowledge acquisition was carried out using interview techniques and iterative prototyping. Iterative prototyping was found to be a useful technique, but for maximum benefit the author suggests that a system should be able to give a piece of recognisable and plausible advice before it is demonstrated to the domain experts for the first time.

ACKNOWLEDGEMENTS

Grateful thanks are due to Professor Geoffrey Trimble and Dr Roger Allwood of the Department of Civil Engineering at Loughborough for their help and encouragement with the development of CRANES, and also to Dr Joe Cullen of the Department of Social Sciences at Loughborough who assisted with the knowledge acquisition. My thanks are also due to the Building Planning Department of Wimpey Construction UK Ltd and in particular Mr John Greene and Mr Don Edwards. I also acknowledge the role of our sponsors in this work, the US Army Corps of Engineers Research Laboratory.

REFERENCES

1. Godfrey, K.A. Expert systems enter the market place, Civil Engineering, American Society of Civil Engineers, May 1986, pp 70-73.

2. Welbank, M., A review of knowledge acquisition techniques for expert systems, British Telecom Research Laboratories, 1983.

3. Gray, C. and Little, J. A systematic approach to the selection of an appropriate crane for a construction site, Construction Management and Economics, 3, pp 121-144.

4. Wijesundera, D.A. and Harris, F.C., The integration of an expert system into the construction planning process, Proc. of 2nd Int. Conf. on Civil and Structural Engineering Computing, 1985, 2, pp 399-405.

5. Trimble, G. and Cooper, C.N., Experience with knowledge acquisition for expert systems in construction, SERC Workshop on Knowledge Acquisition for Engineering Applications, Abingdon, June 1987.

6. Allwood, R.J., Stewart, D.J., Hinde, C., and Negus, B., Evaluation of expert system shell programs for construction industry applications, Department of Civil Engineering, University of Technology, Loughborough, 1985.

7. Bowen, J.A., Cornick, T.C., and Bull, S.P. BERT - an expert system for brickwork design, Expert Systems 86, Brighton, UK, 1986.

8. Thompson, J.V., A water penetration expert system using prolog with graphics, Proc. of the 2nd Australian Conf. on Applications of Expert Systems, New South Wales Institute of Technology, Sydney, 14-16 May 1986, pp 51-73.

9. Nii, H.P. Quoted in Feigenbaum, E.A. and McCorduck, P., The fifth generation, 1983, p 81.

Figure 1   The final stages of a consultation with CRANES

```
* * * * * * * * * * * * * * * * * * * * * * * * * * * * * * * * * * * * * * * * * * *
* No. of tower cranes from graphics          = 2                                    *
* No. of hooks to perform all duties         = 1.36                                 *
* No. of hooks if horizontal slabs pumped    = 0.97                                 *
*                                                                                   *
* The results so far suggest that the number of static tower cranes required is = 2.*
*                                                                                   *
* The steel frame is likely to be assembled ahead of floor construction making use of a concrete *
* skip difficult.  Hence all in-situ concrete to horizontal slabs must be placed by pump and the *
* cranes will not be fully utilised.                                                *
* You should therefore consider the following alternative solutions:               *
* A: Re-enter the graphics module and try to reduce the number of cranes required to cover the site*
* by:                                                                               *
*  (i)    using static tower cranes with longer jibs;                               *
*  (ii)   using a travelling tower crane.                                           *
* B: Adopt the number of cranes suggested by the graphics but re-enter the hook time module and *
* try to increase crane utilisation by:                                             *
* (i)    reducing the construction period;                                          *
* (ii)   installing one or more cranes for only part of the construction period.    *
*                                                                                   *
* Please indicate which system module you wish to enter:                            *
*       Preliminary questions          1                                            *
*       Enter graphics module          2                                            *
*       Calculate hook time            3                                            *
*       End consultation               4                                            *
*                                                                                   *
*       (1..4 or an option)       2                                                 *
* * * * * * * * * * * * * * * * * * * * * * * * * * * * * * * * * * * * * * * * * * *
```

User re-enters the graphics module and succeeds in covering the whole site with a single large tower crane.

```
* * * * * * * * * * * * * * * * * * * * * * * * * * * * * * * * * * * * * * * * * * *
* No. of tower cranes from graphics          = 1                                    *
* No. of hooks to perform all duties         = 1.36                                 *
* No. of hooks if horizontal slabs pumped    = 0.97                                 *
*                                                                                   *
* The results so far suggest that the number of static tower cranes required is probably = 1. *
*                                                                                   *
* All in-situ concrete to horizontal slabs must be pumped.                          *
*                                                                                   *
* The number of cranes suggested is very close to the minimum number required as derived from the *
* hook time calculation.  Problems may be encountered if the crane duties are not evenly spread *
* throughout the construction period.                                               *
*                                                                                   *
* You should therefore re-enter the hook time calculation and reduce the hook requirement slightly*
* by lengthening the construction period or increasing working hours.               *
*                                                                                   *
* If this is not possible then you could consider whether the hook time requirement could be *
* reduced by making design modifications.                                           *
*                                                                                   *
* Please indicate which system module you wish to enter:                            *
*       Preliminary questions          1                                            *
*       Enter graphics module          2                                            *
*       Calculate hook time            3                                            *
*       End consultation               4                                            *
*                                                                                   *
* (1..4 or an option)   3                                                           *
* * * * * * * * * * * * * * * * * * * * * * * * * * * * * * * * * * * * * * * * * * *
```

```
* * * * * * * * * * * * * * * * * * * * * * * * * * * * * * * * * * * * * * * * * * * * * * * * *
* Which element of the hook time calculation do you want to amend?                              *
*                                                                                               *
* Time for in-situ concrete                      1                                              *
* Time for bar or fabric reinforcement           2                                              *
* Time for formwork                              3                                              *
* Time for structural steel or metal decking     4                                              *
* Time for precast floor units                   5                                              *
* Time for cladding units                        6                                              *
* Crane efficiency                               7                                              *
* Percentage bad weather                         8                                              *
* Hours worked per week                          9                                              *
* Construction period                            10                                             *
*                                                                                               *
* (1..10 or an option)   9                                                                      *
* * * * * * * * * * * * * * * * * * * * * * * * * * * * * * * * * * * * * * * * * * * * * * * * *


* * * * * * * * * * * * * * * * * * * * * * * * * * * * * * * * * * * * * * * * * * * * * * * * *
* What is the length of the working week (hours)?                                               *
*                                                                                               *
* (30.0  to  168.0 or an option)   45.0                                                         *
* * * * * * * * * * * * * * * * * * * * * * * * * * * * * * * * * * * * * * * * * * * * * * * * *


* * * * * * * * * * * * * * * * * * * * * * * * * * * * * * * * * * * * * * * * * * * * * * * * *
* Do you want to see a summary of the hook time calculation?                                    *
*                                                                                               *
* (Y or N or an option)   N                                                                     *
* * * * * * * * * * * * * * * * * * * * * * * * * * * * * * * * * * * * * * * * * * * * * * * * *


* * * * * * * * * * * * * * * * * * * * * * * * * * * * * * * * * * * * * * * * * * * * * * * * *
* No. of tower cranes from graphics         = 1                                                 *
* No. of hooks to perform all duties        = 1.21                                              *
* No. of hooks if horizontal slabs pumped   = 0.86.                                             *
*                                                                                               *
* You should use 1 static tower crane.                                                          *
*                                                                                               *
* All in-situ concrete to horizontal slabs must be pumped.                                      *
* * * * * * * * * * * * * * * * * * * * * * * * * * * * * * * * * * * * * * * * * * * * * * * * *
```

THE DEVELOPMENT OF A KNOWLEDGE BASED EXPERT SYSTEM FOR THE SELECTION OF EARTHMOVING EQUIPMENT

John Christian, BEng, PhD, FICE, MCSCE, CEng, PEng and
Havindra Caldera, BSc(Eng), MASME, MIE, CEng
Faculty of Engineering and Applied Science
Memorial University of Newfoundland
St John's, Newfoundland, Canada

Improving construction productivity is critically important today due to stringent financial resources. Mathematical models and knowledge based expert systems in conjunction with micro-computers can be used as tools to improve productivity and to minimize the costs of operations in construction. The knowledge based expert system described in this paper consists of a computer program, which simulates a consultation between an expert in equipment selection, a domain expert in a particular geographical area or company, and a user. It also incorporates some specialized reasoning or artificial intelligence. The system presents a series of questions and a series of answers from which the user has to respond according to the requirements and the conditions of the operation. The program provides a list of suitable equipment for a fleet and the corresponding costs per unit output, depending on the user's answers.

INTRODUCTION

One of the major management tasks faced by construction managers is to improve construction productivity and thereby reduce construction costs. Various methods and techniques can be incorporated to improve construction productivity at different phases of a construction project [Ref. 4]. The development of feasible methods and the selection of appropriate equipment, to accomplish various activities, are common tasks at the planning stage of any construction project.

The earthmoving operation plays an important role among the wide variety of operations on many construction projects. The selection of the most appropriate types, sizes and number of machines for a particular earthmoving activity is therefore very significant in reducing the overall cost of a project.

Although, mathematical models have been used as tools to improve and optimize operations involved in construction, the application of knowledge based systems, in conjunction with micro-computers, in the field of construction engineering is just beginning. The development of a knowledge based expert system enables the selection of the most appropriate and economical type of equipment to be made, on the basis of suitability and availability, for a particular activity.

STRUCTURE OF THE MODEL

The knowledge based expert system described in this paper for the selection of earthmoving equipment has been developed using three main phases on a micro-computer, as illustrated in Figure 1. Ten different types of earthmoving equipment have been considered in the main menu. The second menu, on models or sizes of equipment contains seventy-one items of equipment. However, the program has provision to include more types and models of equipment should this be required, in which case corresponding relevant technical information would then need to be inserted.

A selection of suitable types of equipment, for the earthworks operation under consideration, is made from the main menu in the first phase of the system. The outputs of all the models or the sizes of the selected machines are then obtained. Using these outputs, the optimum combination of machines, to suit the earthworks operation under consideration, is then determined in the final phase of the system. A detailed explanation of these phases is given in the following sections.

SELECTION OF SUITABLE TYPES OF EQUIPMENT

The concept of the selection of the most appropriate equipment for a particular type of earthmoving operation under consideration is diagramatically shown in Figure 2. Various types of equipment are listed in the menu and relevant technical information corresponding to these types are entered into the data base [Ref. 1,6,7]. The knowledge base is logically structured so that factors such as haul distance, on-off highway requirements, traction ability, and so forth can be considered [Ref. 2,5]. The user is posed with a series of questions and depending on the user's answers, the knowledge base selects the suitable types of equipment that could be used for the earthworks operation from the main menu.

In the proposed system, the selection of the appropriate earthmoving equipment begins by requesting a reply to a question on haul distance requirements. A range of average haul distances is presented to the user as an aid so that the anticipated average haul distance of the earthworks operation can be selected. As some types of equipment cannot be economically used to haul material outside a certain range, the system

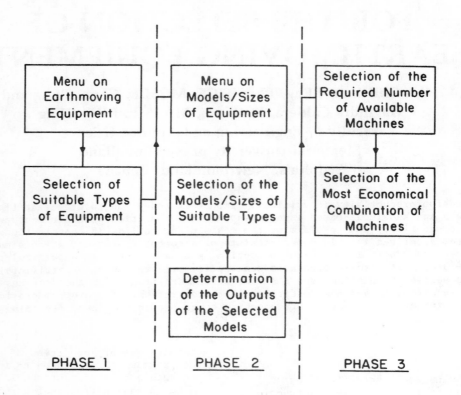

Fig. 1 Block Diagram of System

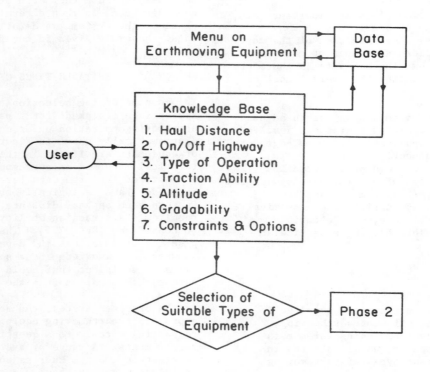

Fig. 2 Phase 1 of the System

selects the types of equipment which can be economically employed. The model then proceeds by asking a question regarding on-off highway restrictions. Since, some of the machine types are not allowed to operate on highways, the system eliminates certain types of equipment to suit the user's on-off highway requirement.

The user is then asked to choose the most apposite operation or operations related to the job under consideration out of a number of common earthmoving operations. According to the user's choice some of the previously selected types of equipment are assigned for possible utilization.

In addition to these factors, the power potential of a machine, limited either by traction ability or gradability, is also used in selecting the types of suitable earthmoving machines. In the questions related to these factors, the user is requested to pick out the appropriate soil types of the haul and return routes from a set of soil types and the appropriate Grade Resistance Factors (GRFs). After checking the traction ability and gradability of the selected types of machines for the haul and return routes, the remaining machines are finally considered for the constraints or options applicable to the working conditions. By considering all the above factors, the system provides the types of equipment that should be used for the earthworks operation.

PRODUCTION OUTPUTS OF THE SELECTED MODELS

When the suitable types of equipment have been selected for a particular earthworks operation, the next step is to obtain the production outputs of all the models of the selected types of machines. These outputs are obtained as outlined in Figure 3. Initially, data concerning the models and sizes of the types of machines selected in phase one are selected from the menu on models and sizes of equipment. Then, in the knowledge base, the height and weight constraints, applicable to the construction site or haul road, are considered by requesting the user to assign limiting values to them. By comparing the limiting values with the operating weights and heights of the selected models given in the data base, the usable models are ascertained. The outputs of these remaining machines are then determined using the information in the data base and the user's responses to the questions provided.

The hourly output that can be expected from earthmoving equipment depends on several factors. Among these, the design features and capabilities of the machine are the most important. Furthermore, the output depends on the nature of the excavated material, the loading and hauling activities, the haul road conditions, the overall job efficiency, and the output of the loading machines. Since these factors influence the outputs of each category of machine in a different manner, the system calculates the outputs using different methods. Most of the information related to the design features and soil properties are stored in the data base. In some cases the user will need to specify some of the design features, such as belt width and belt speed, of available belt conveyors. This is accomplished in

the system by further questions. The nature of the material to be handled is basically represented by the soil properties and the degree of hardness of the stockpile or the ground. A set of soil types and a set of stockpile types are therefore presented to the user so that a suitable combination can be selected.

The travel times of machines are affected by the travel speeds and the haul road conditions and are important in determining the production outputs. Therefore, to obtain the travel times, the user is first requested to assign various sectors to the haul and return routes, the differences in the sectors being dependent on the soil types and the grades. The system then provides a table showing these sectors so that the relevant information can be inserted.

By using these factors and the information in the data base, the system then finds the hourly output of each machine under ideal operating conditions. These values vary from actual production and depend on the overall job efficiency. Hence, in the second phase of the system the user is provided with the option either to suggest a value for job efficiency or to use the facility in the system. Since the overall job efficiency varies with the job conditions, equipment conditions, management conditions as well as the operator's skill, experience, and coordination with other external forces, the system questions the user regarding these factors [Ref. 3]. The user is also asked to consider the probable weather and visibility conditions, which can be very important in North America. The system then determines the overall job efficiency, and hence the actual output, for each machine depending on the excellent, average or poor ratings provided by the user.

By using the actual output of each machine, the total quantity of material to be hauled, the availability of machines, and so forth, the most economical fleet of machines is deduced in the final phase of the program to suit the required schedule.

SELECTION OF THE MOST ECONOMICAL FLEET

At the beginning of the final phase of the system the user is requested to provide the quantity of material to be handled in the time period allotted for the individual earthworks activities in order to find the required rate of earthmoving. However, the system also allows for different rates of production to be considered for one particular activity, over different time periods, according to the schedule requirements. The system then provides the user with an opportunity to give the available number of machines of each model or size in his entire fleet, and to check the feasibility of the number of machines that could be operated within the working area. By considering the user's responses and using the output values of the models obtained in the second phase of the system, the proposed system next determines the number of machines or set of machines that should be used to achieve the required rate of production, as shown in Figure 4. The concept of effective equipment matching is also considered for machines which require a separate loading machine.

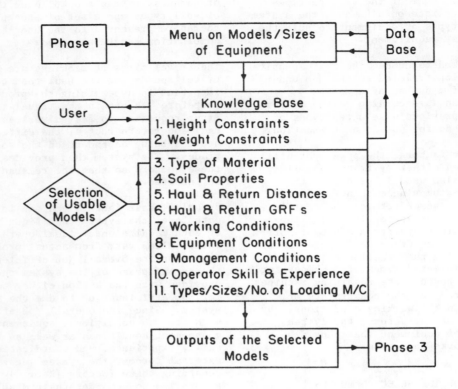

Fig. 3 Phase 2 of the System

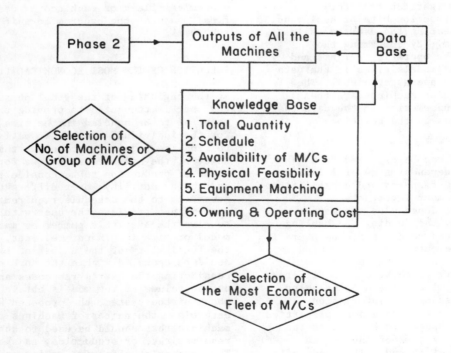

Fig. 4 Phase 3 of the System

In selecting the most economical fleet of machines, the next major objective in the process is to obtain the costs incurred for each group of machines. Accordingly, the system enables the user to utilize a facility to provide the costs due to mobilization, installation and preparation, road maintenance, and owning and operating, or, in the event of renting, the total rental cost. If the user has no idea about the owning and operating, or, the total rental cost of any machine, the cost can be found using a facility in the system.

By knowing the cost incurred per unit time and the output per unit time, the system determines and provides the cost per unit volume of material to be handled by all the selected groups of machines. By comparing these cost figures, the system finally selects the most economical fleet of machines for the earthworks operation.

CONCLUSIONS

The knowledge based expert system described in this paper can be used as a tool in selecting the most economical fleet of earthmoving machines for an earthworks operation by any person who has a little knowledge in earthmoving equipment and computer programming. Even to an expert, the system could be used as a datum in obtaining a quick selection of earthmoving equipment for an earthworks operation. The system can also be used to perform a sensitivity analysis by changing the input parameters or the answers to the questions contained in the system.

REFERENCES

1. Caterpillar Performance Handbook, Edition 17, Caterpillar Tractor Company, Peoria, Illinois, 1986.

2. Christian, John, Management, Machines and Methods in Civil Engineering, John Wiley and Sons, Inc., New York, N.Y., 1981.

3. Day, D.A., Construction Equipment Guide, John Wiley and Sons, Inc., New York, N.Y., 1973.

4. Parker, Henry W. and Oglesby, Clarkson H., Methods Improvement for Construction Managers, McGraw Hill, Inc., New York, N.Y., 1972.

5. Peurifoy, R.L., Construction Planning, Equipment, and Methods, McGraw Hill, Inc., New York, N.Y., 1970.

6. Production and Cost Estimating of Material Movement with Earthmoving Equipment, Terex Corporation, Hudson, Ohio, 1981.

7. Specifications and Applications Handbook of Komatsu, Edition 7, Komatsu Ltd., Minato-ku, Tokyo, Japan, 1986.

THE DEVELOPMENT OF A KNOWLEDGE BASED COMPUTER SYSTEM FOR DECISION MAKING ON CONSTRUCTION METHODS

A Manesero BSc, K P Chapman MSc, DMS, MCIOB and K A Sinclair
Department of Civil Engineering and Building, Coventry Polytechnic, England

SYNOPSIS

The 'Method of Construction' has frequently been identified as one of the major factors in the successful execution of an optimum programme of construction. Unfortunately little work has been carried out in order to aid construction planners with the task of evaluating the suitability of the many different, yet possible, Methods of Construction for any one project.

A research project is presented which is directly aimed at aiding construction planners with the evaluation of potentially suitable methods of construction and the eventual selection of the optimum Method for the current project. This research project is aimed at producing a computerized package using a knowledge base and a knowledge manipulation algorithm in order to select, quantify and evaluate the suitability of alternative Methods of Construction. The basic concepts behind the various knowledge based algorithms is here presented and an emphasis is given to the fact that no standard software package has been used for this development.

INTRODUCTION

In the construction industry it is not uncommon to find the fields of design and production divorced from one another to the extent of alienation of the two practices. This phenomenon can also be noticed at a small scale within the different departments of a construction company. We are referring to the acute problem of communication between the different departments and the little use made of the experience and judgement of the different members who form the organisation.

We are particularly concerned with the information transfer between the site staff and the planning department within a construction company. It is not uncommon for tender documents to be derived at the planning department, decisions on the Method of Construction and the programme of works to be developed and tender to be submitted without ever consulting the site staff who would be responsible for the running of that contract. It is also common to be allowed a very short time period in which to prepare a tender and a long delay to follow between the tender submission date and the actual start on site. In the former the planning department finds it self pressurised in producing an optimum tender for the project and all the documentation that goes with it within a very limited time scale, between two to three weeks for a medium size project. As part of the documentation we find the Method Statement. It has been found (Ref. 1) that this document is generally produced as a contract requirement and does little in clarifying the exact Method of Construction that was considered for developing the programme of works.

THE AUTOMATION OF DECISION MAKING ON THE METHOD OF CONSTRUCTION

It has become obvious that there is a need to aid the planning department in the task of tender planning and the site staff with short term programming. The need for information transfer between office and site, and vice versa, has also been noted along side the need for two basic types of Method Statements. A generalistic Method Statement of a descriptive nature, and a second Method Statement for use by the site staff and supplying a more thorough description and a step by step guidance on the Method of Construction envisaged for the current project.

It was decided to investigate the possibility of implementing a computerized system which was to take the duties of both a planning assistant and a messenger between office and site. Such a system will have the following requirements:

1. be capable of storing factual information on construction matters,
2. store and manipulate heuristic rules,
3. perform general construction analysis,
4. give advice and recommend on Methods of Construction,
5. supply descriptive and documented evidence of its analysis and recommendations.

The above recommendations clearly point towards a knowledge based system which is to tackle both linearly definable problem and heuristic queries (Ref. 2). A decision support system is considered to provide the best means of giving these facilities rather than an expert system, the output from which would be too prescriptive.

The remainder of this paper may be considered as a case study of the development of a knowledge based decision support system for selecting the most suitable method of construction for an in-site reinforced concrete building framed. There are some guidelines given on the approach of Knowledge Engineering within the construction industry, a general description of the algorithm developed to simulate the decision making of construction personnel, and an overview of the potential such a system might have within construction companies.

IMPLEMENTATION STRATEGY

The development of this system has been carried out on a Cambridge Microcomputer Vittese UNIX based processor. This comes in the class of so called 'SuperMicros' and is a 32 User 68020 system. One of the first considerations was the particular language to use. The more traditional languages for AI work such as LISP and PROLOG were rejected in favour of the 'C' language. The rationale behind this decision was complex, but the main considerations were as follows:

1. C was well known by one of the authors,
2. availability of C and its software development support tools under the UNIX operating system,
3. run time efficiency of traditional AI languages cannot compete with C,
4. the ability of C to mix with applications developed in a different environment, eg. Database Systems.

This is in line with the current thinking of many large software development agencies (Ref. 6).

Subsequently our intentions are to port this system onto a transportable UNIX workstation. For this purpose we intend using an Integral PC with 512 RAM and 760 K disc.

THE CONSTRUCTION ADVISORY SYSTEM CAS

The development of CAS has very close link with practising construction companies. Thanks to this close collaboration, it has been possible to identify the type and volume of information requiring transfer from office to site, as well as the limitations in time and information available by the office. The advice and recommendations offered by our collaborating establishment made it possible to define CAS as:

"An Intelligent Knowledge Based Decision Support System for Assisting in the Selection of the Optimum Method of Construction".

KNOWLEDGE ENGINEERING

The knowledge from the construction industry may be acquired from two distinct sources:

a. in published form from statutory documents, manufacturers' data and historic company records. This form of information may be termed "structured data".

b. from interviewing practising construction personnel. This form of information may be termed "heuristic data".

Structured data, in construction related domains, may not always be as structured as it might sound. For example, the guidelines from a code of practice sets out working parameters but it is the judgement of the site Engineer as to which is applicable at a certain situation. Thus heuristic data can arise from the interpretation of structured data. To be successful in structuring an operational knowledge base for construction use a knowledge engineer must approach both sources of information simultaneously (Ref. 3).

The techniques used for acquiring heuristic data from construction personnel required careful consideration. From our experience we discovered that the approach and techniques needed for interviewing the different types of individuals within the one company had to be altered at each stage, but the same approach was found suitable when interviewing individuals at the same level but of a different company. At the main office both senior management and project management were found fairly willing to discuss their operations and supply general information with multiple referencing. Site management was noticed to be more secretive and use limited examples when clarifying their judgement, notably the current project. Tradesmen supply the best quantified advice and use a much wider spectrum to found their judgement. Many problems which go unspotted by management were pointed out by the men and their solutions were unequivocally explained. Figure 1 gives a summary of our findings and may be found

PERSONNEL LEVEL	Senior Management	Project Management	Site Management	Operatives
RELEVANCE OF INFORMATION	Company policies & Legislation	Working practices & Materials	Working practices labour, plant	Methods, times, difficulties
INTERVIEW TYPE	Structured & Argumentative	Structured or Unstructured	Unstructured or Structured	Unstructured
LOCATION OF INTERVIEW	Own Office	Own Office or on Site	Site Office	Pub
RECORDING MEANS	Tape or Video	Tape or Notes	Notes	Tape Recorder

Figure 1

helpful by other knowledge engineers embarked on a similar study.

THE STRUCTURE OF CAS

The basic structure of CAS is as shown on Figure 2. The main operations of the system are contained in a module termed 'The Drive'. Within the Driver can be found the three basic algorithms of the "Method Selector", "Automatic Network Generator" and the "Knowledge Manipulator". It is through this algorithms that CAS may be termed a "Knowledge Based System". CAS contains other modules which are broadly classified into The Store, The Analyser and The Project.

The use of Fuzzy ranges and the evaluation of Fuzzy sets are used where the experts' opinions differ on the conclusion to a problem (Ref. 4). True Fuzzy arithmetic has not been used, but in its place a much more simplified evaluation has been developed which involves averaging the fuzzy range. The second form of representation is a straight forward linear range.

The Construction Modules are another name for construction activities. Each Construction Module represents an operation on site. Associated with this operation is a measure of the resources required, the external influences this operation may be affected by, what measures to take if it is affected and a list of possible preceding and succeeding modules. Each of the links between

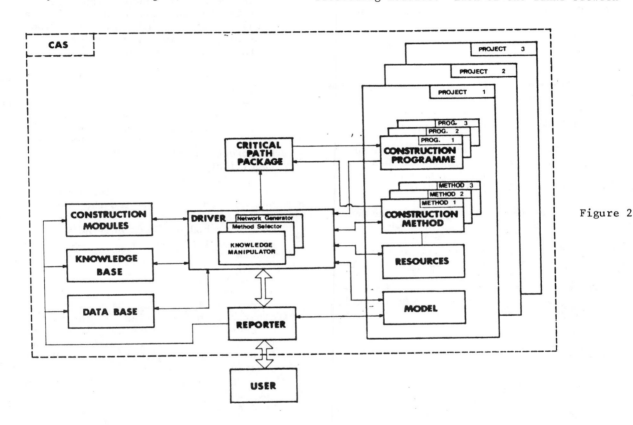

Figure 2

THE STORE

Within the store there can be found The Knowledge base and database as well as the Construction Modules.

The knowledge base and data base have been developed in a hierarchical format isolating related domains into sets or modules. This facilitates easier updating and faster access. Related entries into both the knowledge base and data base have been generated using an inheritance approach (Ref. 7). By building inheritance relations and providing links from the parent to the child, it will not only save memory space but will most importantly ease the entries into the corresponding schema.

Two simple numeric representation have been applied to help with the evaluation of verbal attributes.

modules has been designed so it may accommodate lead and lag times between activities. A differentiation between the accessing of a module at the current bay or at the next bay or next floor has been built in, in order to prevent the buildup of a network with irrelevant quantities and to allow a more even allocation of resources.

THE ANALYSER

The Analyser contains a set of traditional constructional software packages.

The Critical Path Analysis program (CPA) has been home built and adapted so it functions as a background process and is operated by the "Network Generator" without any user 1/0.

THE REINFORCEMENT ANALYSIS PROGRAM (RAP)

This is a program aimed at obtaining an estimate of the volume of reinforcement in each member of the frame. This program is a background process and uses the Model of the project and relevant tables from the database in order to perform structural calculations. RAP makes use of the knowledge base for deciding on certain assumptions which are required in order to proceed. RAP is not a foolproof structural analysis program and, even though it makes use of equations and tables in accordance with BS8110, BS6399 and other documents concerned with reinforced concrete design, the resulting quantities of reinforcement are only estimates for planning purposes (Ref. 5).

THE PROJECT

The Project stores a representation of the current project. The information contained in The Project can be subdivided into two broad groups, The Model and The Method.

The Model contains a representation of the project in its structural configuration, site description and location and abstractions from the specification and Bill of Quantities.

The Method stores the evaluation from the Driver for the current project. It is here where the derived Method of Construction with its associated resource allocation and programme of works are saved. As it is not unknown that the optimum solution to constructing a project might not be the one selected by the project manager, it is necessary for several Methods of Construction to be analysed and saved.

THE DRIVER

The term "Knowledge Manipulator" has been used in preference to the term "Inference Engine" for it is felt that inferencing, or drawing conclusions, is not a good description of the manner in which knowledge-based rules are handled during the operations of CAS.

During the initial developments of a new project, the Knowledge Manipulator sequentially triggers empty master schema which then run in parallel, interacting with the knowledge base. This results in a set of rules-filled schema which appertain directly to the current project. A schema can be visualised as a single questionnaire on a particular topic that requires investigation. The set of rule schemas represent the full list of topics that have to be checked in order to arrive at a conclusion. Each schema contains a different number of slots. Each of those slots will contain a set number of possible questions but only one, or none, will be relevant to the current project. The selection of the relevant question ino each slot will then cut down in the checking through questions which are obviously irrelevant. It is felt that this simplified approach of schema formation is a better simulation of the mental exercises professionals undergo during the initial and subsequent re-analysis of a project.

The "Method Selector Algorithm" follows very closely the techniques used in practice for testing and selecting from the various possible methods of construction. Two distinct stages are normally encountered: firstly, matching the present project against previous projects which show similar characteristics, and secondly, to investigate the proposed solutions against the present project.

The first stage is simulated by filling a project template with the measures which represent the current project. A list of previous projects will exist in the data bank. Each will contain a template representing that project and linked to it the method of construction adopted. By matching the current project against all previous projects with a similar specification, it is possible to arrive at a list of potentially suitable methods of construction.

The second stage firstly involves checking the validity of the various methods against the project specifications and the current company working policies. Those methods which are found suitable are then adjusted, in relation to the allocation of resources and the sequence of construction, to match with the precise project specifications. At this instance the rules from the schema template will be utilised in order to optimise the variable allocations but still preserve the logic behind the current Method.

Once a method has been duly adjusted, it is next passed as input to the "Automatic Network Generator".

The "Automatic Network Generator", which in turn makes use of the 'Construction Modules', will automatically develop the network of construction activities for the particular Method of construction. This will in turn form the input for the 'Critical Path' analysis. The 'Construction Programme' for the Method of Construction under investigation is therefore generated automatically, using subsequent schema CAS then checks the logic of the resulting programme.

Logically obvious items, such as the site working efficiency across the year or the reuse cycle of certain items, are identified during the logic checks and the network is adjusted accordingly. Through subsequent checks of the logic of the resulting programme, it is therefore possible to obtain a most logical programme of works for the Method of Construction under investigation.

Obviously the user may trace through an evaluation and can overrule decisions made by CAS. If the user finds a certain illogical conclusion repeating itself, he may adjust the evaluation of such a rule by abstracting the relevant schema out from the schema template, carrying out the adjustment in the relevant schema slot and repositioning the schema back in its original place.

INFORMATION TRANSFER

Once the construction planner has been presented with several Methods of Construction and their corresponding programme of works he may then make his decision on which Method to adopt for the current project. Once a Method has been accepted, CAS then proceeds at producing the relevant documentation, ie. a bar chart for the programme of works, a resources allocation report, a general Method Statement for the works and a more detailed Method Statement specifying each of the operations involved in more detail.

CAS was never aimed to be of use only within the main offices of a construction organisation. This can be easily identified by the modular nature of its basic structure and from the adoption of the concept of templates in which to hold the directly relevant knowledge based rules as well as the model for the current project. The site offices may be provided with a transportable workstation on which CAS may be ported.

THE FUTURE OF CAS

It can be seen that such a system has immense potential within the planning offices of construction companies. By applying a knowledge base system to aid in the decision making exercise and taking away from the planners the more trivial decisions and calculations, it is envisaged that more time will be spent on investigating the more problematic aspects of the project and eventually a more economic solution may be discovered. It will also be possible to eliminate the tendency that site management has of looking into a black box in order to discover the precise method which was conceived by the planner in order to arrive at the proposed programme of works. CAS may fully

document each of its decision making stages and cross reference the proposed methods to previous projects to act as examples.

REFERENCES

1. Duff, A.R. and Rydal, J. The Potential of Method Statements in Control of Large Building Projects. Research Report, University of Manchester Institute of Science and Technology, 1985.

2. Jones, K. Where can Expert Systems be Used? Computer Weekly, 12 February, 1987.

3. Firlej, M.D. Knowledge Elicitation - What is Involved. Expert Systems for Construction and Service Engineering, CICA/BSRIA 1986.

4. Zadeh, L.A. Fuzzy Sets. Information Control, Vol 3, pp 338-353, 1965.

5. Anon, Manual for the Design of Reinforced Concrete Building Structures. The Institute of Civil Engineers, The Institution of Structural Engineers, Appendix A, pp 74-77, October 1985.

6. Morgan, A. An Overview of Tools and Languages. Proceedings of KBS 87 Conference, June 1987. Online Publications 1987.

7. Kinnucan, P. Software Tools Speed Expert System Development. High Technology, pp 16-20, March 1985.

THE USE OF EXPERT SYSTEMS AND SENSITIVITY ANALYSES IN FORMWORK PRODUCTIVITY AND DESIGN

John Christian, BEng, PhD, FICE, MCSCE, CEng, PEng
and Saif U Mir, BSc(Eng), MEng
Faculty of Engineering and Applied Science
Memorial University of Newfoundland
St John's, Newfoundland, Canada

Although formwork productivity has been measured for many years, and productivity indices have been established and compiled, accuracy in many cases has been questioned. Furthermore, the design of formwork has varied from using intuitive, semi-empirical methods to more rational analytical methods. Today, it is possible to use a general purpose package progam in the design and optimization of formwork.

More refined databases for productivity indices can now be created. Sophisticated measurement tools, such as time-lapse photography, and microcomputers can more accurately measure and considerably reduce the time consuming effort in the compilation and dissemination of data. Refinements and improvements in the accuracy of productivity data will enable productivity and costs to be determined more accurately and, when linked to an integrated package design program, improve the economical design of concrete formwork.

INTRODUCTION

One of the most important factors in the analysis and design of formwork is the pressure of the freshly placed concrete exerted on the formwork. The concrete pressure used in design therefore has a very significant indirect effect on formwork productivity.

The vertical loads on formwork lying in a horizontal, or near horizontal, plane include the weight of the reinforcement, the weight of the freshly placed concrete, the weight of the formwork itself, and dynamic construction loads such as the movement of the concreting crew, the equipment, and the discharging of a pile of concrete from a skip, which may temporarily occupy a far greater depth locally than the finished depth of the concrete member.

The horizontal loads exerted on vertical formwork include the pressure of the freshly placed concrete, construction loads, impact loads resulting from high discharge points, and any abnormal vibration loads which are not subsumed in the design pressure value. Snow and wind loads may also be very important design considerations.

The pressure of the freshly placed concrete is a function of the rate of placement, the temperature of the concrete, and the maximum height of the freshly placed concrete. This value can be modified by introducing a workability (slump) - temperature factor, and an arching limit factor.

An essential link in the economical design of formwork is between analysis and productivity. Although formwork productivity has been measured for many years, and productivity indices have been

established and compiled, the accuracy of the indices in many cases has been questioned. Furthermore, the design of formwork has in many cases varied from using intuitive, semi-empirical methods to more rational analytical methods.

A user-friendly integrated general purpose package progam is now available for use in the design and optimization of formwork. An integrated package program includes a spreadsheet, a word processor, a data manager, a graphics generator and communication services. This system enables a construction engineer to economically design and analyse formwork, using a microcomputer.

The design can utilize an integrated software package spreadsheet consisting of the following four modules:

1. Input data
2. Data bank
3. Calculations
4. Sensitivity Analysis.

Certain inbuilt functions can be used to create a knowledge based system in the decision making process of design, or alternatively, by changing directory, the design can be linked to an expert system through a small program which can provide reasoning, from knowledge and data, and provide a solution.

FORMWORK PRODUCTIVITY

In the economical design of formwork there should be a clear link between analysis and productivity. Because of the rising cost of labor, formwork should be designed to minimize crew sizes and non-productive work. Previously inaccurate data for formwork productivity indices can now be replaced by data from more refined databases.

Firstly, sophisticated measurement tools are available, such as time-lapse photography, which enable professional engineers to analyse and determine productivity performance more accurately. Secondly, the use of a microcomputer considerably reduces the time consuming effort in the compilation of data derived from many more parameters which affect formwork productivity than was previously considered. The dissemination of such data is also greatly facilitated, especially when it is linked to a network system.

Factors which can affect formwork productivity are listed as follows:

1. Type of formwork system and falsework.
2. Formwork dimensions.
3. Type of sheathing.
4. Labor relations, skill, experience and motivation of carpenter crew.
5. Number of wales and studs.
6. Number of formwork uses.
7. Number of inserts, ties, keys, joints.
8. Form and surface finish.
9. Weather.

ANALYSIS AND DESIGN

Integrated software package programs are now available for use in formwork analysis and design. The integrated software package includes a spreadsheet, a word processor, a database manager, a graphics generator, and data communications services.

Use of an integrated software package has distinct advantages over other means of modelling construction systems. Most importantly, little computer programming background is necessary to build such a model, whereas extensive knowledge of programming language, such as Basic or Fortran is necessary in order to create the same model when developing a computer program specifically for formwork design. Therefore, the use of a general purpose program to build a model is certainly more convenient and easier, and requires a minimum of programming experience compared to writing a Basic or Fortran program. Moreover, it is easier for the user to understand the logic within the model because it is written using simple integrated package notation.

Spreadsheets used on microcomputers organize data in a matrix of rows and columns. Each intersection of a row and a column forms a storage location called a cell. A label, a value, or an equation can be placed in each cell, or the cell can be left blank. Long items can be accommodated by combining cells.

The formwork design model was formulated on an integrated software package spreadsheet, which consisted of over eight thousand rows by 256 columns, and contained four design modules as shown in the flow diagram (Figure 1).

Data relating to a company's own stock inventory can be accommodated by creating a small data bank, with exclusive information on sheathing, studs, wales and ties, in one module. A few formulae are developed and included in the calculations module.

After the data bank has been developed it can be linked with the input data module by using a macro facility. This macro facility enables data to be stored for future use. If an expression such as Go To (cell) G20 is written, and given a name such as "A", the macro facility will be invoked whenever "Alt" and "A" keys are pressed simultaneously on the keyboard, and the computer will go to cell G20 for information, say, on the sheathing.

Similar procedures are used in the selection of data for studs, wales and ties from the data bank by pressing keys "Alt" and "B" or "C".

SENSITIVITY ANALYSES AND EXPERT SYSTEMS

In the integrated package program certain inbuilt functions such as an IF ... THEN ... routine can be used to determine which formula for concrete pressure for the design of the formwork should be used. This routine enables the correct entry to be made into a particular cell where the appropriate formula is located. The operation is extremely simple.

The user can change the parametric inputs to compare the effects on the final outputs in a matter of seconds. One of the many advantages of using an integrated package program in formwork design, therefore, is its ease in performing sensitivity analyses. Sensitivity analyses can be performed by changing the values of the sheathing, studs, wales, or tie sizes in the input data module and then comparing the effects in the calculations module.

If the processing technique is required to go beyond the use of an algorithmic analysis and optimization technique, which simply aids choice, an elaboration to solutions can be created which performs sensitivity analyses, creates a diagnostic capability, and identifies the most productive and economic alternative by duplicating the intuitive, heuristic and empirical judgemental knowledge of several construction managers by linking to an expert system shell program.

Part of the expert system consists of sets of IF ... AND ... AND ... THEN ... ELSE rules, in the shell program, which enables an inference mechanism or rule interpreter to be incorporated and cross linked with the database. The shell program can handle fuzzy logic and fuzzy sets of data.

The use of an integrated package program linked to a shell program enables the microcomputer to not only acquire information but to reason from knowledge and provide solutions which would normally require human expertise. By creating an accumulation of data and knowledge on formwork, compiled in one or more modules, the system is able to reason and draw conclusions, and thus enhance the ability to analyze a design problem and optimize the solution. This is done by questioning the user for appropriate information so that inferences and conclusions can be made.

Some inference programs can reason, even from incomplete or uncertain information, by specifying answers to questions with a certain confidence value. The user can be asked to select a confidence level to a question by giving a certain verbal confidence level (such as definite, probable, possible, unlikely, impossible), which is then assigned a specific numerical probability. Unsure or fuzzy sets of information can therefore be accommodated in the design.

CONCLUSIONS

The impact of the use of microcomputers and expert systems will enable the measurement, recording, analysis, prediction and dissemination of productivity data, as well as analysis and design, to be vastly improved.

There should be a definite link between productivity and the analysis and design of formwork. By using productivity data the designer should be able to answer several questions which arise during formwork design, such as modular sizes, appropriate material, and economic fabrication.

Existing prefabricated formwork is often required to be used for a prescribed set of new conditions. In this common design situation the methods described in this paper are extremely appropriate. The structural adequacy of the formwork can be checked by determining the maximum permissible lateral pressure. As the pressure is a function of the xrate of placement and the concrete temperature, the structural integrity of the formwork can be maintained by controlling the rate of placement.

Refinements and improvements in the accuracy of productivity data will enable future productivity and costs to be determined more accurately, show where improvements in productivity can be made, and therefore improve the analysis and economical design of concrete formwork.

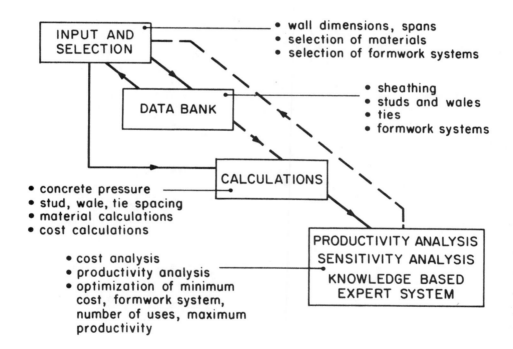

Fig. 1 Formwork Design Modules - Flow Diagram

III STRUCTURAL ANALYSIS AND DESIGN

KNOWLEDGE-BASED SYSTEMS IN STRUCUTRAL ENGINEERING

Professor H Adeli,
Department of Civil Engineering, The Ohio State University, U.S.A.

This paper addresses application of artificial intelligence (AI) in the field of structural engineering. Existing experimental knowledge-based expert systems in the area of structures are reviewed. Applicable AI tools and techniques are briefly discussed.

INTRODUCTION

Artificial Intelligence (AI) is a branch of computer science concerned with making computers act more like human beings. Computer programs using AI techniques to assist people in solving difficult problems involving knowledge, heuristics, and decision making are called knowledge-based systems, expert systems, intelligent systems, or smart systems. Successful expert systems have been developed in the fields of medical diagnosis, mineral exploration, and design of computer layouts. Applications of AI techniques in the field of structural engineering are just starting to evolve.

An expert system, aka knowledge-based system, is an "intelligent" interactive computer program that can play the role of a human expert by using heuristic knowledge, i.e., intuition, common sense, and rules of thumb. The heuristics are usually accumulated by a human expert over a number of years. Using heuristics, an expert system can make educated guesses, recognize promising approaches, and avoid blind search; and consequently it can narrow down the search process in a solution space.

Let us point out the differences between the traditional computer programs and expert systems.

1. Expert systems are knowledge-intensive programs,
2. In expert systems, expert knowledge is usually divided into many separate rules,
3. The rules forming a knowledge base or expert knowledge is separated from the methods for applying the knowledge to the current problem. These methods are referred to as inference mechanism, reasoning mechanism, or rule interpreter,
4. Expert systems are highly interactive,
5. Expert systems have user-friendly/intelligent user interface, and
6. Expert system to some extent mimic the decision making and reasoning process of human experts. They can provide advice, answer questions, and justify their conclusions.

Advantages of rule-based systems and separation of knowledge base from the inference mechanism are

1. Knowledge will be more explicit, accessible, and expandable,
2. Knowledge base can be gradually and incrementally developed over an extended period of time. New rules can be added. Old rules may be refined. The modularity of the system allows continuous expansion and refinement of the knowledge base,
3. A general system with one inference mechanism can be developed for different types of applications simply by changing the knowledge base,
4. The same knowledge may be used in different problems by possibly employing different inference mechanisms. For example, if a design specification such as the AISC specification (5) for design of steel buildings is put into such a knowledge base it may be used directly for design of different types of structures,
5. The expert system can explain its behavior by simply describing the rules it is using (explanation facility),
6. Using the rules the expert system can check the consistency of the rules and point out the faulty rules (debugging facility), and
7. Expert systems may be able to modify the existing rules and learn new rules.

A sophisticated expert system should ideally have the following facilities:

1. Documentation. It should provide automatic comprehensive documentaion of the program. This documentation includes not only comments provided by the programmer but also derived information explaining the logics underlying different pieces of the program.
2. Help facility. It should help and guide the user how to use the system effectively and easily. It should point out the types of the problems it can solve, the options available, and its limitations.
3. Explanation and advice. It should be able to give advice, answer questions, and justify answers. The explanatory power of the expert system makes it transparent to the user.

(6)

4. Debugging. It should find and report errors in the input data and problem formulation.
5. Knowledge acquisition. It should be able to acquire experience after each design and use the experience gained in the future designs.

BASIC STEPS FOR DEVELOPMENT OF AN EXPERT SYSTEM

The major steps in development of an expert system are (23):

1. Selection of an expert system programming environment or tool.
2. Selection of AI techniques for representation and control strategy.
3. Analysis, acquisition, and conceptualization of the knowledge to be included in the knowledge base.
4. Formalization and development of knowledge base.
5. Development of a prototype system using the knowledge base and AI tools.
6. Evaluation, review, and expansion of the expert system.
7. Refinement of the user interface.
8. Maintenance and updating of the system.

SUCCESSFUL APPLICATIONS OF EXPERT SYSTEM TECHNOLOGY

In this section, we describe several successful applications of expert system technology.

1. MYCIN. Developed at Stanford University in mid-seventies, MYCIN is designed to help physicians in the diagnosis and treatment of meningitis (inflammation of the membranes envelopping the brain and spinal cord) and bacteremia infections (involving bacteria in the blood). The knowledge base of MYCIN contains about 450 rules. MYCIN is the first major expert system to perform at the level of a human expert and to explain to the user its reasoning process. Various evaluations made at Stanford indicate that MYCIN is as good as or better than most highly skilled specialists of infectious diseases (23). It is of interest to note that MYCIN was developed over a period of five years with an estimated manpower of 50 man-years.

2. PROSPECTOR. Developed at Stanford Research Institute in late seventies, PROSPECTOR is a diagnostic expert system for mineral exploration (22). It imitates the reasoning process of an experienced exploration geologist for finding an ore deposit in a particular region. Geologists primarily use surface geological observations which are usually uncertain and incomplete. The knowledge base of PROSPECTOR contains about 1600 rules. Bayesian probability is used for treating uncertainties in information and rules on the field evidence and geological data. This expert system has revealed a molybdenum deposit whose value may be worth millions of dollars (24).

3. CADUCEUS (formerly named INTERNIST). It is an expert system for diagnosis of diseases of internal medicine (36). It incarnates more knowledge than a human internist and can diagnose complex test cases which puzzle the human experts. The knowledge base of CADUCEUS includes about 500 diseases, 350 disease manifestations, and 100000 sympto-

matic associations. It contains over 15000 rules and covers some 25 percent of diseases of internal medicine. The developers of CADUCEUS are still working on this most ambitious expert system development project.

4. XCON. Originally called R1, XCON designs the configuration of VAX-11/780 computer components for Digital Equipment Corporation (DEC) according to the requests of a customer (28). Developed in OPS5 environment (a production system programming language developed at Carnegie-Mellon University) (21), XCON includes about 800 rules concerning the properties of some 400 VAX computer components. DEC usually sells one-of-a-kind custom-made systems. XCON takes a client's order as input. Its output is a set of diagrams displaying relationship among different components of the computer system. A technician uses these diagrams to assemble the whole system. Compared with conventional programs, this system can incorporate the frequent changes much more efficiently.

AI LANGUAGES AND TOOLS FOR DEVELOPMENT OF AN EXPERT EXPERT

About 95% of all AI-based expert systems have been developed in LISP computer language. LISP, an acronym for LISt Processing, was invented by McCarthy in 1960 (33) for nonnumeric computations. LISP is now the most widely-used language among AI researchers.

Several dialects of LISP are available, such as COMMON LISP (50), INTERLISP, MACLISP, and ELISP. Among different available dialects of LISP, INTERLISP seems to be the most highly developed implementation. INTERLISP has the rich characteristics of Conversational LISP (CLISP) interpreter, powerful error correction facility, and extensive library. The rich and powerful INTERLISP environment, however, makes it somewhat difficult to learn because for effective use of INTERLISP many new concepts and aspects should be learned (52).

Recently, a new version of Common LISP called Golden Common LISP or GCLISP has been developed for use on an IBM Personal Computer with 256K of memory and a PC-DOS 2.0 operating system (23).

Other languages are available in AI community (7). Japanese are using PROLOG (PROgramming in LOGic) developed in France in 1971 in their ambitious fifth generation computer project which focuses on AI (18). PROLOG is a modern language based on formal logic and a simplified version of the first order predicate calculus (12). Even though LISP seems to be the language of choice among AI researchers in the U.S. and it has been approved by the U.S. Department of Defense, a number of companies including DEC, Xerox, and Texas Instrument are developing expert systems using PROLOG (13).

To facilitate the development of knowledge-based expert systems, expert system programming environments or tools have recently been developed (23). They contain specific representation methods and inference mechanisms. They are easier to use but less flexible than an AI language such as LISP. One such tool is EMYCIN (Empty MYCIN) for building expert systems similar to MYCIN. It uses a backward chaining inference mechanism. The ability to explain its reasoning is an important feature of EMYCIN.

Other generic tools have been developed, for example, KAS (Knowledge Acquisition System) resulted from the development of PROSPECTOR. KAS allows both forward- and backward-chaining. Commercially available AI tools have been compiled in a recent book by Harmon and King (23). Their price varies from $100 to $80000. Most of these tools, however, are useful for development of diagnosis and prediction type expert systems. They are not readily useful for development of expert systems for design of structures.

Traditional popular computer languages (FORTRAN, BASIC, and PASCAL) offer easy portability among different types of computers and compatibility with numerous softwares available in these languages but do not provide the most appropriate environment for development of expert systems. Among these languages, however, PASCAL appears to be the most suitable one. Advantages of PASCAL are

1. Supporting recursion (i.e., functions can call themselves),
2. Allowing user-defined data structures (for example, using records and the type statement), and
3. Providing an easy-to-understand block structure.

In development of a knowledge-based expert system, following issues should be addressed:

1. How should the knowledge be represented?
2. What problem-solving paradigm or inference mechanism should be used for application of knowledge?
3. How can the knowledge be acquired?

Representation of Knowledge

Several approaches for representation of knowledge are available in the AI literature (49,47,48). The major ones are

1. formal methods based on the predicate calculus and mathematical logic,
2. semantic networks consisting of a collection of nodes for representation of concepts, objects, events, etc., and links for connecting the nodes and characterizing their interrelationship,
3. rule-based or production systems, and
4. frame systems consisting of generic data structures in predefined information categories called slots.

It appears that the production and frame systems are the most suitable representation approaches for building computer expert systems in the area of structures. A production system is a collection of rules which consist of an IF part and a THEN part or antecedent-consequent or situation-action parts. Production rules facilitate the generation of explanations because the antecedent-consequent or IF-THEN rules can easily be transformed into questions.

The general form for the rules is
Rule # N
IF ⌐ (antecedent1) ~~~~~~~~~~~~~(antecedent n) ⌐

THEN ⌐ (consequent1 with certainty c1)
~~~~~~~~~~~~~~~~~~~~~~~~~~~~~~~~~~
~~~~~~~~~~~~~~~~~~~~~~~~~~~~~~~~~~
(consequentm with certainty cm) ⌐

The rule number is a unique number for identifying the rule. The value of this number does not specify the order of application of the rule. Each rule should present an independent chunk of knowledge. Antecedents can be considered as patterns and consequents as conclusions or actions to be taken. Rules can be algorithmic or heuristic. Certainty factors indicate the level of confidence in a piece of information. They are simply informal measures of confidence and not probabilities.

Two different types of rules or constraints can be identified in design of structures: domain rules and meta-rules (or rules about the rules). Domain rules consist of well-defined constraints given in design specifications. In design of a steel plate girder according to the AISC specification (5), for example, following rule or constraint exists:

IF   The plate girder is not hybrid, AND
Intermediate stiffeners are provided, AND
$C_v < 1.0$ AND
$a/h < 260/(h/t)^2$ AND
$a/h < 3.0$ AND
THEN We can increase the allowable shear stress by relying on the postbuckling behavior and the tension-field action of the web plate.

Meta-decisions determine the course of design and should be provided by an expert designer. In the previously-mentioned example, rules regarding whether to use a hybrid girder or a non-hybrid girder, or whether to use intermediate stiffeners should be provided by an expert designer. Such rules are empirical in nature and in general cannot be found in textbooks. In AI terminology, domain rules are mostly based on deep knowledge and meta-rules are generally based on surface knowledge.

In design of stiffened plate girders, other heuristic rules may determine

1. What types of steel to use
2. whether to use single-sided or double-sided stiffeners
3. whether to use continuous or intermittent weld for connection of web plate to flange plates and connection of stiffeners to the web plate.

Frame systems are suitable for more complex and richer representation of knowledge. A frame consists of a number of slots in which different characteristics and features of an object or a chunk of information are described. Slots can store values. They may contain default values, pointers to other frames, or procedures. The procedures may determine the values of slots. In other words, a procedure consists of a set of instructions for determining the value of slot. This is called procedural attachement.

Inference Mechanisms

A number of different heuristic problem-solving paradigms are available in the AI literature, for example, describe-and-match paradigm, goal-reduction paradigm, generate-and-test systems, means-ends analysis, backtracking, and rule-based (production) systems (49,35). Different problem-solving strategies for building knowledge-based expert systems for engineering design are surveyed in a recent article by Maher et. al. (32).

Rule-based problem-solving systems use a collection of rules as explained in the previous section. A production system consists of three main elements:

1. A set of IF-THEN rules or knowledge base,
2. Global database or working memory, and
3. An inference mechanism or rule interpreter.

Notwithstanding its simplicity the production system represents a powerful model for human information processing and problem solving ability. Rule-based deduction systems can explain how and why they perform certain actions and they can evaluate their outcomes and results. They can handle unplanned but helpful interactions. In other words, they can utilize a portion of knowledge whenever suitable or necessary not just whenever the programmer foresees it may be useful.

How the rules are found from the knowledge base and which rules shall be used? In order to answer this question we need to choose an inference mechanism or a control strategy which is the heart of an expert system. The inference mechanism fires rules according to its built-in reasoning process. For development of expert systems in the area of structures following inference mechanisms may be used:

1. Forward-chaining (aka antecedent reasoning and data-driven control strategy). In this inference mechanism, rules are scanned until one is found whose antecedents match the information for the problem entered in the global database. Then, the rule is applied and the database is updated. This process is repeated until the goal state is achieved or no useable rule is found. If the goal state is not known and has to be constructed or the number of possible outcomes is large then the forward-chaining mechanism is often recommended. Complex planning problems can be tackled by this approach. This approach is used in XCON.

2. Backward-chaining (aka consequent reasoning and goal-driven strategy). In this inference mechanism, rules are scanned and those whose consequent actions can lead to the goal are found. For each of these rules a check is made whether its antecedents match the information in the database. If they all match the rule is applied and the problem is solved. If there exists an unmatched antecedent a new subgoal is defined as "arrange conditions to match that antecedent". This process is applied recursively. If the values of goal state are known and their number is small then backward-chaining seems to be quite efficient. This approach is employed in MYCIN and SACON.

3. A combination of backward-chaining and forward chaining. In structural design since possible goal states cannot be easily represented, application of either forward-chaining or backward-chaining mechanism alone does not appear to be the most prudent control strategy. Combination of the two approaches together with division of the design process into design subtasks, however, seems to be the most appropriate inference strategy.

EXPERIMENTAL EXPERT SYSTEMS IN STRUCTURAL ENGINEERING

Application of AI in computer-aided design (CAD) of structures is a very recent development. Elias

(17) reviews the possibilities of using AI techniques in design of aerospace structures. Dixon and Simmons (15) explore application of expert systems in mechanical design. They are also experimenting an expert system for design of V-belts and shafts. MacCallum (30) discusses the development of an expert system for design of ships. An overview of the knowledge-based expert systems has been presented in a recent survey article by Dym (16).

Recently, at the Ohio State University, Brown and Chandrasekaran (9,10) presented a general approach to the creation of computer-based expert consultants. They formulated a framework in which knowledge is decomposed into substructures and each substructure is in turn divided into a hierarchy of conceptual specialists. They applied this methodology to develop an expert system for mechanical design with design refinement as the central problem solving activity.

In the area of structural design, Fenves was the first who realized the usefulness and feasibility of expert systems for CAD of structures. Fenves and Norabhoompipat (19) discuss potentials for AI applications in structural engineering design and detailing. Rooney and Smith (41) proposed an expanded model of design process by introducing a feedback mechanism consisting of three steps : acquisition of experience, application of experience, and database management. They applied this model to a very simple structure, i.e., design of a single span simply-supported steel wide-flange beam.

A preliminary study for development of an expert system for design of reinforced concrete beams has been carried out by Robarts and Saiidi (40). They wrote a BASIC program for design of reinforced concrete beams based on a data bank containing the previously used designs. The selection is merely based on the frequency of the designs made in the past.

Application of expert systems in education has been discussed by O'Shea (34). Starfield et. al. (46) point out how engineering concepts can be mastered through the development of simple expert systems. Rehak and Schields (38) discuss the design of a pedagogical aid for mechanics of materials using a tree-traversal hierarchial problem generation and representation.

Following experimental expert systems in the area of structural engineering have been reported in the recent literature:

SACON

Developed by Bennett and Engelmore in LISP computer language (8), SACON interacts with the user for the proper application of MARC finite element structural analysis program. It consists of 170 production rules and 140 consultation parameters such as types of materials, loadings, and load components. It uses backward chaining as inference mechanism. SACON is intended to help the less experienced engineers to use a large general purpose structural analysis software, that is, MARC. A similar experimental expert system has been developed by Fjellheim and Syversen (20) for using the Sesam-69 Structural Analysis Program.

Rivlin et. al. (39) also attempted to develop a knowledge-based consultation system and to establish a finite element structural analysis knowledge base for the use of MARC finite element program in FORTRAN. They employed the backward chaining inference mechanism. Their finite element structural analysis knowledge base included information about the three stages of the structural analysis problem:

1. Pre-analysis. In this stage the type of the analysis is defined. Using the knowledge of geometrical configuration, loading environment, material behavior, and expected response of the structure, an appropriate type of analysis such as static, dynamic, linear elastic, elastoplastic, small-displacement, and large-displacement is recommended by the consultation system,

2. Analysis stage. It includes input data of the structural problem to be analyzed and the response of the structure subjected to a given loading condition. The consultation system requires only necessary input from the user. It makes the required decisions for complying with the MARC program input requirements. Thus, the user is relieved from the large quantity of numerical data and various input formats, and

3. Post-analysis stage. Nodal and element quantities obtained such as nodal displacements, velocities, and accelerations, and element stresses, strains, and temperatures are examined for adequacy of the analysis and recommendations are made for additional analysis if necessary.

HI-RISE

Being developed by Maher and Fenves (31) at Carnegie-Mellon University, HI-RISE is an expert system for the preliminary design of rectangular commercial or residential highrise buildings more than ten stories high. The language of this expert system is PSRL, a frame-based production system language developed at Carnegie-Mellon University (51). HI-RISE uses a hierarchial frame representation as proposed by Preiss (37). Selection of a structural system in actual practice is usually based on a variety of factors including aesthetics, economics, efficiency, and structural integrity. HI-RISE uses weighing factors in a linear evaluation factor to evaluate the merits of different structural systems. HI-RISE selects two functional systems, that is, lateral load and gravity load resisting systems. HI-RISE presents all structurally feasible systems as well as the "best" design according to the criterion of the linear evaluation function.

SPERIL

Developed by Ishizuka et. al. (25,26) at Purdue, SPERIL is an experimental expert system for assessment of structural damage subjected to earthquake excitation. It is based on rule-based production system with a bottom-up search and written in language C with about 800 statements. The knowledge base of SPERIL consists of information obtained from earthquake accelerograms and visual inspection of damaged buildings. Due to the imprecise nature of the inferential structural damage knowledge, they wrote the rules using Dempster and Shafer's probability (14) and fuzzy subsets (53). They point out that Dempster and Shafer's probability is superior to the Bayesian probability for expressing subjective uncertainty.

SPECON

Being developed by Fenves and co-workers (43), SPECON (SPEcification CONsultant) is a small expert system for checking structural steel members for compliance with AISC specification (5). It is written in LISP (50) and the production system language OPS5 (21). Its inference mechanism is analogous to MYCIN's backward chaining paradigm (42). The knowledge base of SPECON is divided into two levels. The top level contains rules for identifying the applicable constraints. The next level consists of the specific design constraints. SPECON has an explanation module which is intended to answer questions of how a certain hypothesis is deduced or a particular question is asked by the system. The user simply types in "why" or "how-did-you-deduce".

DURCON

Being developed by Clifton (11), DURCON (for DURable CONcrete) is a knowledge-base expert system for selecting the constituents of concrete exposed to aggressive environments. It addresses the deterioration of concrete due to four factors, i.e., freeze-thaw, sulfate attack, corrosion of reinforcing steel, and cement-aggregate reactions. The knowledge base in DURCON consists of specification rules from the American Concrete Institute Guide to Durable Concrete and heuristic knowledge being obtained from human experts on the durability of concrete. DURCON is developed in PASCAL using the forward-chaining inference mechanism.

SASE

This expert system is being developed at the National Bureau of Standards for Standard Analysis, Synthesis, and Expression (45). It ensures that new building standards or modified versions of the existing ones are correct and consistent and facilitates the machine-processing of the standards. The developers of this system hope that it will replace the textual version of the engineering standards.

SICAD

Being developed by Lopez et. al. (29), SICAD (Standards Interfaces in Computer-Aided Design) is an experimental expert system for interfacing the engineering standards in CAD programs. In SICAD, standards are treated as intrinsic functions of the system and not part of the CAD program. Similar work is also being carried out at the National Bureau of Standards (44).

WAVE

Being experimented by Jain et. al. (27), WAVE interacts with the user for proper definition of loading, foundation system, and structural configuration of offshore structures.

SSPG

In order to investigate the practicality of LISP for CAD of structures, Adeli and Paek have developed an experimental expert system for design of stiffened steel plate girders, called SSPG (1). Due to highly nonlinear and implicit nature of design constraints as well as existence of discontinuities, optimization of stiffened plate girders cannot be easily achieved by most available mathematical programming techniques. SSPG is written in

ELISP which is an implementation of Rutgers/UCI LISP for DEC-20 systems. The design of a stiffened steel plate girder does not involve a lot of common sense knowledge. To start the design, however, the human designer usually selects a number for the ratio of the depth of the web, h, and the length of the span, L, based on his previous experience. The choice of ratio h/L depends on a number of parameters including the span length, yield stress of steel, Fy, and the loading (e.g., intensity of the distributed load, w).

Using an interactive BASIC program for design of stiffened steel plate girders (2,3), the optimum h/L ratios for "practical" minimum weight of the plate girder were found in terms of the previously mentioned parameters, span length, yield stress of steel, and the intensity of the distributed load on the girder (4). This information was then fed into SSPG as 300 IF-THEN or production rules. SSPG designs the web plate, flange plates, bearing stiffeners, and intermediate stiffeners using steel plates with thicknesses available in the market.

The production rules in SSPG are for four different types of steel commonly-used in steel structures, i.e., A36 with yield stress of 36 ksi, A529 with yield stress of 42 ksi, A441 with yield stress of 50 ksi, and A572 with yield stress of 60 ksi. The rules were found for four different load intensities of 3 k/ft, 4 k/ft, 5 k/ft, and 6 k/ft and eighteen different span lengths ranging from 50 ft to 500 ft. These rules are used in the following form:

IF   The type of the steel is A36,   AND
       The load intensity is 6 k/ft,   AND
       The length of the span is 200 ft
THEN   The ratio of the span length to the depth
       of the web should be selected around 14.

Of course, design by SSPG is not limited to the aforementioned combinations. If a plate girder must be designed, say, for a span of 345 ft and a load intensity of 5.6 k/ft, then SSPG generates several candidate h/L ratios from the production rules using a breadth-first search technique(49) and designs the plate girder using these ratios. SSPG gives a number of designs around the "practical" minimum weight design.

SSPG does not give the theoretical optimum solution as one may find from a formal optimum design based on a mathematical programming technique. SSPG, in fact, designs the plate girder the way an experienced human designer would design it. In design of many types of structures such as frames used in buildings, without using a formal optimization approach, an experienced designer usually comes up with a design which is quite close to the least weight design. Also, it should be noted that the best design is not necessarily the one with the lowest material weight or cost.

CONCLUSIONS

Development of expert systems for solution of practical problems in the area of structures is a substantial undertaking. It requires new ways of looking at computers and computation, and generation, propagation, and dissemination of knowledge. Existing experimental expert systems and recent efforts in this direction have been summarized in this article. It is expected that these efforts will increase rapidly because benefits of advances made in this direction appear to be tremendous.

ACKNOWLEDGEMENT

This study has been supported by the Ohio State University Office of the Research and Graduate Studies.

REFERENCES

1. Adeli, H. and Paek, Y., "Computer-Aided Design of Structures Using LISP", Journal of Computers and Structures (accepted for publication).
2. Adeli, H. and Phan, K., "Interactive Design of Structures on Microcomputers", Journal of Civil Engineering for Practicing and Design Engineers, Vol. 4, No. 5, 1985, pp. 413-437.
3. Adeli, H. and Phan, K., "Interactive Computer-Aided Design of Non-Hybrid and Hybrid Steel Plate Girders", Journal of Computers and Structures (accepted for publication).
4. Adeli, H. and Phan, K., "A Comparative Study of LRFD and AISC Specifications", Civil Engineering for Practicing and Design Engineers, Vol. 4, No. 10, 1985 (to appear).
5. AISC, Manual of Steel Construction, American Institute of Steel Construction, 8th ed., 1980.
6. Andriole, S. J., Ed., Applications in Artificial Intelligence, Petrocelli Books, Inc., Princeton, New Jersey, 1985.
7. Barstow, D.R. et. al., "Languages and Tools for Knowledge Engineering", in Hayes-Roth, F., Waterman, D.A., and Lenat, D.B., Eds., Building Expert Systems, Addison-Wesley,
8. Bennett, J.S. and Engelmore, R.S., "SACON: A Knowledge-Based Consultant for Structural Analysis", Proceedings of the 6th International Joint Conference on Artificial Intelligence, Tokyo, 1979, pp. 47-49.
9. Brown, D.C. and Chandrasekaran, B., "An Approach to Expert Systems for Structural Design", IEEE Computer Society, Trends & Applications Conference, Gaithersburg, Maryland, 1983.
10. Brown, D.C. and Chandrasekaran, B., "Expert Systems for a Class of Mechanical Design Activity", Proceedings of the International Federation for Information Processing WG5.2 Working Conference on Knowledge Engineering in Computer-Aided Design, Budapest, Hungary, September 11-14, 1984.
11. Clifton, J.R., Oltiker, B.C., and Johnson, S.K., "Development of DURCON, An Expert System for Durable Concrete: Part I", Report No. NBS IR 85-3186, National Bureau of Standards, U.S. Department of Commerce, Gaithersburg, Maryland, July 1985.
12. Clocksin, W.F. and Mellish, C.S., Programming in Prolog, Springer-Verlag, New York, 1981.
13. Christopher, A., "Artificial Intelligence and Computer Graphics", Computer Graphics World, August 1985, pp. 11-20.
14. Dempster, A.P., "Upper and Lower Probabilities Induced by a Multivalued Mapping", Annals of Mathematical Statistics, Vol. 38, 1967, pp. 325-339.
15. Dixon, J.R. and Simmons, M.K., "Computers That Design: Expert Systems for Mechanical Engineers", Computers in Mechanical Engineering, November 1983, pp. 10-18.

16. Dym, C.L., "Expert Systems: New Approaches to Computer-Aided Engineering", Proceedings of the 25th Structures, Structural Dynamics, and Materials Conference, May 14-16, 1984, pp. 99-115.

17. Elias, A.L., "Computer-Aided Engineering: The AI Connection", Astronautics and Aeronautics, American Institute of Aeronautics and Astronautics, July-August 1983, pp. 48-54.

18. Feigenbaum, E.A. and McCorduck, P., The Fifth Generation, Addison-Wesley, Reading, Massachusetts, 1983.

19. Fenves, S.J. and Norabhoompipat, T., "Potentials for Artificial Intelligence Applications in Structuring Engineering Design and Detailing", in Latombe, J.C., Ed., Artificial Intelligence and Patern Recognition in Computer-Aided Design, North Holland Publishing Co., 1978.

20. Fjellheim, R. and Syversen, P., "An Expert System for Sesam-69 Structural Analysis Program Selection", Technical Report CP-83-6010, Division for Data Technology, Computas, Norway, January 1983.

21. Forgy, C.L., "OPS5 User's Manual", Technical Report CMU-CS-81-135, Carnegie-Mellon University, July 1981.

22. Gaschnig, J., "Prospector: An Expert System for Mineral Exploration", in Michie, D., Ed., Introductory Readings in Expert Systems, Gordon and Breach Science Publishers, New York, 1982.

23. Harmon, P. and King, D., Artificial Intelligence in Business, John Wiley & Sons, 1985.

24. Hayes-Roth, F., Waterman, D.A., and Lenat, D.B., "An Overview of Expert Systems", in Hayes-Roth, F., Waterman, D.A., and Lenat, D.B., Eds., Building Expert Systems, Addison-Wesley, Reading, Massachusetts, 1983.

25. Ishizuka, M., Fu, K.S., and Yao, J.T.P., "SPERIL I — Computer Based Structural Damage Assessment System", Report No. CE-STR-81-36, School of Civil Engineering, Purdue University, West Lafayette, Indiana, November, 1981.

26. Ishizuka, M., Fu, K.S., and Yao, J.T.P., "A Rule-Based Inference with Fuzzy Set for Structural Damage Assessment ", in Approximate Reasoning in Decision Analysis, Eds., M.M. Gupta and E. Sanchez., North-Holland

27. Jain, A.K., Agarwal, A., and Gupta, A., "WAVE: An Expert Offshore Structural Analysis System", Proceedings of the Third Conference on Computing in Civil Engineering, San Diego, California, April 2-6, 1984.

28. Kraft, A., "XCON: An Expert Configuration System at Digital Equipment Corporation", in, The AI Business: The Commercial Uses of Artificial Intelligence, Eds., Winston, P.H. and Prendergast, K.A., The MIT Press, Cambridge, Massachusetts, 1984.

29. Lopez, L.A., Elam, S.L., and Christopherson, T., "SICAD: A Prototype Implementation System for CAD", Proceedings of the Third Conference on Computing in Civil Engineering, San Diego, California, April 2-6, 1984.

30. MacCallum, K.J., "Creative Ship Design by Computer", in Rogers, D.F., Nehrling, B.C., and Kuo, C., Eds., Computer Applications in the Automation of Shipyard Operation and Shipyard Design IV, North-Holland Publishing Company, 1982.

31. Maher, M.L. and Fenves, S.J., "HI-RISE: An Expert System for the Preliminary Structural Design of High Rise Buildings", Proceedings of the International Federation for Information Processing WG5.2 Working Conference on Knowledge Engineering in Computer-Aided Design, Budapest, Hungary, September 11-14, 1984.

32. Maher, M.L., Sriram, D., and Fenves, S.J., "Tools and Techniques for Knowledge Based Expert Systems for Engineering Design", Advances in Engineering Software, United Kingdom (submitted).

33. McCarthy, J., "Recursive Functions of Symbolic Expressions and Their Computation by Machine", Communications of the ACM, Vol. 3, No. 4, 1960, pp. 184-195.

34. O'Shea, T., "Intelligent Systems in Education", in Introductory Readings in Expert Systems, Ed., D. Michie, Gordon and Breach Science Publishers, New York, 1982.

35. O'Shea, T. and Eisenstadt, M., Artificial Intelligence - Tools, Techniques, and Applications, Harper & Row, Publishers, New York, 1984.

36. Pople, H.E., Jr., "Heuristic Methods for Imposing Structure on Ill- Structured Problems: The Structuring of Medical Diagnostics", in Szolovits, P., Artificial Intelligence in Medicine, Westview Press, Boulder, Colorado, 1982.

37. Preiss, K., "Data Frame Model for the Engineering Design Process", Design Studies, IPC Business Press, Vol. 1, No. 4, 1980, pp. 231-243.

38. Rehak, D.R. and Schields, T.V., "Design of a Pedagogical Aid for Civil Engineering Education", Proceedings of the Third Conference on Computing in Civil Engineering, San Diego, California, April 2-6, 1984, pp. 163-172.

39. Rivlin, J.M., Hsu, M.B., and Marcal, P.V., "Knowledge Based Consultation for Finite Element Structural Analysis", U.S. Air Force Flight Dynamics Laboratory Report AFWAL-TR-80-3069, Wright-Patterson Air Force Base, Ohio, 1980.

40. Robarts, P. and Saiidi, M., "Artificial Intelligence for Design of R/C Beams Using an IBM-PC - A Preliminary Study", Proceedings of the 2nd National Conference on Microcomputers in Civil Engineering, Orlando, Florida, October 30-31, November 1, 1984, pp. 29-33.

41. Rooney, M. and Smith, S.E., "Artificial Intelligence in Engineering Design", Computers and Structures, Vol. 16, 1983, pp. 279-288.

42. Shortliffe, E.H., Computer-Based Medical Consultations: MYCIN, American Elsevier, New York, 1976.

43. Sriram, D., Maher, M.L., and Fenves, S.J., "Knowledge-Based Expert Systems in Structural Design", Computers and Structures, Vol. 20, No. 1-3, 1985, pp. 1-9.

44. Stahl, F.I., "The Standards Interface for Computer-Aided Design", NBSIR 83-2671, National Bureau of Standards, U.S. Department of Commerce, April 1983.

45. Stahl, F.I., Wright, R.N., Fenves, S.J., and Harris, J.R., "Expressing Standards for Computer-Aided Building Design", ComputerAided Design, Vol. 15, No. 6, November 1983, pp. 329-334.

46. Starfield, A.M., Butala, K.L., England, M.M., and Smith, K.A., "Mastering Engineering Concepts by Building An Expert System",

Engineering Education, November, 1983, pp. 104-107.

47. Stefik, M. et. al., "Basic Concepts for Building Expert Systems", in Hayes-Roth, F., Waterman, D.A., and Lenat, D.B., Eds., Building Expert Systems, Addison-Wesley, Reading, Massachusetts, 1983.

48. Stefik, M. et. al., "The Architecture of Expert Systems", in Hayes-Roth, F., Waterman, D.A., and Lenat, D.B., Eds., Building Expert Systems, Addison-Wesley, Reading, Massachusetts, 1983.

49. Winston, P.H., Artificial Intelligence, 2nd ed., Addison-Wesley, 1984.

50. Winston, P.H. and Horn, B.K.P., LISP, 2nd ed., Addison-Wesley Publishing Company, Reading, Massachusetts, 1984.

51. Wright, J.M. and Fox, M.S., "SRL/1.5 User Manual", Technical Report, Carnegie-Mellon University Robotics Institute, June, 1983.

52. Xerox Corporation, INTERLISP Manual, 1983.

53. Zadeh, L.A., "Fuzzy Logic and Approximate Reasoning", Syntheses, Vol. 30, 1975, pp. 407-428.

A KNOWLEDGE-BASED APPROACH TO STRUCTURAL DESIGN

B Kumar*, P W H Chung†, R H Rae† and B H V Topping*
*Department of Civil Engineering
†Artificial Intelligence Applications Institute
University of Edinburgh, Scotland

The application of knowledge-based techniques to computer-aided structural design have recently received increasing attention. This paper presents a brief overview of some of the existing and proposed knowledge-based systems for structural design in civil engineering. Their main features and shortcomings are identified by examining the concepts involved in their development. INDEX, a knowledge-based system for the design of industrial buildings, is outlined. Knowledge representation issues are discussed and a domain-independent representation of structural design entities proposed. Examples are given to illustrate how the blackboard architecture of INDEX allows the knowledge modules surrounding it to communicate with each other. The use of the Edinburgh Prolog Blackboard Shell in the development of INDEX is explained. The implementation of INDEX is summarised and some representative production rules given. Some advantages and disadvantages of using the shell are also described briefly.

1. Introduction

1.1 The Structural Design Process

A civil engineering structure may be defined as an entity which will withstand the imposed design loads and transmit them to the foundations. In doing so, the structure must fulfil certain engineering and other architectural constraints. The structural design process includes the proportioning and sizing of such a structure to ensure the appropriate levels of safety and serviceability specified in the various design documents such as codes of practice and building regulations. The whole design process may be divided into three distinct stages :

1. Preliminary design: In this stage, the functional requirements and constraints are synthesised into a preliminary design concept. This involves the selection of a potential structural configuration satisfying layout and spatial constraints. This stage frequently includes an approximate analysis to evaluate the response of the alternative candidate structures selected for further consideration.

2. Detailed design: This involves the detailed design of candidate structure chosen in (1) and consists of the following three sub-stages :

 a. structural analysis ;

 b. proportioning and sizing the structural members ; and

 c. checking all the applicable design constraints.

This stage typically consists of several iterations between analysis and proportioning and sizing to ensure that all applicable constraints are satisfied with economy of design. Most of these constraints are specified in the applicable design codes. There may be a few external constraints as well, such as restrictions on the height of a structure. A large and significant deviation in the properties of the components assumed at the analysis and proportioning stages might necessitate another analysis-proportion and sizing-check cycle. This is typical of most design problems. The iteration continues until a satisfactory design is arrived at. In some cases, there may be a return to the preliminary design stage resulting in a revision of the chosen structural concept.

3. Design documentation: Detailing of the different components and preparation of the design documents.

1.2 Knowledge-based systems for structural design

Hitherto, the use of computers in structural design has been quite extensive. In fact, structural engineers were among the earliest users of computers. However, their use has generally been confined to strict numerical analysis and graphical output of results. Conventional structural design programs generally consist of a user interaction module and the main analysis module (see figure 1) [5]. These programs are particularly helpful in the analysis stage of the design process and are generally analysis based rather than design based programs.

There are, however, many problems in structural design which do not fit into the strict, rigid framework of algorithmic solution. For example, deciding about the structural system for a building or deciding about the spacing of frames or the pitch of a portal frame or the bases of a frame are a few of the numerous decisions that require weighing many different criteria utilising the designer's previous experience and his judgement. Figure 2 [4] shows the different stages of the structural design process as well as indicating the influencing factors (experience, heuristics etc.) at every stage.

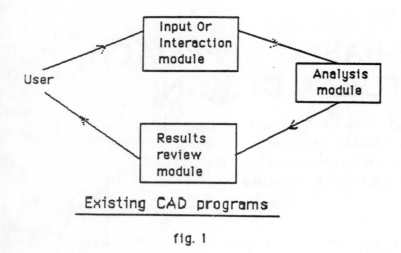

Existing CAD programs

fig. 1

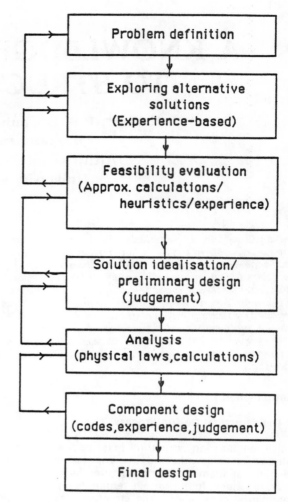

Structural design process

fig. 2

In recent years, there have been some attempts at developing Knowledge-Based Systems (KBSs) for structural design. Although at present a full-fledged system capable of designing a structure from initial concept to final design has yet to be developed but some prototypes do exist and some conceptual models have been proposed.

The following sections describe some existing knowledge-based systems and the proposed models for structural design.

1.2.1 Prototypes : Preliminary Design

HI-RISE [9] is a knowledge-based system which may be used in the preliminary design of high-rise buildings. It is implemented in a frame-based language PSRL. The knowledge base of HI-RISE contains declarative and procedural knowledge. The declarative knowledge represents a physical hierarchy of known structural types. The procedural knowledge is organized into "knowledge modules". The top level modules concern the design of two functional systems: a lateral load resisting system and a gravity load resisting system. The design of each of these systems is further decomposed into different knowledge modules. Its inference mechanism is that used by PSRL.

One of the major handicaps of HI-RISE is that it has a fixed agenda. This means it cannot handle situations that demand a different sequence of operations. Another limitation is that its context tree built during the consultation can only represent rectangular buildings; it is unable to represent buildings of other geometries. However, HI-RISE is a major contribution in the sense that it has succesfully demonstrated the application of a knowledge-based approach to structural design and has quite succesfully addressed important issues such as the representation of design information and the choice of a design strategy.

1.2.2 Prototypes : Detailed design

As already stated, the detailed design stage has three sub-stages; analysis, proportioning and sizing and checking of constraints.

SACON [12] stands for Structural Analysis CONsultant. It is an early example of a knowledge-based system in structural engineering. It was implemented using the EMYCIN system. The knowledge base of SACON

consists of :

1. rules for inferring analysis strategies indicating the most appropriate analysis and the associated recommendations,

2. rules for inferring the critical stress, deflections and other behaviour of structures and

3. mathematical models for estimating non-dimensional stress and deflection constraints on each substructure based on boundary and loading conditions.

The control strategy in SACON is backward-chaining and performs a depth-first search. SACON was mainly developed to act as a front-end to the finite element analysis program MARC. Therefore it cannot be used as a general-purpose knowledge-based analysis system.

SesCon [10] is another prototype system developed on the lines of SACON to be used as a front-end to the Seasam-69 structural analysis package.

Garrett [6] has developed a knowledge-based

standards processor, SPEX. It is proposed that this processor would act as an interface between CAD programs and the design standards. This processor is to be utilised for either designing or checking structural components for conformance with a design standard and other external constraints. One of the major features of this system is that the standard-dependant and the standard-independant knowledge are separated. This has the following advantages :

1. Changes in the design standard may be dealt with separately without affecting the CAD program.

2. The interpretation and the formal representation of the design standard has to be undertaken once only and not every time a CAD program is written.

3. The CAD program may be used for any standard by simply changing the standard-dependant knowledge which the standard processor uses to satisfy the CAD program's request.

One of the handicaps of SPEX is that it may only be used to design components of a structure and cannot be used for the complete structural design. Another handicap of SPEX is its over-reliance on its optimisation routine. Whenever its optimisation routine cannot find a solution, it immediately assumes that either the constraint set was incorrect or the hypothesis was wrong instead of considering the fact that the optimisation routine itself may have failed, which is quite possible. However, SPEX is probably to date the most comprehensive example of knowledge-based standards processing developed.

SPECON [12] is a small prototype knowledge-based system intended to assist the designer in checking structural steel elements for conformance with the AISC steel design specifications. It was developed at Carnegie-Mellon University as a part of a class project. Its organisation is similar to that of MYCIN and consists of :

1. the knowledge base,

2. the context and

3. the inference machine.

The knowledge base of SPECON is divided into two levels, one of which identifies the applicable constraints, whereas the other comprises the specific design constraints. The context is a Short Term Memory that keeps track of the various facts generated in a particular consultation. The control strategy in the inference machine is similar to MYCIN's backward-chaining strategy. It also has an explanation module which can answer questions relating to :

1. how a certain hypothesis was deduced and

2. why a certain question was asked.

SPECON is a very small prototype system and has only

one clause of the AISC specifications in its knowledge base. It is, however, a good demonstration of the application of the production rule approach towards standards processing.

1.2.3 Proposed models

Sriram [11] proposed a conceptual model for the integrated structural design called DESTINY. It integrates all the stages of the structural design process into an unified framework. Its scope is limited to the design of buildings. DESTINY utilises a blackboard system of architecture. The knowledge base of DESTINY consists of a number of different knowledge modules. These are organised into a hierarchy of three levels:

1. Strategy level knowledge modules : These modules analyse the current solution state to determine the next course of action. In the present version, only one knowledge module - TACON - exists at this level. This level schedules the execution of the specialist level knowledge modules.

2. Specialist level knowledge modules: These modules contribute to the development of the solution on the blackboard. Most of the knowledge modules at this level are themselves small KBSs having a knowledge base consisting of engineering heuristics. The different knowledge modules at this level are:

(i) ALL-RISE : This knowledge module synthesises different alternatives from the input related to space planning. The implementation of this module is under development.

(ii) MASON : This knowledge module models and analyses the feasible structural configurations.

(iii) DATON : This knowledge module proportions and details linear and surface structural elements such as beams, columns and the like.

(iv) CRITIC : This knowledge module criticizes and evaluates the current best design.

It is at this level that detailing and proportioning is undertaken by the DATON module.

3. Resource level knowledge modules: These contain the analytical knowledge and reference information required for analysis and design. The knowledge modules at this level consist mainly of algorithmic programs and database management systems (DBMS).

The inference mechanism of DESTINY has two main components:

1. Agenda and

2. Monitor.

The strategy level knowledge module schedules the execution of the specialist level tasks and sets the

Agenda. The Monitor then executes the element with the highest priority.

2. INDEX – A Knowledge-Based System for Industrial Building Design

2.1 Introduction

The work presented in this paper is concerned with the development of a Knowledge-Based System for the design of Industrial Buildings. The design concepts of the proposed system are described in this paper. The development of the system was greatly influenced by HI-RISE [9] and DESTINY [11]. These two systems were confined to the domain of residential and commercial buildings whereas INDEX is concerned with the design of industrial buildings.

The DESTINY model was found by the present authors to be comprehensive and sufficiently general for structural design. It is difficult to conceive any significant modifications to it primarily because of its close relationship with the structural design process which is well defined. However, while adapting it to different areas of structural design, certain modifications will have to be made in the domain-specific areas. The abstraction levels on the blackboard demand certain modifications for each different application.

As different prototypes in the different areas of structural design have already been developed, the main focus of attention in our work will be the inter-action between the different knowledge modules of an integrated system. Because of the comprehensive nature of the DESTINY model, the issue that needs most attention in future research is basically that of implementation. The main areas to be addressed will be knowledge representation and the inter-action between the different knowledge modules. For example, for standards processing, the SPEX model is being used but the area addressed by us is its interaction with a design program.

2.2 Some major features and components of INDEX

The architecture of INDEX is a blackboard system. It consists of different knowledge-modules surrounding and communicating through the blackboard. The system would be utilised after the general layout of the building has been fixed. In other words, the system takes the general layout and other spatial constraints of the building as its input. This is very similar to the input that HI-RISE or DESTINY require. Since the layout of the design is fixed, the domain of the system may be restricted to structural design. In general, the space planning is in the domain of architectural design.

2.2.1 Blackboard

The blackboard is divided into different parts which will contain entries posted on it by the different knowledge modules in the course of the consultation. The upper part consists of entries relating to the problem definition, which depends on the input from the user. The other parts consist of entries posted on it by the specialist as well as the resource level knowledge modules as the solution of the problem gradually emerges on the blackboard. The levels on the blackboard may be seen as a hierarchial decomposition of the industrial building design process.

2.2.2 Knowledge Base

Using the same terminology as Sriram [11] to describe the DESTINY model, the conceptual model of the system described in this paper is given in figure 3. However there are significant differences between the two models. The most important one is the difference in the number of levels of hierarchy in the organisation of the knowledge base. DESTINY's knowledge base is organised into a hierarchy of three levels whereas that of INDEX is in only two. The result is the absence of the Strategy level of DESTINY. The reason for this is that the rules for setting up the Specialist Agenda which the Strategy level module TACON consists of, are not required in this case. This task is accomplished by giving appropriate 'est' values to the rules as discussed later. The Specialist Agenda in our case is :

ALTSEL->STRANEX->DETEX->OPTEX->EVALUATOR

This agenda is currently fixed but research into ways of incorporating facilities for keeping this agenda flexible according to the situation is being considered. The other difference is the inclusion of the module OPTEX for structural optimisation at the Specialist level and a related module STOPT at the Resource level.

The knowledge base consists of a number of knowledge modules as shown in figure 3. As mentioned earlier, the knowledge modules are organised into a hierarchy of two levels, the specialist level and the resource level. The knowledge modules at the specialist level consist mainly of heuristics and other knowledge that are specialist-dependant. The knowledge modules at the resource level consist mainly of textbook knowledge. All the knowledge modules contain declarative as well as procedural knowledge. A brief description of the knowledge modules at the different levels is given below :

Specialist level : This consists of knowledge modules primarily containing experience-based heuristics. Of course, some textbook knowledge will also be stored at this level.

This level consists of the following knowledge modules (KMs) :

ALTSEL : This module is responsible for the ALTernative SELection of the feasible structural systems and deciding about different design parametres as the required frame spacing, whether to go for a single or a multi-bay system etc.

STRANEX : This module carries out the modelling and analysis of the chosen structural system by ALTSEL.

DETEX : This undertakes the detailed design, i.e. detailed proportioning of the components of the chosen structure.

EVALUATOR : This module evaluates the different alternatives generated by the system.

OPTEX : This module consists of various heuristics and rules to be used for the optimisation of the structures.

Resource level : This level generally consists of algorithmic programs, e.g. structural analysis programs, standard codes, optimisation routines etc.

The knowledge modules at this level will include the following when completed:

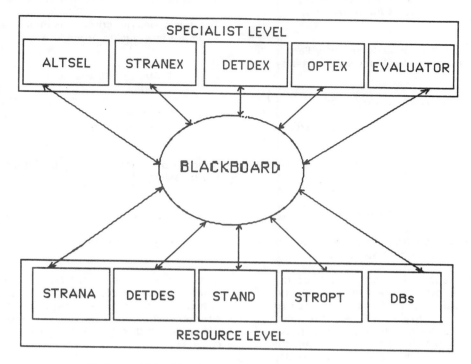

Schematic Model of the Proposed System

fig. 3

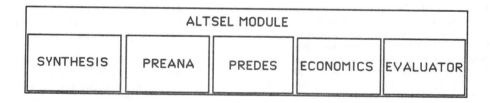

Sub-modules of the ALTSEL module

fig. 3a

STRANA : This module includes the STRuctural ANAlysis programs.

DETDES : This module is responsible for the DETailed DESign of the structure, i.e. detailed sizing of the components of the structure.

STAND : This module includes the provisions of the applicable STANDards and will be responsible for checking these standard constraints.

STOPT : This module consists of STructural OPTimisation routines.

DBs : These DataBases include the different dimensions and sectional properties of various structural sections, e.g. UBs, UCs etc.

Further, these modules consist of a number of sub-modules as for example shown in figure 3a and discussed in section 3.2.

2.2.3 Control Mechanism

A blackboard shell is being used for the implementation so that the control mechanism is already built into the shell. It consists mainly of an agenda, dynamically built during the consultation process. The agenda sequences the firing of the rules inside a knowledge module. The shell itself is written in the Edinburgh Prolog [1]. A typical rule in the blackboard shell syntax is of the following form [8] :

```
if        Condition
then      Goal
to        Effect
est       Est.
```

The effect of a rule may be one of the following :

add[Index,Fact,Cf], which adds an entry Fact on the blackboard under the index Index with certainty factor Cf,

or amend[Index,Fact,Cf], which amends an entry Fact on the blackboard under the index Index with certainty factor Cf,

or action Action, which takes an action Action,

or delete, which deletes an entry on the blackboard,

where Index, Fact, Cf and Action are prolog terms.

The 'est' in the rules indicate the 'usefulness' of each rule and, thus, helps in building up the agenda. So, by giving appropriate 'est' values to the different rules, we can sequence the firing of these rules. The rule with the lowest 'est' value will be fired first. The rule with the next higher 'est' value after that and so on.

Some important advantages of using a shell of this nature are that the effort required in building the rule-base is enormously reduced and the control mechanism is already provided. Thus, one may concentrate more on making the rule-base strong and robust enough to tackle real-life problems and on the design issues of the system, rather than getting involved in the detailed programming aspects. However, one has to acknowledge one important drawback of using such a shell: developing a multi-formalism system becomes practically infeasible. For example, the shell used in INDEX is a forward-chaining production rule system and any need to use a different formalism, like frames for example, would present a formidable task. One notable feature of this shell, however, is that one can easily switch to a backward-chaining formalism by writing the relevant portions in Prolog. It is important to emphasise here that using this shell has not proved to be a handicap at all so far and incorporating some additional important features into the system has proved to be quite simple. For example, setting up the Specialist agenda or incorporating the ability to change this agenda at the user's discretion have already been found to be quite straightforward to implement without requiring a separate set of production rules as in DESTINY.

3. Representation issues

A good representation of the design knowledge is essential for its efficient storage and manipulation. Representation of any piece of information basically involves the determination of the levels of abstraction of the object under consideration. Abstraction may be seen as a mapping between sets. An abstract view of a complex object is its simplified model. This simplified model could be obtained by applying a set of rules to any one of the salient properties of the complex object. In fact, design may be seen as a set of transformations from abstract to concrete and vice-versa [3]. Abstraction may also be seen as a simplified model of a complex object in terms of specifications and products. Each level in the abstraction hierarchy may be seen as a set of specifications for the next level and the product of the previous level. Applying these principles of abstractions to a complex structure, we may get different simplified models of the same structure, obtained by applying different sets of rules to different salient properties of the structure.

3.1 Representation of structural design entities

The basic design criteria used to assess a proposed structure in a design procedure are :

1. Strength (the load bearing capacity) and

2. Stiffness (the resistance to deformation).

Strength of a structure may be further sub-divided into the following :

1. lateral load resisting strength and

2. gravity load resisting strength.

If we take these properties separately and apply different sets of rules to them, we can obtain a simpler model of the required structure for the particular strength parameter in question (see figure 4). This model would denote a sub-part of the structure finally required.

Figure 5 shows domain-independant abstraction hierarchy levels for structural design entities for a general system. This could be extended for any domain-specific structural design problem. The relationships between the nodes at the different levels may be described by the following links (after [11]) :

Aggregation : This means a node which is developed from its constituent parts and is denoted by the 'part-of' link.

Alternation : This means a node which is an alternate node for a generic type of node and is denoted by the 'is-alt' link.

This abstraction hierarchy may be seen as a modular organisation of the knowledge required for any structural design problem. In fact, this organisation covers almost the whole domain of structural design and represents the levels of information and knowledge required for any design problem in any specific area of civil engineering structural design whatsoever. It should, however, be realised that a system based on the representation shown would be a massive system in terms of the amount of information contained in it and that it would be very difficult to implement it with the present state of knowledge-based systems technology. It would not only require a very considerable storage capacity but would also need efficient knowledge representation formalisms and would almost certainly need to be a multi-formalism system. We are not aware of any attempt at developing such a system.

The abstraction hierarchy on the blackboard of INDEX is given in figure 6. This is also a representation of the structural design process for buildings. This representation is given in terms of 'specifications' and 'products'. It can be seen as a hierarchial decomposition of the design process as it moves ahead and the solution emerges on the blackboard. Every level in this figure is a 'product' of the level above it and forms the 'specifications' for the one below it. This fact is represented by the 'prod-of' and 'spec-for' links between the different levels. This figure does not cover the whole design process and is

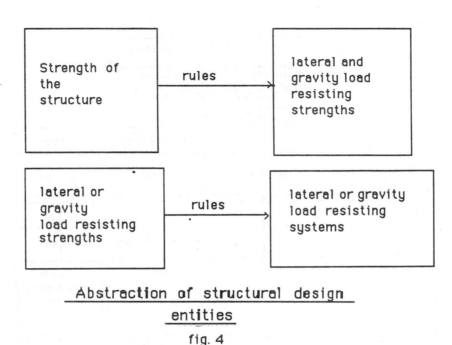

Strength of the structure → rules → lateral and gravity load resisting strengths

lateral or gravity load resisting strengths → rules → lateral or gravity load resisting systems

Abstraction of structural design entities

fig. 4

confined to the preliminary design undertaken by the ALTSEL module.

3.2 Implementation

An initial implementation of the ALTSEL module has been undertaken incorporating approximately one hundred rules at the time of writing this paper. It is being implemented on a Sun 3/50 workstation. The system has knowledge about the following types of steel frames :

1. Single and multi-span portal frames,

2. Roof trusses and simple columns,

3. Lattice beams and simple columns,

4. Roof trusses and latticed columns,

5. Simple beams and columns.

Apart from these, it also has rules for incorporating gantries for the design of gantry cranes if required.

The ALTSEL module has five sub-modules as shown in figure 3a, viz., SYNTHESIS, PREANA, PREDES, ECONOMICS AND EVALUATOR. Based on the rules in these sub-modules, the system is able to select the feasible alternatives for the lateral load resisting main frames for the industrial building in question. An approximate analysis is undertaken by the PREANA sub-module for each of the alternatives generated by the SYNTHESIS sub-module. The plastic method of analysis is used for this approximate analysis except for the lattice beam and truss roof altrernatives. An approximate proportioning and sizing of all the alternatives is then undertaken by the PREDES sub-module. These sizes are picked up from a database containing Universal Beams, Universal Columns and Square Hollow sections. The relative economics of the alternatives generated are then considered by the ECONOMICS sub-module. The rules in this sub-module are based on a study by Morris and Horridge [7] on comparative costs of single-storey steel framed structures.

Efforts are also underway to calibrate these rules against experts. Although some of the rules are based on discussions with working design engineers, most of them are taken from published literature from various steel section, frame manufacturing and fabricating firms including the Steel Construction Institute (formerly known as the Constructional Steel Research and Development Organisation) [2]. However, the system has proved to be quite effective on some real-life problems which have been used to test the system. A sample run of the system is given in Appendix I. A list of entries on the blackboard is given in Appendix II. The problem was to design a factory building of 15 metres span to withstand a vertical load of 5.43 kN/m. Other inputs were to find out any relevant detailed design constraints and no internal stanchions were allowed inside the building. By following the list of entries on the blackboard and the sample run in conjunction with the abstraction hierarchy on the blackboard given in figure 6, one may understand the sequence of the emergence of the solution on the blackboard. One difference between DESTINY and INDEX here is that whereas DESTINY only posts the current best design (CBD) on the blackboard, INDEX posts all of them. This is done so as to provide greater flexibility in terms of being able to review the whole context tree at a glance. An entry on the blackboard is identified by the index attached to it. In the example given below, the index of each entry is 'synthesis', their status is 'in' which means that they have been added into the list of entries on the blackboard, their certainty is 'true' and the 'facts' added are a list of lateral load system alternatives, viz., the lattice beam, the castellated beam and the tied portal. The numbers at the begining of these entries are not relevant in the present context.

226 in true
synthesis
lateral_load_sys(lattice_beam)

225 in true
synthesis
lateral_load_sys(castellated_beam)

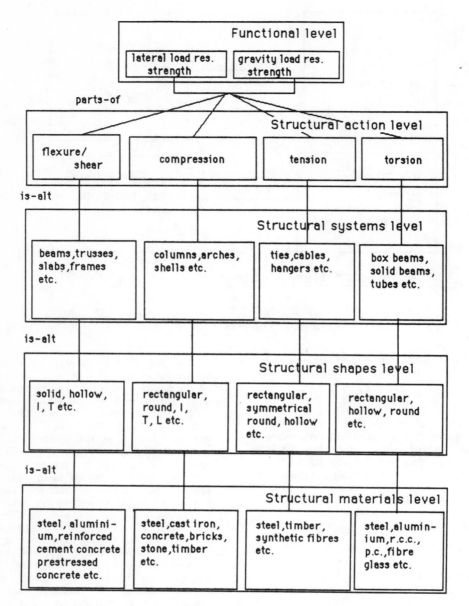

Abstraction hierarchy of structural design entities

fig. 5

222 in true
synthesis
lateral_load_sys(tied_portal)

3.3 Representative production rules

Much work has already been done on the ALTSEL module of the specialist level. This module is responsible for the preliminary design of the building, e.g. selecting the different alternative structural systems for the building, selecting the appropriate frame spacings, selecting the most economical system, etc. ALTSEL takes the column grid layout of the proposed building as its input. This module consists mainly of heuristics obtained from different literature and some practicing engineers. This is a simple representative rule from this module:

```
if    [synthesis,span(X),true]
and   holds(X =< 60)
then  output_message('Single span portal is an
      alternative.')
to    add[synthesis,lateral_load_sys(single_
      span_portal),true]
est   100.
```

which means that, if the span is known and is less than or equal to sixty metres, then a single span portal is a feasible alternative; 'output_message' is a simple Prolog procedure.

The strategy adopted by the system when moving from one level to the next in the design of the building is constraint handling [13], which may be sub-divided into :

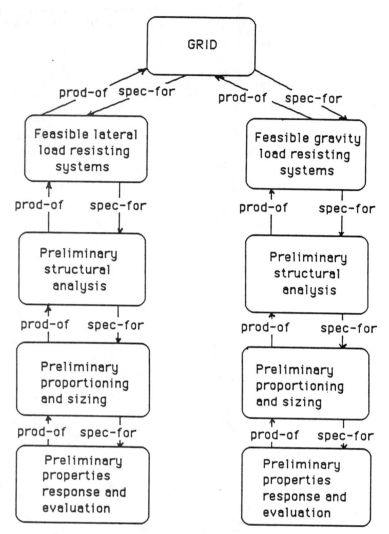

Abstraction hierarchy on the blackboard for the
solutions generated by the ALTSEL module

fig. 6

1. constraint formulation,

2. constraint satisfaction and

3. constraint posting.

This idea of constraint handling is accomplished in the
system by first satisfying the constraint for a particular
alternative, looking for any constraint associated with
the alternative which will be used by other modules,
i.e., constraint formulation, and posting it to the
appropriate module which is supposed to use it later
on, i.e, constraint posting. This may be illustrated by
the following rule, which indicates that deflection
checking should be carried out using elastic methods.

```
if    [synthesis,span(X),true]
and   holds((30 =< X,X =< 60))
then  output_message('A multi-bay portal would
      be  economical.')
to    add[synthesis,lateral_load_sys_eco(multi_
      bay_portal),true]
      and[design,multi_portal_design_cons(el_
      defl_check),true]
est   200.
```

In this example, the constraint has been posted on the
blackboard with the index 'design'. It may be accessed
by any other module by this index. For example, the
following rule from the standard provision checking
module states that, if there is an entry on the
blackboard that says that the deflection should be
checked by elastic methods, then the provisions of
clause 5.1.2.3 of the standard must be satisfied:

```
if    [design,multi_portal_design_cons(el_defl_
      check),true]
then  check_clause(sec. 5.1.2.3)
to    add[design_check,multi_portal_defl_
      check(satisfied),
      true]
est   300.
```

Summary

A brief review of some of the existing and proposed
knowledge based systems for structural design has
been given. The design concepts involved in the
development of a system for the design of industrial

buildings were also described. Some implementation issues were highlighted with examples of some representative production rules. The advantages of using a shell for a system development were also discussed and the power and potential of a knowledge-based approach to structural design were illustrated with examples.

Acknowledgements

The authors acknowledge the collaboration with The Engineers of Babtie Shaw and Morton, Glasgow and Ove Arup and Partners, Edinburgh in the implementation of INDEX. The research described in this paper is part of a larger collaborative project being undertaken by the Department of Civil Engineering and the Artificial Intelligence Applications Institute at the University of Edinburgh. Bimal Kumar wishes to acknowledge the University of Edinburgh for his postgraduate research scholarship.

REFERENCES

(1) Artificial Intelligence Applications Institute, University of Edinburgh, "Edinburgh Prolog (The New Implementation) User's Manual", 1986.

(2) Bates, W., "Introduction to the Design of Industrial Buildings", Constrado, Croydon, 1978.

(3) Begg, V., "Developing expert CAD systems", Kogan Page, London, pp. 45-80, 1984.

(4) Bell, T., Plank, R., "Microcomputers in Civil Engineering", Construction Press, London, pp. 6-20, 1985.

(5) Burgoyne, C.J., "Expert systems for Structural Design", presented at the Construction Industry Computer Conference, London, 1986.

(6) Garrett, Jr., J.H. and Fenves, S.J., "Knowledge-Based Standards Processing", International Journal of AI in Engineering, Vol. 1, No. 1, pp. 3-14, 1986.

(7) Horridge, J. F. and Morris, L. J., " Comparative costs of single-storey steel framed structures", The Structural Engineer, Vol. 64A, No. 7, pp. 177- 181, 1986.

(8) Jones, J. and Millington, M., "An Edinburgh Prolog Blackboard Shell", Department of Artificial Intelligence, University of Edinburgh, 1986.

(9) Maher, M.L. and Fenves, S.J., "HI-RISE - An Expert System for the Preliminary Design of High Rise Buildings", Knowledge Engineering in Computer -Aided Design, Gero, J., ed., Elsevier Science Publishers B. V. (North Holland), pp. 125-146, 1985.

(10) Sriram, D., et. al., "Knowledge-Based Expert Systems in Structural Design", Computers and Structures, Vol. 20, No. 1-3, pp. 1-9, 1985.

(11) Sriram, D., "DESTINY - A Model for Integrated Structural Design", Knowledge Engineering and Computer Modelling in CAD, Proceedings of CAD'86, London, pp. 226-235, 2-5 September, 1986.

(12) Sriram, D., et. al., "Expert Systems for Civil Engineering - A Survey", Report No. R-82-137, Department of Civil Engineering, Carnegie-Mellon University, U.S.A., 1982.

(13) Stefik, M., "Planning with constraints - MOLGEN, part 1", Artificial Intelligence, No. 16, pp. 111-140, 1981.

A sample run of the system

```
**********************************************************
Trying to find which are the possible lateral load systems :-
**********************************************************
```

single-span portal lateral load system is possible

tied portal lateral load system is possible

truss and column lateral load system is possible

The frame spacing for the span under consideration should be in the range
of 3 to 5 metres and angles or cold formed purlins should be used. Type in
a desired value followed by a full-stop.   4.5.


```
**********************************************************
The following alternatives can be considered for
the sides :-
**********************************************************
```

One alternative is to just have side rails attached to
the side stanchions.

Another alternative could be have side bracings between
the stanchions.


```
**********************************************************
The following alternatives can be considered for the
side cladding :-
**********************************************************
```

One alternative for side cladding is to have plastic
coated sheeting all over.

Another alternative for the side cladding is to have
brickwork in one of the following ways :-
                    1.supported from the structure both vertically and
horizontally,
                    2.supported only horizontally,
                    3.self_supporting both vertically and horizontally,
                    4.self_supporting and also supporting some elements
such as the ends of purlins at the gables.

precast or cast-in-situ concrete wall all over.


```
**********************************************************
Following are the approximate section sizes for the
different alternatives of feasible lateral load systems :-
**********************************************************
```


Following are the feasible sections
for the single span portal alternative :-

305x102UB@33
Zp provided = 479.6

The following are the feasible sections for the tied
portal rafters and columns based on aproximate analysis :-

203x133UB@25
Zp provided = 259.1

Following is the dimensions for the tie based
on approximate analysis :-

60x60x10 angle or a rod of 36mm. dia.

Following is the feasible section for the bars of the
roof truss for the roof truss and simple columns alternative :-

120x120x5.0@18.0SHS

Area provided is 22.9 cm. squares

Following is the feasible UC
column section for the truss and simple columns alternative :-

152x152UC@23

The most economical alternative for the span under consi-deration for lateral
load resisting system is the truss and column alternative.

****
The following design constraints should be considered
in the detailed design stage :-
****

The following things should be considered in the
detailed design stage of single span portal alternative :-
                    1.pitch should be kept low because greater slope
will give rise to greater spread at knees which can cause problems with
cladding,
                    2.horizontal thrusts should be carefully examined
and the foundation designed accordingly,
                    3.haunch should be provided at
the eaves and the ridge should be deepened because the maximium bending
moment will occur at the knees.

Appendix II

List of entries on the blackboard for the accompanying sample run under their respective indices

```
Index - design
_____

design_cons(single_span_portal)

design_cons(search)


Index - economics
_____

lateral_load_sys_eco(roof_truss)


Index - predes
_____

roof_truss_columns(152x152UC@23)

roof_truss_sec(120x120x5.0@18.0SHS)

tp_tie_section(36_60x60x10)

tp_zp_provided(259.1)

tp_feas_sec(203x133UB@25)

ssp_zp_provided(479.6)

ssp_feas_sec(305x102UB@33)


Index - preana
_____

tie_tension(38.2132)

tp_pla_mod(127.266)

ssp_pla_mod(442.819)

tp_pla_mom(19.0898)

sspfb_pla_mom(66.4229)


Index - synthesis
_____

side_clad(conc)

side_clad(brick)

side_clad(sheet)

sides(bracing)

frame_spacing(4.5)

lateral_load_sys(roof_truss)

lateral_load_sys(tied_portal)

lateral_load_sys(single_span_portal)


Index - problem
_____

find_lateral_load_sys
```

```
bases(fixed)
load(5.43)
find_design_cons(yes)
int_stanch(no)
apex_ht(3.75)
eaves_ht(7.6)
pitch(19)
span(15)
```

A KNOWLEDGE-BASED EXPERT SYSTEM FOR COMPUTER AUTOMATED STRUCTURAL DESIGN

Professor Donald E Grierson and Gordon E Cameron
Department of Civil Engineering, Solid Mechanics Division
University of Waterloo, Canada

The paper concerns the development of a knowledge-based expert system (KBES) involving the coordinated use of finite element analysis, sensitivity analysis and optimization techniques to design minimum weight planar steel frameworks. The numeric-intensive analysis and optimization tasks of the design method are well formulated and well handled through computer codes written in FORTRAN. On the other hand, the design synthesis process itself is driven by a variety of criteria that are less well defined and quantified numerically. The essential feature of the work is the separation of the well-structured numeric tasks of analysis and optimization from the non-structured and often symbolic knowledge that drives the synthesis process. A separately maintained knowledge base is developed that is easily updated and revised, and which provides the means to generate explanations of the decisions taken during the synthesis process. The development of the expert system is achieved through the use of the rule-based programming language OPS83, which has the capability both to interface the numeric FORTRAN algorithms and to perform the symbolic computations required to fire the rules in the knowledge base. The features of the KBES for optimal structural design are illustrated for steel framework design.

INTRODUCTION

Traditional computing is naturally limited to what it does best, numeric manipulation and computation. It is unable to represent and interpret knowledge in an explicit and coherent form and is unable to perform symbolic computation. On the other hand, design is concerned with concepts, ideas, judgements and experience, all of which are outside the realm of traditional computing. The aim of the present research is to develop and implement a knowledge-based expert system (KBES) environment wherein both numeric computation and knowledge-based problem solving are together applied to perform optimal structural design.

The structural optimization aspects of this work are based upon research initiated by Grierson and Schmit (Ref. 7) and further developed by others (Refs. 3,5,8,9,10). This previous work developed a program for the STRUctural SYnthesis of skeletal steel frameworks, STRUSY, that employs optimization techniques in conjunction with finite element analysis and sensitivity analysis to achieve a computer-based design capability that is computationally efficient with wide application. The current version of the program determines a minimum-weight design for planar skeletal frameworks under service and factored performance constraints. Stress and displacement constraints account for first-order and/or second-order (P-Δ) effects (Ref. 8). Recent extensions account for dynamic load effects (Ref. 9). Members may be sized in a variety of ways, including the automatic selection of commercially available standard sections. Full account can be taken for fabrication details concerned with member continuity and structure symmetry.

Cross-section areas a_i are taken as the principal sizing variable in the formulation of the optimization problem. In their general form, stress and displacement performance constraints are implicit functions of the sizing variables. To facilitate the numerical implementation of the synthesis process, these constraints are formulated as explicit linear functions of the sizing variables through the use of sensitivity analysis techniques. Recognizing that elastic displacements and stresses generally vary inversely with the member cross-section areas, corresponding "good" quality performance constraints are achieved by formulating them as explicit-linear functions of the *reciprocal* sizing variables $x_i = 1/a_i$. The minimum weight design problem expressed explicitly in terms of reciprocal sizing variables is then

$$\text{Minimize:} \quad \sum_{i=1}^{n} \gamma_i l_i / x_i \ . \tag{1}$$

$$\text{Subject to:} \quad \underline{\delta}_j \leq \sum_{i=1}^{n} d_{ij}^o x_i \leq \overline{\delta}_j \ , \qquad (j = 1, 2, \ldots, d) \ , \tag{2}$$

$$\underline{\sigma}_k \leq \sum_{i=1}^{n} s_{ik}^o x_i \leq \overline{\sigma}_k \ , \qquad (k = 1, 2, \ldots, s) \ , \tag{3}$$

$$x_i \in X_i \ , \qquad (i = 1, 2, \ldots, n) \ . \tag{4}$$

Equation (1) is the cost or objective function to be minimized, where γ_i and l_i are the material density and length of member i, respectively. Equations (2) define the d constraints on elastic displacements δ_j, where d_{ij}^o is the computed sensitivity of δ_j to change in x_i for the current design stage, x_i is the variable to the next weight optimization, and $\underline{\delta}_j$ and $\overline{\delta}_j$ are the specified lower and upper bounds on displacement δ_j, respectively. Similarly, equations (3) define the s constraints on elastic stresses σ_k, where the upper and lower limits define allowable tensile and compressive stresses, respectively. Finally, equations (4) define the set of available reciprocal areas $X_i = \{x_1, x_2, \ldots\}$ for each member i

from which the value of the sizing variable x_i is to be selected.

Equations (1-4) represent a well-defined mathematical statement of the optimal design problem. However, the proper expression of these equations for any particular application requires considerable judgement on the part of the designer. The same can be said concerning the means of solving equations (1-4) and, finally, in interpreting the merits of the structural design so found. The present paper addresses itself to these somewhat subjective areas of concern. Specifically, a KBES methodology for structural design is described with emphasis on using expert systems techniques: to obtain a good initial estimate of the structural model and, hence, mathematical model of the design problem, equations (1-4); to drive the numerical computation process to a reasonable optimal design for the current structural model; and to evaluate the current design and to suggest alternative (improved) structural modelling scenarios as the starting point for other possible designs.

KNOWLEDGE BASED EXPERT SYSTEMS (KBES)

This section presents a brief background to Knowledge Based Expert Systems in the context of optimal structural design. In general, expert systems aim to emulate the ability of human experts to ask pertinent questions, to explain why they are asking them, and to justify their conclusions. Even though the applications may differ, the fundamental architecture of these systems remains the same and possesses the following common components (refer to Figure 1):

- Knowledge Base
- Context
- Inference Engine
- Explanation Facility
- Numeric-Intensive Tasks

The Knowledge Base contains a body of rules provided by experts from the knowledge domain. The knowledge may be *deep* or *surface*. Principles of statics or structural analysis procedures are examples of deep knowledge. Surface knowledge is heuristic knowledge developed from experience. Knowledge about the selection of a trial beam-column is an example of surface knowledge. There are a variety of different types of knowledge that need to be included in the knowledge base of a KBES for optimal structural design. First, there is the "procedural" knowledge required to establish the basic precepts for the structural design; for example, *if the structure is tall and slender → P-Δ analysis is required*, or *if bending member → check shear*. Then, there is the "structural modelling" knowledge required to establish the basic parameters for the structure to be designed; for example, *if a structure has a concrete core → employ a gravity framing system*, or *depending on span length, select spanning element...L > l* → truss section*. Then, there is the "mathematical modelling" knowledge required to establish the formulation of the design problem and to then solve it; for example, *if a skeletal structure with one-dimensional elements → adopt a linear sensitivity-based formulation*, or *if to select discrete sets of available cross-sections for member design → establish on basis of capacity and economy*. Then, of course, there is the knowledge embodied in the governing design code for the structure; for example, *if required to size member → apply strength, stability and deformation rules*. Finally, there is "designer preference" knowledge that invokes rules of good practise; for example, *if uplift at a support → change the bracing scheme*, or *if connection costs are excessive → change relative sizes of columns and girders at joints*.

The Context contains facts that reflect the current state of a problem solution. Whereas the rules in the knowledge base may be thought of as an expert's *long term memory*, the facts in the context reflect

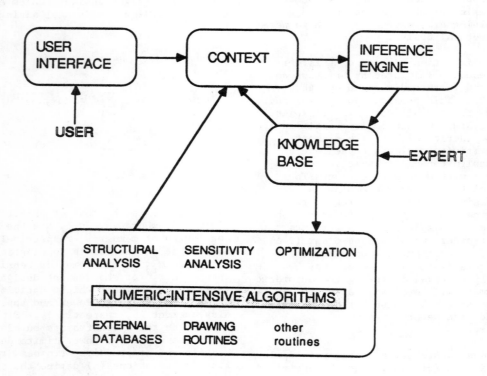

Figure 1: Components of a Knowledge-Based Expert System

an expert's *short term memory*. The context is like a blackboard where one builds up a list of facts about a particular problem, and "erases" it at the end of the session. A typical fact in the context for an optimal design KBES would be the description of the structure topology, supports, loading, etc. Other typical facts derived during the actual design process would concern the current status of the structure relative to governing code clauses; for example, *if $(a_{old} - a_{new}) \neq 0 \rightarrow$ fire rule in knowledge base to perform an analysis to find new member forces.*

The Inference Engine manipulates the context through the knowledge base. It contains no knowledge about the problem domain and is simply a feature of the programming language. For example, the inference engine of a rule-based forward-chaining system operates in the following cyclic *recognize-act* mode: monitor changes in context → match premises of rules with context → select and execute a matching rule in the knowledge base (which modifies the context) → repeat until stated goal is reached or until no premise-matches occur. In fact, studies have shown that a rule-based, forward-chaining architecture is well suited for solving design problems (Refs. 11, 12). The rule-based language should support alpha-numeric computation and have "hooks" into other programming languages, such as FORTRAN, in which proven numeric-intensive solver routines have already been written. The expert system HI-RISE for the preliminary structural design of high-rise buildings has been successfully implemented in the rule-based language OPS5 (Ref. 12), which can access routines written in other languages. An updated version of OPS5 is the language OPS83 (Ref. 6), which supports both a rule-based architecture and the traditional imperative (sequential) programming paradigm of languages like FORTRAN. This means that OPS83 can switch from a rule-based format to an imperative-based format, thus permitting the procedural portions of an application to be programmed in the imperative format rather than cluttering the knowledge base with rules that must be contrived to "fire" in a sequential order. This dual-control format makes OPS83 an ideal authoring tool for creating an expert system that must incorporate both the well formed and the unstructured aspects of optimal structural design. Moreover, OPS83 can also perform both forward and backward chaining, which is a desirable feature since forward chaining is well suited to the original design problem while backward chaining is well suited to the design verification problem where the goal is to find evidence to support a selected design. The OPS83 language was selected by this study as the principal authoring tool for the development of the described KBES for optimal structural design.

The Explanation Facility interacts with the knowledge base and the context to answer user requests for explanations or justifications as to why certain decisions were reached or why particular data is required. An example scenario may be as follows:

    system: Is there a concrete core in this structure?
      user: why?

    system: I am trying to determine if this is a gravity or lateral resisting system, or both.

    system: Is there a concrete core in this structure?
      user: yes

    system: Can I assume this is a gravity-only resisting frame?
      user: yes

The Numeric-Intensive Tasks represent a relatively new but vital component of expert systems required to function practically in the engineering domain. The optimal design problem can be broadly defined as problem formulation, structural analysis, sensitivity analysis, optimization, design constraint evaluation and database management. Previous studies have established excellent FORTRAN routines for each of these various tasks. It remains to implement all of these tasks together in the design process within an expert system architecture.

OPTIMAL DESIGN WITHIN A KBES FRAMEWORK

The relevant aspects of the optimal structural design process are: identify the scope of the design task (ie., identify the actual structural conditions that the design must have a concern for) and infer a numerical model of the structure; derive a mathematical statement of the design problem and develop a synthesis process to solve it; determine the results of the design process and evaluate the merits of the structure so found. These three broad areas are further detailed in the following.

The Structural Design Task

It is presumed that the usual architect-engineer relationship prevails for the building project and that a number of parameters are established even before the structural designer begins work on the project; for example; the general configuration of the load carrying system, basic floor plan, bay widths, story heights, nature of the applied loads; whether steel or concrete construction, etc. Some of this initial data may have been established using yet another expert system devised to create reasonable preliminary designs (e.g., HI-RISE). The initial task of the designer is to enter this initial data into the context of KBES. The inference engine then attempts to match facts in the context with premises of rules in the knowledge base. Rules whose premises are satisfied are "fired" (i.e., the consequence of a rule is executed) to establish the scope of the design problem with respect to numerical solution. Some typical rules in the knowledge base that may be fired by the initial data in the context, or lack of it, are as follows:

- If the structure type is unspecified and it cannot be inferred from the context → query user to specify (e.g., TRUSS or FRAME?).

- If structure type is a frame → query user if it is braced or unbraced.

- If a tall structure without a concrete core is inferred from the context → invoke P-Δ analysis/design criteria.

- If steel construction and member type is unspecified and span lengths are reasonable → select wide-flange section type for members of primary frame...if spans are long → suggest truss-beam sections for spanning members.

The firing of these and other fundamental rules in the knowledge base further adds facts to the context until eventually the full scope of the design task has been identified.

One of the important consequences of this initial phase to establish the scope of the design task is that the subset of rules in the knowledge base that are active for the application on hand is clearly identified. The inactive part of the knowledge base should thus be discarded immediately, which is possible because of the modular nature of knowledge bases, thereby reducing the knowledge base search domain and thus leading to improved efficiency of the expert system in carrying out the design task.

Formulating And Solving The Design Problem

Having the basic model of the structure and the scope of the design task as data in the context, this data is then used to fire further rules in the knowledge base to essentially establish the mathematical statement of the design problem to be solved. Some typical knowledge base rules in this regard are as follows:

- If steel construction and structure is a truss → flag the axial design-check rules of the Design Code.

- If steel construction and structure is a frame → flag all axial and flexural design-check rules, as well as member deflection-check rules.

- If structure is a frame → identify end-sections and mid-span of flexural members as stress-check points.

- If not sway-prevented with a lateral load resisting core → suggest structure nodes where sway displacements should be checked, and for which load cases.

- If fabrication criteria is unspecified → suggest "good-practise" rules concerning member continuity, cut-off points, joint connectivity, symmetry, etc.

Having established the formulation of the design problem, which then becomes data in the context, the inference engine then fires further rules in the knowledge base to drive the synthesis process towards obtaining the minimum-weight design for the structure. Some typical knowledge base rules in this regard are:

- For the specified section types, and any specified limitations on their selection → select initial sections for the members of the structure to commence the design process (e.g., largest sections in database, or, alternatively, select beam sections on basis of the member span-to-depth ratios).

- For initial member sizes → conduct analysis of structure.

- From initial analysis results → identify appropriate subsets of sections as being available for the design of each member.

- From analysis results and member properties → conduct sensitivity analysis and formulate linear approximations of the design constraints.

- For current design constraints → conduct optimization to find new member sections for which

the structure has lower overall weight.

- If new design infeasible, or if design process is divergent → suggest/implement means to overcome difficulties.

- If structure weight has not converged → repeat the design step again.

- If structure weight has converged → submit minimum-weight structure to post-analysis critique to establish the merits of the design relative to other possible modelling scenarios.

In essence, the expert system is here concerned with conducting numeric-intensive tasks and invoking robust computation rules to ensure the numerical stability and convergence of the analysis-optimization synthesis process. Earlier studies (Refs. 3,5,10) embedded these rules within the numeric flow sequence of the synthesis process. The expert system architecture treats these computation rules as being separate from the numeric-intensive tasks themselves, thereby allowing them to be individually monitored and easily modified.

The expert system can be specified to solve the design problem in one of three ways, depending on the wishes of the designer. It can directly conduct the design in exactly the way specified by the designer without making any judgements on its own. Or, with a view to improved design, it can query the designer's requests and suggest alternative approaches to solving various aspects of the design problem. Finally, the expert system can directly conduct the design without inviting any input into the process by the designer. The particular mode of operation selected for the expert system at this stage of the overall synthesis process is reflected in the way the final stage is conducted concerning the design results and evaluation, discussed in the following section.

Design Results And Evaluation

Once the numeric-intensive tasks involved in solving the design problem are completed, the expert system then evaluates the structural design so found in a variety of different ways concerned with giving design explanations, warnings and improvement advice.

The explanation facility informs the designer as to the basis for the decisions taken to arrive at the final design: for example, if a member was found to be only in tension for the design → a double-angle section shape was selected for its design; or, if lateral sway was found to be the critical design constraint → the girder stiffnesses were increased to meet drift requirements.

The warning facility serves to pinpoint design defficiencies and, where possible, to suggest remedial action; for example, if excessive deflections are found → suggest tightening the constraint bounds at offending nodes and redoing the design; or, if support uplift detected → suggest changing the bracing system and redoing the design.

The design improvement facility identifies aspects of the final design that suggest the design may be improved if alternative choices are made in certain areas; for example, if the minimum available size of a particular section shape was selected for a member → suggest another section shape for which even smaller sizes are available; or, if a very deep section was found for a spanning member → suggest replacing the solid shape with a truss system.

The design evaluation stage introduces additional data and information into the context which, upon reapplying the expert system, is then used to determine an improved design of the structure. Generally only one or two such iterations are required before the design will converge to a state that is fully acceptable to the designer.

ACKNOWLEDGEMENT

This study is based on research being conducted by the second author under the supervision of the first author for the degree of Doctor of Philosophy in Civil Engineering, University of Waterloo. The work is sponsored by the National Sciences and Engineering Council of Canada under grant A5306.

REFERENCES

1. American Institute of Steel Construction, Specification for the Design, Fabrication and Erection of Structural Steel for Buildings (effective November 1, 1978).

2. American Institute of Steel Construction, Load & Resistance Factor Design Specification for Structural Steel Buildings (September 1, 1986).

3. Cameron, G.E., Optimal Structural Synthesis of Planar Trusses Subject to Canadian and American Design Standards Using Standard Steel Sections. Master's thesis, University of Waterloo, Dept. of Civil Engineering, Waterloo, Ontario, Canada, 1984.

4. CAN3-S16. 1-M84 Steel Structures for Buildings (Limit States Design). Canadian Standards Association, 1984.

5. Chiu, C.W., Structural Synthesis of Skeletal Frameworks Under Service and Ultimate Performance Constraints. Master's thesis, University of Waterloo, Department of Civil Engineering, Waterloo, Ontario, Canada, 1982.

6. Forgy, C.L., OPS83 User's Manual and Report. Production Systems Technologies, March 1985.

7. Grierson, D.E. and Schmit, L.A., Jr., Synthesis under service and ultimate performance constraints. Computers & Structures, 15(4):405-417, 1982.

8. Hall, S.K., Automated Synthesis of Structural Frameworks Under Large Displacements. Master's thesis, University of Waterloo, Department of Civil Engineering, Waterloo, Ontario, Canada, 1986.

9. Kramer, G.J.E., Computer Automated Synthesis of Structural Frameworks subjected to Dynamic Loads. Master's thesis, University of Waterloo, Dept. of Civil Engineering, Waterloo, Ontario, Canada, 1987.

10. Lee, W.H., Optimal Structural Synthesis of Skeletal Frameworks Using Discrete and Commercially Available Standard Sections. Master's thesis, University of Waterloo, Dept. of Civil Engineering, Waterloo, Ontario, Canada, 1983.

11. McDermott, J., R1: A Rule-Based Configurer of Computer Systems. Report CMU-CS-80-119, Carnegie-Mellon University, Dept. of Computer Science, 1980.

12. Maher, M.L. and Fenves, S.J., HI-RISE: A Knowledge-Based Expert System for the Preliminary Structural Design of High Rise Buildings. Report R-85-146, Carnegie-Mellon University, Dept. of Civil Engineering, January 1985.

APPLICATION OF AI PROGRAMMING TECHNIQUES TO THE ANALYSIS OF STRUCTURES

R Fruchter and Professor J Gluck

Department of Civil Engineering

and Y I Gold

Department of Computer Science

Technion—Israel Institute of Technology, Haifa, Israel

One of the primer objectives of AI is to build systems that are able to enlarge and modify their knowledge base and to profit in an "intelligent" way from the acquired experience. This paper presents a prototype system that provides the capability of adaptively learning from training experience, process that is currently carried out by the user when performing a structural analysis.

The presented system is based on the development of a hierarchy of "intelligent" modules, suited for modeling structures. Emphasis is placed upon the following problems: (1) representation of these modules, (2) the relation between them in the modeling process and the flow of information in the analysis process, (3) defining the concept of training and developing a suited mechanism of training. The system is written in CPROLOG and runs on a VAX 780.

The modular structure of the developed system, as well as the capability to learn from training experience in a dynamic enviroment, establishes the basis of a formalized methodology for developing training systems which may be extended to include other types of training objectives in the process of structureal analysis.

1. INTRODUCTION

The present CAD tools used for the analysis of structures are very powerful tools, containing the experience of the last two decades. The insufficiency presented by these tools is that their implied knowledge is static, without the capability to learn from experience. Meaningful analysis requires interpretation of structure and result by the human expert. The acquired knowledge, through training and learning of new case studies remain the personal experience of the user. It is hoped, that using AI techniques, will allow to develop program models for training and learning, in order to transfer to the program (Ref. 1) some of the abilities of the human expert to acquire knowledge.

In order to explore the appropriateness of AI techniques in the domain o structural analysis, a research project was initiated at the Department of Civil Engineering and the Computer Science Faculty, Technion, to develop a system with the capability of adaptively learning from training experience through structural analysis. The system is written in CPROLOG (Ref. 2) and runs on a VAX 780.

This paper presents major issues ot the project, which describe the purposes of this research project. In the next section the approach taken in the development of the system and a system overview presenting the objectives of the project are discussed. General concepts and parts of the system, that have been implemented are presented in section 3 and 4. Emphasis is placed on the following problems: (1)representation and development of a hierarchy of "intelligent" modules, suited for modeling structures (section 3); (2)defining and implementing the training and learning processes (section 4); (3) the flow of information through the system (section 3 and 4). Example cases are presented in section 5. In the conclusions some further objectives for future work are presented.

2. APPROACH AND SYSTEM OVERVIEW

The goal of this research is to explore, the mechanism of acquiring training experience throughout ("local") and at the end of the structural analysis process ("generalization"), as well as "how" this experience is later used, changed and dynamically updated within the "local" training and in the "generalization", or learning process.

In this perspective, it seemed correct to model the concepts of training and learning in the process of structural analysis, by taking into consideration

both procedural and declarative knowledge representation. The reason of this statement is based on the following observations: the declarative knowledge representation enables to define facts and rules of the specific domain, whereas the procedural knowledge representation enables dynamic modification of the stored declarative knowledge.

Other issues that this research considered important, were the relevance of the acquired knowledge from training, its influence and its use in a dynamic environment. The knowledge contained in the trained knowledge base (TKB) must be used when analysing a new structure. A mechanism must be provided to enable the use of newly acquired training experience as the new structure is being modified.

The purpose of the current research project was to develop a system with the capability of adaptively learning from training experience in the domain of structural analysis, by applying AI techniques.

This goal was accomplished by developing a hierarchy of "intelligent" modules (see section 3) suited for modeling of structures. These modules permit the performance of structural analysis at different levels of abstraction, like: primitive element level (e.g., primitive, joint), structural element level (e.g., beam, column) or structural level (e.g., frame). The combination of modules of a "lower" level enables the construction of a more complex structure. The hierarchy has a modular structure and can be extended at any time with new "intelligent" modules, without requiring changes in the existing modules.

The central feature of the system is the capacity to increase the knowledge base through training with new case studies. The training of a module augments the basic knowledge needed for the analysis process, resulting in improved future performance. New knowledge can be incorporated either automatically from the system's own training experience or by user interaction. The training is carried out at each abstraction level. This means that a module at a "higher" level, starts out with the training knowledge already acquired by its components, which belong to a "lower" level.

These trained "intelligent" modules, can be used for modeling more complex structures, leading to new knowledge acquisition.

Figure 1. provides an overview of the current version of the training model. In the diagram: the circles represent declarative information (e.g., facts and rules representing the structures and the acquired knowledge about their state and behavior). The boxes represent procedural knowledge, concerning training, and learning from training experience. The information flow through the system, is shown by the direction of the arrows.

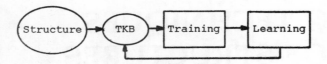

Figure 1.   System overview

The parts of the system that have been studied and implemented will be discussed in the following sections.

3. HIERARCHY OF "INTELLIGENT" MODULES

Modeling structures for the purpose of structural analysis involve a number of independent but interrelated data objects. Different ways of structuring and organizing these data objects have been proposed in the literature (Ref. 3), like: database management systems (DBMS), "object-oriented" data models, "stream-processing" data models (Ref. 4).

An example of "object-oriented" data models is the data abstraction model (Ref. 4). This model was used for the purpose of this project. The data abstraction is a methodology for structuring systems of data. It is based on the idea of isolating parts of the program which consist of the way how the data objects are used, from the parts of the program which deal with the details of how the data objects are implemented, by using more primitive data objects. The advantages of using the data abstraction model include:
- It is a powerful tool for controlling complexity. By creating abstraction levels, the task of designing a large program can be divide into smaller tasks, that can be realized and checked separately.
- Programs are easier to maintain and to modify.
- It permits multiple representation and manipulation of the same data object, by different parts of a program.
- The manipulation of the data objects is more efficient, since more assumptions can be made at any level of the hierarchy of abstractions.
- Assumptions and acquired knowledge at "lower" levels are inherited by the "higher" levels.

The proposed hierarchy of abstraction levels for the development of the "intelligent" modules, is presented in Figure 2. The key idea was to create abstraction levels that isolate the way data objects are used at "higher" levels from their underlying representation in terms of "lower" level data objects or in terms of list structures. It can be seen (Figure 2) that the design of a program for structural analysis, that uses structural elements as data objects, can be separated from the implementation part of structural elements in terms of more primitive data objects. The same can be said about developing a program for the analysis of structural elements; it can be separated from the implementation level of: primitive and joint, which represent a "lower" abstraction level.

```
┌──────────────────┐
│    structure     │
└──────────────────┘

   rules for combining structural elements
   rules for obtaining the structural response
   rules for training and learning structures

┌──────────────────┐
│ structural elements │
└──────────────────┘

   rules for combining primitives and joints
   rules for analysing structural elements
rules for training and learning structural elements

┌──────────────────┐
│  primitive, joint │
└──────────────────┘

   rules for analysing primitives and joints
   facts representing physical parameters
      that characterize these modules
```

Figure 2. Hierarchy of abstraction levels

3.1 Data object modules

In order to develop the hierarchy of modules, the following types of data objects were chosen for the "lowest" abstraction level: *primitive* and *joint*. These modules have a flexible representation structure, which permits any addition of new physical parameters needed in new analysis.

A *primitive* is considered a basic element constructing structural elements. It contains all the information (physical and behavioral parameters) needed in order to obtain the result of structural analysis. A *primitive* can have for example the representation shown in figure 3a. The *primitive* is considered a basic unit, to which input data (I) is supplied. This input data is transferred to the underlying procedures, which perform the analysis of the primitive and return the desired output data (O). In the presented example (Figure 3b) the input data is represented by:
-the geometry of the primitive (L);
-the forces that act at the left section of the primitive: NI=axial force, SI=shear force, MI=moment;
-the exterior forces that can act on the primitive at a distance (D) from the left section: FN=tension or compression force, FS=normal force.

The output data in the present example, will be the forces at the right section of the primitive: NO=axial force, SO=shear force, MO=moment.

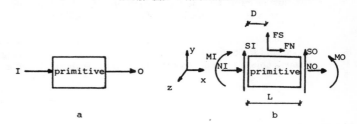

Figure 3.   Representation of the primitive (p)

In order to obtain the result of the analysis, the processing of the data is based on the principles of static equilibrium (Ref.5,Ref.6). The equations used in the present example are:

$$\sum F_x = 0$$
$$\sum F_y = 0$$
$$\sum M = 0$$

The *joint* was considered as a second basic element in modeling structural elements and structures. It provides the means to combine the primitives. The *joint* represents the basic unit, which permits the transfer of information (forces) from one primitive (or structural element) to an other. The combination of primitives through joints can be made at any angle, as shown in figure 4a. The implementation of the joint module is also based on the idea of basic unit, to which input (I) is supplied. The input is transferred to the underlying procedures that perform the analysis and return the output values. The input data considered in this example is represented (see Figure 4b) by:
-the geometry of the combination (α);
-the input forces: NI, SI, MI;
-the exterior forces that can act on the joint: FN, FS.

The output data (O) is represented in the present example by: JNO, JSO, JMO. The processing of the data is based on the principles of mechanics of materials (Ref. 5, Ref. 6).

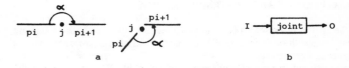

Figure 4.   Representation of the joint (j)

The next data abstraction level consists of structural elements (e.g., beam, column). A structural element is created by combining primitives and joints. The flow of information through the components of a structural element is shown in Figure 5a. The structural element can be viewed as an entity (Figure 5b), receiving input information and creating output information. The processing of input information is performed at the underlying level, by the primitives and joint components. As shown in figure 5a, the output of a *primitive i* represents the input for the joint, that connects the *i* and *i+1 primitives,* and the output of this joint is transmitted to the *primitive i+1* as input data.

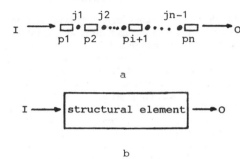

a

b

Figure 5. Representation of the structural element

Having created this abstraction level, more complex structures can be modeled by using the structural element modules. An example of such a model, is a frame. Its abstract representation in terms of the above defined modules and the flow of information through it, is given in Figure 6.

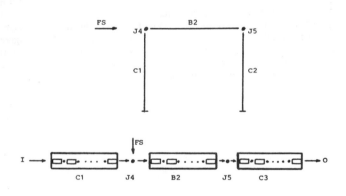

Figure 6. Model of a structure (frame) and the flow of information through it

4. DEFINING THE CONCEPTS OF TRAINING AND LEARNING

Training and learning from training experience are complex processes, which represent the ability of people to enlarge their knowledge and improve their expertise (Ref. 7). Understanding these processes and trying to model them, represent challanging goals for AI research. The training and learning modules, described in this paper, are developed in light of these definitions and the criteria presented in the Approach.

The difficulty of defining a training mechanism lies in: defining the goal of the training process; the steps of the training process; and the way to implement them in order to create a system with dynamic behavior.

The goals established for the training and learning modules of the present system are:
-To identify and evaluate through training critical regions of the structure.
-Define, formalize, and store patterns that are the result of the training.
-The stored patterns, representing the result of training and analysis of structures, will allow future analysis to be direct, and thus the essential information about the response of the structure will be faster to obtain.
-Search for similar patterns in the TKB and reduce the given situation to known ones acquired through training and learning.
-Discover new cases through training, formalize and store them in the TKB.

Considering the system presented in Figure 1, the information flow through the training and learning modules consists of the following steps:
 1) The structure introduces the initial information about its state.
 2) The TKB of the corresponding abstraction level is searched for a pattern that matches the given state of the structure, and:
   a) if a match is found, the training module will not be activated and no new pattern will be stored; the structure will be analysed according to the rules of the pattern found;
   b) if no matching is found the training module is activated. The component elements of the structure are processed according to the implemented training rules.
 3) If the output of the structural analysis is obtained through training it is transferred to the learning module, whose function is to extract the relevant information that characterizes the studied case, to formalize it and to store it in the TKB of the corresponding abstraction level.

4.1 Training and learning mechanism

The model of training and learning (generalization) is based on the following idea: take an input pattern, modify it to obtain an output pattern, which is then used to extract the relevant parameters in order to generalize it and store it as a new learned pattern in the TKB. A schematic illustration of this mechanism is given in Figure 7.

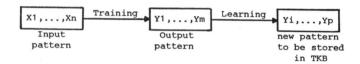

Figure 7. Schematic illustration of training and learning mechanism

4.1.1 Training

The training consists, in its current (implemented) version, of the following two rules:
 1. If an exterior force (FN or FS - as defined in section 3.1) is acting at any given point on a primitive, this point is considered a critical region (e.g., forces on joints, forces on primitives) and relevant to the output information (Figure 8a). In order to transform this point into a critical region, the primitive will be "broken" into two primitives (with the corresponding physical parameters) and connected through a joint at the "breaking-point". The exterior force will act in the new situation on the new joint. The result of this training process is shown in Figure 8b.
 2. If no exterior forces act on the primitives and on the connection joint between them (Figure 8c), no critical region can be defined and the primitives can be "combined" (Figure 8d). The input and output information is dynamically updated through the training process.

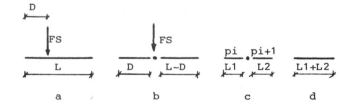

Figure 8. Training rules

4.1.2 Learning (generalization)

Learning (generalization), as implemented in the present version, works as follows: it accepts the result of the training, from which the relevant parameters are extracted, characterizing the case and finally storing the formalized pattern to the TKB at the corresponding abstraction level.

4.2 Steps in the training and learning processes

The training and learning processes based on the defined rules, consist of the following steps:

1) search for critical regions and "break" component by applying training rule 1, if necessary;

2) if previous step was the result of applying training rule 1, update the input information by accepting the new components created by rule 1 (two primitives and a joint);

3) evaluate the first comming primitive and joint;

4) dynamic update relevant output information in the following way:

  a) if training rule 2 is applied, then:
  - "combine" the last evaluated primitive with the previous part of the structural element, and
  - replace the output information, given by the previous part of the structural element, with the output information of the last evaluated primitive;

  b) otherwise: continue to train the rest of the structural element;

5) at the end of training either a structural element or a structure the output information is passed to the learning module and the new formalized pattern, representing the analyzed case, is strored in the TKB at the corresponding abstraction level. An example of such a pattern could be: the number of primitive components of a structural element after training (N), the type of exterior force acting on the primitive (FE) and the type of exterior force acting on the joint (FJ).

5. EXAMPLES

Two simple examples are presented next:

Consider the structure presented in Figure 9a, composed from: two columns - C1 and C3, a beam - B2, and two joints - J4 and J5. The force F that acts on the node J4 represents a stream of growing force values: (F1, F2,...,Fi,...,Fn). It is required to obtain the response values (NO,SO,MO - as defined in section 3.1) of the structure at all relevant sections for all given force values F. In order to obtain the required response, for the first force value F1, the structure will pass the training process. The result of the training session is the list of pairs: input values and response values at the relevant sections of the structural elements, and the corresponding trained structure (Figure 9b):

$$<<NI1,SI1,MI1>,<NO2,SO2,MO2>> \text{ for C1,}$$
$$<<NO2,SO2,MO2>,<JNO4,JSO4,JMO4>> \text{ for J4,}$$
$$<<JNO4,JSO4,JMO4>,<NO4,SO4,MO4>> \text{ for B2,}$$
$$<<NO4,SO4,MO4>,<JNO5,JSO5,JMO5>> \text{ for J5,}$$
$$<<JNO5,JSO5,JMO5>,<NO6,SO6,MO6>> \text{ for C3.}$$

The learning module will assert two rules in TKB, one at the structural element level, having the pattern (N,FE,FJ), where N will be one, FE will be zero, FJ will be zero; and the second rule at the structure level having the pattern <CJBJC,FE,FJ>, where CJBJC will denote the type of the structure, FE will be of type zero and FJ will be of the type FS representing the force F1.

In the following cycles of the structural analysis, that will return the response of the structure to any other force value Fi, the evaluation will be made on the previously trained structure (Figure 9c).

Another example, of how the knowledge of TKB can be used and extended, is shown in Figure 10a,c. In this case different exterior forces act at different moments on the structure (F and P). In the first cycle of the analysis, which evaluates the response of the structure to the force F, the trained structure and the trained structural elements acquired in the previous case study are being used. The results of this structural analysis will not contribute new rules to the TKB. In the second cycle of the structural analysis, which evaluates the response of the structure to the force P, the training module is activated. The result of this training session is the list of pairs: input values and output results at the relevant sections of the structural elements, and the corresponding trained structure (Figure 10d):

$$<<NI1,SI1,MI1>,<NO2,SO2,MO2>> \text{ for C1,}$$
$$<<NO2,SO2,MO2>,<JNO4,JSO4,JMO4>> \text{ for J4,}$$
$$<<JNO4,JSO4,JMO4>,<NO4,SO4,MO4>> \text{ for B2L,}$$
$$<<NO4,SO4,MO4>,<JNO6,JSO6,JMO6>> \text{ for J6,}$$
$$<<JNO6,JSO6,JMO6>,<NO6,SO6,MO6>> \text{ for B2R,}$$
$$<<NO6,SO6,MO6>,<JNO5,JSO5,JMO5>> \text{ for J5,}$$
$$<<JNO5,JSO5,JMO5>,<NO8,SO8,MO8>> \text{ for C3.}$$

The learning module will assert two rules in TKB, one at the structural element level, having the pattern that characterizes the trained beam: N=2, FE will be of type FS representing the force P, and FJ will be of type zero. The second asserted rule will be at the structure level, having the pattern: <CJBJBJC,FE,FJ>, which represents the trained structure shown in Figure 10d. CJBJBJC represents the type of the trained structure, which contains the information about the two components of the beam - "__BJB__". FE will be of type FS representing the force P, and FJ will be of type zero.

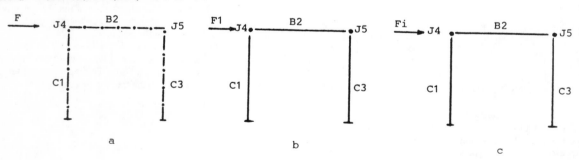

Figure 9. Example 1

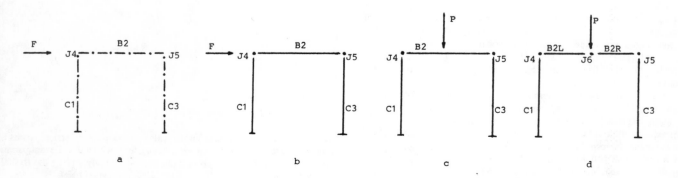

Figure 10. Example 2

6. CONCLUSIONS AND FUTURE WORK

This paper presented the first version of an adaptive system with the capability of learning from training experience.

The concepts that where explored in this research project are: data abstraction methodology for structuring a hierarchy of "intelligent modules, suited for modeling structures; training and learning related to structural analysis.

The development of the system was accomplished by creating a hierarchy of "intelligent" modules. The "data abstraction" model was used to structure this hierarchy. Specific abstraction levels and their interrelationship were discussed. The central features of the system: training and learning, where defined and their implementation discussed. At the end two simple examples where provided.

Further work is proposed for future versions of the system:
-extending the TKB at the different abstraction levels with a large number of case studies - resulting from structural analysis of regular structures;
-using and extending the TKB at the different abstraction levels with more complex structures;
-further diversification of "intelligent" modules, that represent additional behavior patterns encountered in structural analysis;
-defining and implementing new target subjects for training and learning, like: nonlinear response of structures, response of structures to dynamic loading;
-connecting the training system to more specialized analysis tools;
-connecting the training system to graphic facilities.

REFERENCES

1. Hayes-Roth, F; Waterman, D A and Lenat, D B, Building Expert Systems, Addison-Wesley, 1983.
2. Clocksin, W F and Mellish, C S, Programming in PROLOG, Springer-Verlag, 1984.
3. Law, K H; Jonaneh, M K and Spooner, D L, Abstraction database concept for engineering modeling, Engineering with Computers, 1987, Vol. 2, No. 2, 79-94.
4. Abelson, H; Sussman, G J with Sussman, J, Structure and interpretation of computer programs, MIT Press, 1985.
5. Timoshenko, S P and Gere, J M, Mechanics of materials, D. Van Nostrand Co., 1972.
6. Ketter, R L; Lee, G C and Prawel, Sh P Jr, Structural analysis and design, McGraw-Hill,1979.
7. Cohen, P R and Feigenbaum, E, The handbook of artificial intelligence, HeurisTech Press, 1982, Vol. 3, 323-494.

IV   WATER ENGINEERING

IMPLEMENTATION ISSUES OF HYDROLOGICAL EXPERT SYSTEMS – A CIVIL ENGINEERING CASE STUDY

K Ahmad, BSc(Hons), MSc, PhD and
A J Langdon, BSc(Hons), MSc
Computing Unit, University of Surrey
W D Moss, BSc(Hons), MA, PhD, MICE, MIWES
Department of Civil Engineering, University of Surrey
R K Price, BA(Hons), MA, PhD, AFIMA, MIAHR
Computing Unit, University of Surrey and Hydraulics Research Ltd.

Abstract

Methodologies, tools and techniques used in the development of expert systems, for use by engineers in storm-sewer management and sewerage rehabilitation planning, are outlined. A number of issues of relevance to expert system builders' are discussed, including comments on intelligent front-ends, logic programming techniques, treatment of uncertainty, and explanation and justification techniques.

1. Introduction

Our prime concern is the development of knowledge based expert systems for solving so-called 'real-world' problem; we have concentrated on the development of such systems for use by water engineers concerned with storm-sewer design and sewerage rehabilitation planning. We believe that our results will be of interest to builders of civil engineering expert systems in particular, and to other expert systems builders in general.

A knowledge-based expert system (KBES) is essentially a computer program, which, with its associated data, embodies knowledge concerning some specific area of human activity. Such a system may be thought of as a program which mimics the performance of a human expert.

The word "knowledge" in the KBES context is used in its traditional sense and covers items such as facts, heuristics (rules of thumb or 'short cuts' acquired by experience) meta-rules (rules about rules), theories and relationship in a given area of human enterprise - the 'domain'. An important milestone in the development of expert systems was the emergence of tools and techniques of representing knowledge, with its qualitative details, incompletness and uncertainity, on a computer system - the 'knowledge-base' which is used to store knowledge of experts in a given domain. Once this knowledge is acquired from human experts and captured inside a machine, the expert system builders develop programs which deploy the knowledge in the knowledge-base in order to solve complex problems. These programs contain strategies of selecting and deploying specific items of knowledge in a certain order; the so-called 'inference-engine' of an expert system.

There are three major reasons for the success of currently available expert systems. First, given the intuitive link between intelligence, knowledge and problem-solving capability, expert systems perform well, that is behave intelligently because they contain 'large bodies of knowledge on given topics' (Feigenbaum and McCorduck 1984:25). Second, an important distinguishing feature of an expert system, as compared to other traditional programs, is the clear distinction between the knowledge-base and the inference engine of a KBES (Bonnet 1985:20). This separation is invaluable for debugging, updating and modifying either of these components, especially because changes in the knowledge-base, for example, will not have any serious effect on the inference engine and vice-versa. The third reason expert systems are successful is implicit in the fact that per se these systems are user-orientated; they can explain their input requirement, justify the conclusions reached, and usually have a more robust user-interface: expert systems can serve as an invaluable teaching aid, as well, being used to disseminate expertise.

The development of expert systems is very relevant to the water industry. The changing economic climate presupposes more and efficient services from a reduced workforce, more specifically: (i) Planning and operational activities and getting more and more complex, (ii) Expertise in a wider field is required and (iii) There is a greater access to computers, and instrumentation, control and automation. Expert systems can help the water engineers by a) providing ready access to data and offering help in its acquisition, b) providing expert advice in a variety of fields, c) combining answers from simulation models with engineering judgement to obtain best solutions, d) ensuring that steps in published procedures are not missed and e) providing useful training tools.

In this paper we focus on items (c) and (a) above. By way of illustration, we describe below our current development work on two expert systems. First, a simple expert system for advising on the use of Modified Rational Method (MRM) for storm-sewer design (The Wallingford Procedure. Vol.4. 1981), and second, an intelligent advisor for the WAllingford Storm Sewer Procedure (WASSP). This is a nationally agreed procedure and has been well-documented (The Wallingford Procedure Vols 1-5. 1981). The MRM system was primarily developed in order to study, analyse and understand aspects of expert systems technology relevant to items (a-e) above. This includes issues of knowledge representation and deployment, explanation, justification, and treatment of uncertainity among others. The WASSP intelligent advisor, on the other hand, is an industrially sponsored project to provide consultancy and advice for solving a complex real-world problem; the use of simulation models in storm-sewer design. MRM is written entirely in PROLOG, whereas WASSP Intelligent Advisor is written in a mixture of an expert system shell and PROLOG. The comparison between the two systems has helped us to understand the debate within the KBES community on the relative merits and demerits of shells versus programming language (Bundy 1984b:2-3).

The structure of this paper is as follows: In section 2 we discuss the crucial relationship between Artificial Intelligence techniques (as used in building expert systems) with other computing methodologies for successfully developing civil engineering expert systems. The next section contains an outline of the problems of knowledge acquisition, a theme which we discuss in some depth in section 5. Section 4 is an outline of the MRM expert system emphasizing the use of KBES techniques reported in the literature and some developed by the authors. In section 5 the on-going work on the WASSP intelligent advisor is presented, which involves the use of an expert systems shell, PROLOG and FORTRAN, and also contains our strategy for acquiring knowledge. Finally in section 6 we describe planned developments and conclude.

2. Engineering Expert Systems: The role of intelligent front-ends

Expert system builders' rely heavily on AI techniques for the acquisition, representation and deployment of knowledge. The development of early expert systems concentrated on knowledge which was declarative, descriptive and qualitative. (This is in contrast to conventional computing where the emphasis is on procedural and quantitative knowledge number crunching). However, Shortliffe has noted that there is work in progress "for ways to combine AI techniques with more traditional numerical approaches to produce enhanced system performance" (Shortliffe, 1981:326). This 'melded' approach is of particular relevance to problems in water engineering where there is a recognition that to solve problems in this field, one has, on one hand, to use quantitative analysis, in order to develop and present detailed alternatives, but, on the other hand, 'equally important may be purely qualitative factors including subjective inferences drawn from quantitative analysis', (Loucks, Stedinger and Haith, 1981:5). Our KBES development strategy is in consonance with this 'melded' quantitative/qualitative approach; results from simulation model combined with engineering judgement as an important basis for engineering decision-making.

The central feature of our work is the development of intelligent interfaces for currently available simulation packages for general use by engineers. Another, long-term, design goal is to incorporate such an interface, together with the model, in an expert system. There are a number of examples in the literature

reporting the development of intelligent front-ends for simulation, statistical and other packages. (Bundy 1984a; Bennet and Englemore (1979, 1989)). An intelligent front-end (IFE) makes a complex computer program, such as a simulation package, more accessible to end-users: "IFE's promise to act as a translator between software and the lay user and, hence, enable to widespread use of powerful software. If IFE's succeed they will be of major commercial and social significance". (Bundy 1984a:1). An example of this approach is the Structural Analysis CONsultation (SACON) expert system, developed by Bennet and Englemore (1979, 1984), which advises engineers in using a non-linear finite element program MARC. SACON is interesting in that it is based, computationally at least, on MYCIN - a well known expert system (Shortliffe 1976).

The development of IFEs "involves the integration of several different areas of AI. It also impinges on non-AI areas of computer science", (Bundy 1984a:3), such as (i) Man-Machine Interface, involving the provision of robust user-interface, graphics, file-handling capabilities and so on; (ii) Computer-Assisted Instruction techniques, with its emphasis on teaching and learning for naive users; and, (iii) work in data-base management systems which is aimed at providing 'user-friendly' interfaces to large data-bases.

Expert systems are user-orientated programs, and hence must be virtually fool-proof and they must have an interface, as in (i) above, to accept a range of input and to display results in a comprehensible manner. Item (ii) is of importance because water-engineering requires expertise in solving problems of a multi-disciplinary nature; generalists are increasingly asked to do specialists work or specialists' may be borrowing concepts from other disciplines; an amplification of expertise, in a teaching and learning context, will be indespensible. Item (iii) is important because water-engineering problems require large amounts of data which should be readily available. In this respect Ahmad, Moss and Knowles (1979, 1981) have discussed issues relating to Computer-Assisted Learning (CAL) in Civil Engineering hydrology; also the relationship of CAL programs to data-base management systems was considered with specific reference to a teaching and learning environment. These authors have helped us to apply the experience of designing CAL packages to expert system.

The IFE's are bound to play a major role in engineering problem-solving. However, before one builds a KBES (or an IFE), it is essential to acquire knowledge from the domain experts. This task is non-trivial, as we explain in the next section.

3. Knowledge Acquisition

An important bottleneck in the development of KBES is the problem of knowledge acquisition: how to acquire and engineer the knowledge into a form that can be embedded in the expert system. Bennet and Englemore have argued that "advances in understanding and overcoming this knowledge acquisition bottleneck rest on an analysis of both the process and the product of our current, rather informal interactions with experts". (1984:314). We consider knowledge acquisition problems in the context of the two expert systems we discuss in this paper. (See section 4.2.2)

4. MRM Expert System

4.1 Outline

MRM is a simple expert system developed at the University of Surrey for Urban Storm Sewer Design. It is based on the Modified Rational method of design developed by Hydraulics Research Ltd. and is written entirely in PROLOG. In simple terms, it calculates the Peak runoff, Qp, for any particular pipe and a specified design storm using the formula:-

$$Qp = C.i.A$$

where C is a dimensionless coefficient
   i is the average rainfall intensity during
      the storm
   A is the contributing catchment area

The problems in evaluating these terms are expanded in the next section.

4.2 Knowledge Representation and Explanation Facilities

MRM is like any other computer program which processes input to give some output and it evaluates an apparently very simple equation:

$$Qp = C.i.A$$

However, this simplicity is quite deceptive in that in order to evaluate C, one has to evaluate 4 equations, and for i, 9 equations, whereas A, is a simple constant. Some of these equations are of an empirical nature and depend on the specific geophysical and geomorphological locality and some demand detailed engineering knowledge. (The Wallingford Procedure: Vol. 1, 1981). The novice user is consequently faced with a bewildering plethora of input requirements, some of which is unnecessary because it could be deduced by some previous input data or by having access to hydrological and geomorphological data via (digitized) maps and tables. For an expert the input may pose no problem at all, but for a novice it would be useful to have a facility which can justify and amplify input requirements. Figure 1 shows a typical interaction between user and MRM. The explanation and justification facility is an important strength of expert systems and is an important factor in the dissemination of expertise (Shortliffe 1976: 95-204).

The empirically derived equation used in MRM are generally based on correlations observed among a few variables. In some instances, this study was extended over a number of different catchment areas. It is possible that there would be times when an engineer, with more local knowledge, will have a different and better correlation, and would like to use his or her own equation rather than the published version which is incorporated in our system. It is, therefore, important that

an expert system has the facility for the user to interactively change any, or indeed all the equations temporarily; Figure 2 illustrates the "whatif" facility which enables a typical user to do just that. It should be noted that MRM will now produce two outputs, one on the basis of the original equation and one on the basis of the changed equation.

There are a number of parameters in MRM whose value depends on "heuristic" or rule of thumb reasoning. These heuristics enable the engineer to establish an upper and lower bound for the values of the given parameter. In some cases there are tables of recommended values published in textbooks, for example percentages of impervious area for different surfaces (Bartlett, 1970). We have used heuristic reasoning techniques in MRM to establish the value of this particular parameter. (The format is similar to that of the famous 20 question game; (see Figure 3).

We have mentioned above that some of the input can be deduced from previous input or from other sources like maps or data files. Parameters in the system can therefore, be in any of three states. They could be known to the system, that being the first premise of MRM, or they could be deduced from existing values, or finally the system can ask for the parameter's value. However, there are certain parameters whose value the system can never deduce e.g. grid reference, storm return period, catchment area... etc. - these are classed as "labdata" parameters.

On the other hand there could be parameters whose value the system may ask for but such questions could be very trivial, for example, the MRM system is not allowed to ask for the value for the discharge, Qp being "inferrable only" data. The intermediate case falls in between these two extremes where the system can ask for the parameter or deduce it, for example PIMP, the percentage impervious area. The user has the effective veto on predetermined system parameters. In classifying the MRM system parameters into "labdata", "inferrable" and for "askable" parameters we have followed the strategy by Shortliffe (1976).

Civil Engineering data, generally, and hydrological data in particular has problems of uncertainity associated with it. This is a problem which is common to many domains and is hence of interest to expert systems builders. There is also an equally important uncertainty associated with the various formula used and technique of approximate reasoning which are applied in engineering decision making see for instance (Blockley 1982: 103-115, Ishizuka, Fu, Yao 1982: 261-268) who discuss these questions with reference to Civil Engineering. (See also Shortliffe 1976) and (Buchanan, Shortliffe 1984: 233-264). We deal with uncertainity using the classical statistics approach (Chie Yen, 1975) section 4.1.3.

4.3 Pattern-Matching

The processing of input data, done by MRM, uses techniques of logic programming, more specifically PROLOG. The internal data base of the system is stored in terms of the so-called n-place predicate for example the value of Cr, the routine coefficient, is stored as:

cr(1.30).

which essentially means that this proposition is true regardless of consequence. Also, we have stored part of the Winter rain acceptance potential map (The Wallingford Procedure Vol.3, 1981). This is used to obtain the soil index parameter which is needed to calculate the percentage runoff. (The Wallingford Procedure Vol.1, 1981:51). The value of the parameter on the map at a specific locality is defined by its grid reference co-ordinator. In MRM the chosen area has been defined using the map's grid squares in the 'pointer-ref' predicate (Fig.4). These squares are given a reference number (1,2,3,4) and the value of the parameter "soil" is linked to the squares' reference number in the predicate "database". Once the user gives the grid reference co-ordinates of the catchment area they are then used to find the soil parameter value in the soil database. Several database sections for other map orientated parameters are also represented in this way in MRM.

4.4   The Utility of PROLOG

In the terminology of logic programming Qp is regarded as a top level goal, i.e. in order to satisfy this top-level goal we have to satisfy the sub-goals labdata, mean intensity, for example; each sub-goal could be atop level goal in its own right.(Fig.5). The program is more readable although probably slower in execution than an equivalent FORTRAN program and we were fortunate to have an implementation of PROLOG that has floating point facilities (Bailey 1983). It is important to note that PROLOG has been used to implement a rule base and quite unusually as a simulation language (Robertson 1985: 1-9). For instance the output of the program apart from explanation and justification is a single number, the value of Qp (or two numbers if "whatif" is used).

Using techniques based on logic we specified the MRM program. With few adjustments, the specification then became executable code. This similarity between specification and program is a powerful facility (Kowalski, 1985: 11-27).

4.5   Dealing with uncertainty

Expert systems in engineering lend themselves especially well to treatment of uncertainty using classical probability and statistics. This is because many standard design equations in engineering are formulated empirically and are thus subject to uncertainty. (Even those based on rigorous theory will have uncertainties when used in the field).

The MRM expert system is a good example of this because it produces design results based almost entirely on hydrological equations. There are two sources of uncertainties in these equations. First, since the equations are often empirical an implicit "equation error" will exist, and second, to calculate results from the equations uncertain values are assigned to each of the parameters in the equations. (These values are uncertain because invariably they will be field measurement subject to all the usual associated errors). So, for each equation we end up with uncertainties due to equation error and due to each input parameter.

An implementation of MRM has been developed that takes account of these uncertainties in the form of coefficients of variation. These coefficients are calculated internally by the system, i.e. they are not required to be input by the user. They are based essentially on prior information: for example, equation error is "known" by the system; variations of field measurements were entered to the system after extensive empirical studies of the distributions of such measurements; other field measurements may be known to follow standard statistical distributions and so the system will also store this information. (Chie-Yen, 1975).

As a consequence the system will return a design value along with its coefficient of variation.

5. WASSP Intelligent Advisor

5.1   Outline

The Wallingford Storm-Sewer Procedure, commonly known as WASSP, is a suite of six large complex mathematical models developed by Hydraulics Research Ltd. for use in Urban Storm Sewer design and analysis. This is a nationally agreed procedure and over 60 copies of the package are now in use in the U.K. However, users of WASSP, especially novices, are frequently faced with the problem of choosing the correct model, inputting the correct data for their task and objectively interpreting the results produced.

The choice of model is not as straightforward as it seems; a number of factors may restrict the user as to which he or she should choose. The input data especially the hydrological parameters are of a very complex nature and require consultations of large scale maps of the U.K. Confronted   with the specialised information required by each model the user can easily become confused and make mistakes. Furthermore, the volume of output produced by each model requires some experiential   knowledge to understand what is happening, especially when a sewer systems' performance is being analysed for rare storm events.

In collaboration with Hydraulics Research Ltd. Surrey University is working on an Intelligent Advisor for the WASSP package to overcome these problems.

There are two phases to this work firstly, to make WASSP a more interactive package and secondly, to construct an intelligent interface around this base. (Fig.5). WASSP is essentially a batch oriented package so facilities for interactive file handling and creation, and graphical interpretation have been built in to form a "well-engineered interface" (Bundy, 1984). The intelligent interface is currently under construction. It is based on PROSE, a rule-based system developed by Wells (1985) and is written entirely in PROLOG. The inferencing strategy is in the form of a typical heuristic tree operating in a controlled left to right, top to bottom sequence. It also has backtracking facilities where answers to previous questions can be changed without affecting the tree search.

At present, a simple rule base advising the user on model choice has been installed. The explanation and justification facilities are in embryonic form and will be extended to include MRM's explanation mechanism. Further, the facility to make a direct call to WASSP models (See Fig.6) can be mode possible via a PROLOG-FORTRAN 77 interface. The rule in PROLOG would be typically:

    A:-B, call (C).

where C is a WASSP model

This is currently in the development stage. We believe that engineering expert systems will require a mixture of programming paradigms for implementation; logic programming techniques for implementing rule bases and algrothmic programming for simulation and modelling.

5.2   Knowledge Acquisition

The key bottleneck in developing an expert system occurs in building the knowledge base by having a knowledge engineer interact with the expert. This tends to be a very inefficient and time consuming exercise.

The sort of information that is required is the expert's experiential knowledge, often referred to as "Engineering Judgement" - how he or she solves problems and what rules of thumb or heuristics are used. This type of knowledge is not available in textbooks or in codes of practice and so different experts will have different, possibly conflicting, views. Morever, the experts, although being good at what they do, may find it difficult to explain their actions it clearly and concisely.

In our work, the previous sessions conducted with experts were only for small problems so the dialogue was noted down in a simple journalistic style. On analysis of these interviews it was obvious that much important information was missed. Church of British Telecom used video equipment however, to record interviews when building TRACKER, a circuit fault finding experts system, and this has proved to be a very efficient and valuable tool. For a typical one hour session we ask the expert to talk through a case study of using WASSP and the interviewer intervenes when he wishes to pick up or clarify a point. Constant interruption only serves to upset the flow of the experts thought, but at the same time it is necessary for the interviewer to have a script of question that he wishes to cover and he should notify the expert of these beforehand.

In the case of WASSP maps, diagrams and computer printouts are all referred to in illustrating the problem. Where simple tape recordings would lose all this usual information video not only records but allows interviewer to refer back to a point very easily and to the precise frame where it occurred.

A transcript of the video is then made (the whole process analysis and transcription took 8 hours for a 1 hour recording session(and the knowledge base is built up by searching for rules of the form:-

$$IF(A)^{AND}_{OR}(B)^{AND}_{OR}(C) \; THEN \; (D)$$

The following statement is a simple example taken from a recorded session, and is in the expert's own words.

Is there any surface flooding in the area - if not, and there's unlikely to be any surcharging and you're not terribly interested in that area anyway then use the sewered-sub-area model.

This could be expressed in rule form:-

    IF (NO SURFACE FLOODING) AND (NO SURCHARGING) AND (AREA IS UNIMPORTANT TO PROBLEM) THEN (USE SEWERED-SUB-AREA MODEL).

When a list of rules has been built up they are sent to the expert for verification and the same procedure is followed for each interview. To avoid clashes of opinion and methods of practices, rules obtained from one expert are passed to another for comment until some common ground is reached. Finally, the rulebase is tested on-line in the system by expert users to approve the final configuration.

6. Concluding Remarks

A brief account has been given of a programme of work currently in hand on expert systems and intelligent front-ends, which has itself grown out of a body of work, extended over several years, on the production of interactive packages for such purposes as Computer Assisted Learning.

It is hoped, that although the description of the particular systems relates to the specialised topic of urban drainage, it will be of interest for its relevance to expert systems more generally.

Again, while the systems described are still of a development stage, it is intended that they will be of use in a larger project planned by the Water Industry Expert Systems Club, an Alvey-sponsored IKBS Awareness Club, for which one of the authors (Ahmad) is to serve as principal investigator. One of the applications which the club is to explore is a Sewerage Rehabilitation Expert System; this, while seeking to incorporate the knowledge of experts in the field of sewer rehabilitation, will permit the integration of mathematical models such as those of WASSP, to explore the effect of any proposals.

Acknowledgement

The authors wish to thank Miss A. Storey of the Computing Unit, University of Surrey and Mr. A. Tarzi of the Civil Engineering Department, University of Surrey for their contribution to the work described in this paper.

The MRM system was initially developed by Mr. D.M. Obene, ex-Dept. of Civil Engineering, University of Surrey, as a part of his MSc dissertation; the authors gratefully acknowledge his contribution.

BIBLIOGRAPHY

(Ahmad, Moss, Knowles, 1979)

Ahmad, K., Moss, W. D., Knowles, P. R., (1979). CAL Packages for Civil Engineering Hydraulics and Structural Design. Computers and Education 3 (1979), pp 391-399.

(Ahmad, Moss, Knowles, 1981)

Ahmad, K., Moss, W. D., Knowles, P. R., (1981). Simulation, Modelling and Computer Graphics in undergraduate engineering education. In Proceedings of Computer Simulation in Undergraduate Education, North-Holland Pub.Co. 1981, pp 43-64.

(Bailey, D., 1983)

Bailey, D., (1983). The University of Salford LISP/PROLOG Reference Manual. University of Salford, Manchester.

(Bartlett 1970)

Bartlett, R. E., (1970). Surface Water Sewerage. Applied Science, London.

(Bennet, Englemore, 1979)

Bennet, J. S., Englemore, R., (1979) SACON: A Knowledge-based Consultant for Structural Analysis.

In Proceedings of the sixth IJCAI, pp 47-49. International Joint Conference on Artificial Intelligence, Tokyo, Japan.

(Blockley 1982)

Blockley, D., (1984) Fuzzy Systems in Civil Engineering. In (Ed's) Gupta, M. M., Sanchez, E., Approximate reasoning in Decision Analysis. North-Holland, Oxford.

(Bonnet 1985)

Bonnet, A., (1985) Artificial Intelligence: Promise and Performance. Prentice-Hall, London.

(Buchanan, Shortliffe 1984)

Buchanan, B. G., Shortliffe, E. H., (1984) Rule Based Expert Systems: The MYCIN Experiments of the Stanford Heuristic Programming Project. Addison-Wesley, Massachusetts.

(Bundy 1984a)

Bundy, A., (1984) Intelligent Front-Ends. Research paper-227, Department of Artificial Intelligence, Edinburgh.

(Bundy 1984b)

Bundy, A., (1984) What has learning got to do with expert systems? Research paper 214, Department of Artificial Intelligence, Edinburgh.

(Cendrowska, Bramer 1982)

Cendrowska, J., Bramer, M. A., (1982) A Rational Reconstruction of the MYCIN Consultation System. The Open University, Milton Keynes.

(Chie-Yen 1975)

Chie-Yen, B., (1975) Risk based design of Storm-Sewers, Report No.141, Hydraulics Research Ltd., Wallingford.

(Feigenbaum, McCorduck 1984)

Feigenbaum, E. A., McCorduck, P., (1984 The Fifth Generation. Artificial Intelligence and Japan's computer challenge to the world. Michael Joseph, London

(Ishizuka, Fu, Yao 1982)

Ishizuka, M., Fu, K. S., Yao, J. T. P., (1982) A rule-based inference with fuzzy for Structural damage assessment. In (Ed's) Gupta, M. M., Sanchez, E., Approximate reasoning in Decision Analysis. North-Holland, Oxford.

(Kowalski 1985)

Kowalski, R., (1985) The relation between logic programming and logic specification. In (Ed's) Hoare, C. A. R., Shepherdson, J.C., Mathematical Logic and Programming Languages. Prentice-Hall, London.

(Loucks, Stedinger, Haith 1981)

Loucks, D. P., Stedinger, J. R., Haith, D. A., (1981) Water Resource Systems Planning and Analysis. Prentice-Hall, New Jersey.

(Robertson 1985)

Robertson, D., (1985) Running Eco Simulations in Prolog. Department of Artificial Intelligence, Edinburgh (Unpublished).

(Shortliffe 1976)

Shortliffe, E. H., (1976) Computer-based Medical Consultations: MYCIN. Elsevier Pub.Co., New York.

(Shortliffe 1981)

Shortliffe, E. H., (1981) Consultation systems for Physicians: The Role of Artificial Intelligence Techniques. In (Ed's) Webber, B.L., Nilsson, N. J., Readings in Artificial Intelligence. Tioga Pub.Co., Palo Alto, California.

(Uschold et al 1984)

Uschold, M., Harding, N., Muetzelfeldt, R., Bundy, A., (1984). An Intelligent Front-Ends Ecological Modelling. Research Paper 223, Department of Artificial Intelligence, Edinburgh.

(Wallingford Procedure 1981)

(1981) Design and Analysis of Urban Storm drainage - The Wallingford Procedure, Vol's 1-5, Department of Environment, National Water Council, Standing Technical Committee Report No.29, National Water Council.

(Wells 1985)

Wells, I. G., (1985) University of Surrey, Personal Communication.

Please give the X
Grid reference value
--Units(100m. Easting)
---2000

Please give me the Y
Grid reference value
--Units(100m. Northing)
--- 700

          '   '
          '   '
          '   '

Please give me the value of the Soil Index.
This information is available in Vol.3 (Maps)
of the WASSP Manual (1981).
--- why

To find the value for soil
--- how
By asking for or deducing the value.
--- why

To find the value for percentage_runoff
by the equation:
percentage_runoff = 0.829 * pimp + 25 * soil +
0.78E-1 * ucwi - 20.7

        '   '
        '   '
        '   '

Fig.1 Typical MRM Interaction

Please give me the Storm
Return period in years
---why

I need this as basic data
To find the value for qp
--- how
By the equation:

qp = 0.278 * C * meanintensity * area

--- whatif qp=c*meanintensity*area
Remember this question...
You will have to answer it again!

Please give me the Storm
Return period in years
--- 5

Please give me the
Duration of the storm
--Units(min.)
--- why

I need this as basic data
To find the value for qp
--- how
By the equation:

qp = c * meanintensity * area
        '   '
Type "c" then RETURN to continue
--- c
     Using the New Equation
The Peak_Discharge_Qp is 3.599 cu.m

Type "c" then RETURN to continue
--- c

The Peak_Discharge_Qp is 1.000 cu.m

Fig.2 MRM: "WHATIF" Facility

Please give me the
percentage of Impervious Area in
the catchment that will be
drained by the storm sewer
--- unknown

Is your drainage system to be designed for
a residential area?
--- n
Is your drainage system to be designed for
an industrial area?
--- n
Is your drainage system to be designed for
a green-field site?
--- y
There is a variation of impermeability factors
to choose from
Limits are given below:
Lower value = 5
Upper value = 35
Please choose a value
--- 32

Fig.3 MRM: An example of "Heuristic" Reasoning

```
/*                                     */
/*    Grid pointer reference data      */
/*                                     */
pointer_ref(1090,7000,1090,7010,2000,7010,2000,
7000,1).
pointer_ref(2000,7000,2000,7010,2010,7010,2010,
7000,2).
pointer_ref(1090,7010,1090,7020,2000,7020,2000,
7010,3).
pointer_ref(2000,7010,2000,7020,2010,7020,2010,
7010,4).

/*                      */
/* Soil data base       */
/*                      */
database(soil_database,1,0.5).
database(soil_database,2,0.5).
database(soil_database,3,0.5).
database(soil_database,4,0.5).
```

Fig.4 Pattern Matching used in MRM

```
/*                                      */
/*       Qp Predicate                   */
/*    Top Level Goal is to              */
/*       calculate Qp                   */
/*    the Peak Discharge                */
/*                                      */
qp(Valueqp):- labdata(Gridx,Gridy,T.D. Totalarea),
             c(Valuec), meanintensity(Valuei),
             area(Totalarea),
             Valueqp is 0.278 * Valuec * Valuei
             * Totalarea.

/*                                      */
/*          C Predicate                 */
/*    Fires calculation of "c"          */
/*                                      */
c(Valuec):- cr(Valuecr),cv(Valuecv),
            Valuec is Valuecr * Valuecv.
cv(Valuecv):- pimp(Valuepimp),
              percentage_runoff(Valuepr,
              Valuepimp),
              Valuecv is Valuepr / Valuepimp
```

Fig.5 Expression of Formulae as Predicates in
MRM

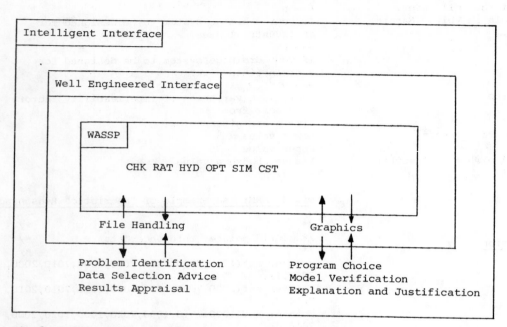

Fig.6 Architecture of WASSP Intelligent Advisor

EXPERT SYSTEMS AS A PRELIMINARY DESIGN TOOL FOR DRINKING WATER SUPPLIES IN DEVELOPING COUNTRIES

G R Kelsey, BSc, MSc
Civil Engineering Department
University of Newcastle upon Tyne, England

Three major distinguishing features of expert systems are identified. The potential applications of expert systems in developing countries are discussed, with particular reference to the drinking water supply sector. The importance of carefully defining the area of application is emphasised, and it is argued that the most appropriate area within the development of a drinking water supply system is the preliminary design stage. Some of the anticipated advantages and drawbacks of using expert systems in developing countries are outlined. Finally, a description is given of the continuing development of a prototype expert system for the preliminary design of a drinking water treatment system.

1 DISTINGUISHING FEATURES OF EXPERT SYSTEMS.

An expert system, or intelligent knowledge-based system (IKBS), is a computer program which mimics the reasoning ability of a human expert. It consists of a data base (or short-term memory), a knowledge base and an inference engine. Knowledge is represented in the knowledge base as rules which may be causal links, plausible inferences or rules-of-thumb methods of efficient problem-solving, and the inference engine uses heuristic methods of searching through the rules. The division between the knowledge base and the inference engine is analagous to the distinction between declarative and procedural knowledge.

Allwood et al. (Ref. 2) state that expert systems differ from conventional programs primarily in (1) their methods of representing knowledge and in (2) their methods of searching the knowledge to infer conclusions. Basden (Ref. 3) stresses a third distinguishing feature of expert systems, namely their explanation facility or "human window".

2 THE POTENTIAL APPLICATIONS OF EXPERT SYSTEMS IN THE DRINKING WATER SUPPLY SECTOR IN DEVELOPING COUNTRIES.

2.1 Consultancy.

In developing countries the provision of drinking water supplies for poor communities is constrained primarily by a shortage of funds, a lack of political commitment, the application of inappropriate technologies and methodologies, and institutional underdevelopment.

One aspect of institutional underdevelopment is a shortage of expertise as opposed to technical ability and manual labour. Whereas human expertise is both scarce and expensive throughout the developing world, microcomputers are readily available in most cities. They are relatively cheap, are easy to install and operate, have a "stand alone" capability, and are not so reliant as mainframe computers on continuous power supplies and a sophisticated back-up organisation. Expert systems could be used as a source of expert guidance to the novice, of specialist knowledge to the non-specialist, or of multi-disciplinary experience to the specialist.

Consultancy is perhaps the major role of expert systems. In developing countries, an expert system could provide an impartial source of independent advice (subject to the bias of the programmer) to which a client could refer before approaching consultants. When dealing with a human consultant, the client would then be able to make an informed choice between recommended alternatives, to evaluate advice rather than take it on blind faith, and to express his or her requirements more effectively and assertively.

Grover (Ref. 9) states that "the limited human and financial resources in developing countries can be used more efficiently if water and sanitation projects are initially prepared to standards meeting requirements of approving authorities and financing agencies". He stresses the need to obtain guidance at the outset from the relevant authorities and agencies. It is envisaged that an expert system could provide some part of that guidance. It could be built by a Development Bank or International Funding Agency, to be used by preliminary design engineers and project planners at the early stages of a drinking water supply project. The expert system would implicitly incorporate the Bank´s or Agency´s preferred criteria, and would help to ensure that the basis of a proposal was sound and that its design was in accordance with funding requirements.

2.2 Checklist.

Throughout the world there is a tendency for inexperianced engineers to be selective - without always realising it - about the information they obtain from textbooks and guidelines. An example is the way in which "typical" designs are sometimes taken directly from a textbook without considering the basis of the design and the qualifying circumstances of the local situation. Another common problem is that inexperienced engineers, working with printed guidelines, are able to determine the applicability of a factor only after they have attempted to apply it. Even highly experienced engineers have gaps in their knowledge and are subject to forgetfulness.

An expert system as a "package" is more attractive to users than textbooks or guidelines. Once started running, the expert system ensures an exhaustive search of the possible solution space pertaining to a problem. It selects and orders the factors requiring consideration, ignoring those that are irrelevant in a particular case. It ensures the correct weighting of factors and their interactions, and the consistent application across time and space of decision-making criteria. Thus an expert system could facilitate problem-solving by acting as an aide-memoire at the simplest level and by ensuring a systematic and efficient approach at a more sophisticated level.

2.3 Decision support.

Another aspect of institutional underdevelopment (referred to in section 2.1) is a reluctance on the part of individuals to make decisions. The expertise available from an expert system would both increase the confidence of a decision-maker in his own decisions and provide a means of justifying his decisions to those in authority. It would thus provide a spur for decisive action. An expert system could "help the user to increase the accuracy or certainty of his own predictions or pinpoint areas where other work should be done" (Ref. 3). An expert system could "support the inexperienced engineer by helping him to have a better understanding of the problem before deciding to solve it himself or involving the expert" (Ref. 1).

Expert systems should not be expected to abolish the need for human beings to make decisions: they should be used as decision-support tools rather than substitutes for decision-making. This requires that an expert system's explanation facility should be well-developed. To say that expert systems should not be used as substitutes for decision-making, however, does not mean that they will not be used in such a way. This and other drawbacks are discussed in section 4.

2.4 Technology transfer and training.

The process of implementing an expert system on a microcomputer, in the offices of a water supply authority or rural development department, for example, would both involve the transfer of technology and facilitate the transfer of expertise to developing countries. There is no real lack of information about water supply systems in developing countries, but there is a lack of knowledge concerning how to extract, collate, manipulate and apply such information.

An expert system could be used to impart knowledge in two ways. It could be written specifically to perform the function of a human tutor, whereby the user's weaknesses are "diagnosed" by his or her response to questions, and rectified by an appropriate course of "treatment", or, if designed for another application, it could be used as a training facility to enrich a person's understanding of a problem-domain.

An expert system would be appropriate for training purposes because of the consultative nature of the computer-user interactions and because of its explanation facility. The user of an expert system would learn from it by experience, in a similar manner to the way in which an apprentice learns by example (whereas a pupil is taught by instruction). The expert system could be used to play any number of "what-if" games which, though an effective method of learning, are often not the most productive use of a human expert's valuable time.

Expert systems would more appropriately be used as a training facility by people with some knowledge of a domain than by complete novices. The reason for this is that a novice must be provided, by explicit instruction, with a basis of knowledge before he or she can build upon and expand it through experience. Instruction would be required, for example, in the meaning of jargon words and specialised phrases.

Expert systems would enable the easier duplication of expertise, by the copying of computer files instead of the training of human beings.

As a medium of communication (of information rather than expertise) an expert system has several advantages over the use of paper. A textbook, for example, may contain numerous facts, but the relationships between them may be too complex to explain easily in a (uni-directional) string of words. The user of a book may find difficulty in locating the information required, and he or she may have to read a section in order to determine whether or not it is relevant or else risk using inadequate information in attempting to solve a problem. An expert system would automatically ensure that all relevant factors were considered and that irrelevant factors were ignored.

2.5 Intelligent front-ending.

In the design of a drinking water supply system, the number and complexity of the combinations of alternatives are too great for automatic mathematical programming to be applied in order to obtain a first-time optimal solution. An investigative approach must be adopted, which is more appropriate to the symbolic manipulation of expert systems than the numerical processing of conventional software.

An expert system could be integrated with a conventional, algorithmic computer program, to reduce heuristically the large solution spaces associated with optimisation techniques. In this case the expert system would be contained within a conventional package, to reduce the computational demands of problem-solving.

The process of design is usually an iterative one, involving alternately the manipulation of numerical data (which is more suited to conventional programming) and the discrimination of the design engineer. Some conventional software already exists in the field of drinking water supply design, such as that described by Hebert & Yniguez (Ref. 13), but they require the user to have an understanding of engineering principles. An expert system could perhaps be used as a computer-user interface, directing the generate-and-test process on behalf of the user. The conventional programs would be incorporated as external functions of the expert system, which would then provide a service similar to that of a human consultant with access to computer-aided design tools. In this case the expert system would itself contain conventional subroutines and be used to enhance the human involvement in problem-solving.

Similarly, an expert system could be employed as a user-friendly, natural-language interface to support people who are unfamiliar with computer languages and operating systems.

2.6   Inter-disciplinary linkage.

An expert system is able to combine knowledge from a variety of disciplines, thereby enhancing the knowledge of specialists in each.

In the drinking water supply sector in developing countries it is envisaged that expert systems could provide a source of basic engineering knowledge to planning officials, who require access to such knowledge in order to make informed decisions about levels of service and budgeting requirements. They could also be used by preliminary design engineers, to ensure that non-technical factors affecting technical decisions are taken into consideration. Overall, the expert system would provide a link between planning officials in centralised locations and preliminary design engineers in the field.

3   DEFINING THE AREA OF APPLICATION.

As previously noted in section 2.1, the provision of drinking water supplies in developing countries is constrained by, among other things, the application of inappropriate technologies and methodologies. The Third World is littered with monuments to the attempted imposition of developed-country solutions onto a developing country's problems. Much has been written on the subject of appropriate technology, but it is important to remember (Ref. 21) that technology is not an entity in itself and by itself promises nothing. No technology is intrinsically either appropriate or innappropriate.

Furthermore, the term "appropriate technology" is not synonymous with "low-cost" or "intermediate

technology" (Ref. 22). Sophisticated and capital-intensive technology may, in certain circumstances, be appropriate. For example, the use of microcomputers to perform time-consuming and repetitive work can help engineers to develop a least-cost and affordable water supply system, thereby releasing funds for further coverage, and can shorten the design process, thereby enabling engineers to perform other tasks (Ref. 4).

Expert systems are a high-level, emerging technology in industrialised nations. The discussion in section 2, however, indicates that they could also be appropriate in developing countries. But for expert systems to be appropriate they must be employed in an appropriate manner, which requires that the areas of application within which expert systems are acceptable, affordable, manageable and useful must be carefully defined.

The stages in the development of a drinking water supply system may conveniently be summarised as (1) identification, (2) planning, (3) preliminary design, (4) detailed design, (5) approval by a funding agency, (6) implementation, (7) operation and (8) evaluation.

At the identification and planning stages the domains of expertise involved are wide and generalised. The proposed drinking water supply system is examined both in terms of strategic considerations, such as economic and rural development policies, and in terms of specific considerations, such as technical, institutional, financial and socio-cultural feasibility. Expert systems, however, have traditionally been built for "deep and narrow" domains, that is, they have been made highly knowledgeable about a well-defined field of limited scope. Basden (Ref. 3) suggests three reasons why it might be difficult to build a successful expert system in a field of "wide and shallow" knowledge: (1) it would be difficult to distinguish relevant from irrelevant factors; (2) it would be difficult to test the expert system exhaustively; and (3) the expert system would be slow in operation, since it would have to search a very large knowledge base. (Basden also suggests that, in wide and shallow domains, even the performance of human experts is sometimes low, in which case expert systems might, after all, be more successful.)

It is envisaged that expert systems would be most useful at the preliminary design stage of a drinking water supply system, involving the selection and combination of components, where the domain of expertise is relatively wide but still contained within the bounds of physics, chemistry, microbiology and engineering. Each of the consultancy, checklist, decision-support, training, intelligent front-ending and inter-disciplinary linkage applications of an expert system could be of potential benefit at this stage.

At the detailed design stage of a drinking water supply system the components and layout determined at the previous stage are designed in detail by less-experienced engineers. The domain of expertise is so narrow that there is little room for "qualitative manoeuvre". Detailed design work requires technical ability but very little expertise, and the detailed design process is more amenable to numeric processing by conventional software, rather than symbolic manipulation by expert systems.

At the approval stage, as at the planning stage, a proposed drinking water supply system is examined within a wide field of knowledge, in terms of both strategic and specific criteria. It is considered, therefore, that an expert system would be of little benefit at this stage.

In developed countries, expert systems have been written to facilitate the construction of buildings (Ref. 8) and the control of sewage treatment plants (referred to in Ref. 19). But in developing countries a number of extraneous and uncontrollable factors would be involved at the implementation stage, and at the operation stage the primary concern (in rural areas) should be with motivating local people to take responsibility for operation and maintenance upon themselves. The evaluation stage of a project could be thought of as a problem of interpretation and diagnosis, but in reality a wide area of expertise would be required, not only to diagnose problems but to identify and diagnose both problems and successes. Thus, it is considered unlikely that an expert system would be appropriate at the implementation, operation or evaluation stages of a drinking water supply system in a developing country. An exception might arise in the operation of an urban system, where the treatment works and pumping station, for example, are generally more centralised, more mechanised, more complex, and designed to operate at a higher level of efficiency than their rural counterparts.

4 ADVANTAGES AND DRAWBACKS OF THE USE OF EXPERT SYSTEMS IN DEVELOPING COUNTRIES.

4.1 Advantages.

An expert system could be of benefit in all the applications discussed in section 2 (namely consultancy, checklist, decision-support, technology transfer and training, intelligent front-ending and inter-disciplinary linkage) and in the areas outlined in section 3 (specifically preliminary design of a drinking water supply system). Certain characteristics of both expert systems and developing countries enable such benefits to be realised.

In many situations in developing countries precise, reliable and complete information is difficult to obtain. Strict specifications are difficult to implement and are often inappropriate. The requirements of such a situation are not definitive answers and absolute standards but recommendations and explanations, which are better provided by expert systems than conventional software. An expert system will generally offer advice and most-plausible solutions rather than give absolute answers.

The explanation-facility of an expert system enables a decision-maker to develop trust in the program. He or she should be able to understand enough of the expert system's methods to accept or override its decisions.

The separation of the knowledge base from the inference engine, and the use of natural-language programming, would enable an expert system to be adapted or "fine-tuned" to suit site-specific circumstances. Where it would otherwise be necessary, this might be more straightforward than re-training a human being.

The formalisation of expert knowledge as rules is itself a major benefit of expert systems.

4.2 Drawbacks.

The possible disadvantages of an expert system tend to flow from the same characteristics which yield the advantages.

An expert system might be used not so much as a decision-support tool but as a substitute for decision-making, in the same way that cost functions, for example, are often applied to a problem without regard to their ranges of applicability and other limitations. Similarly, an expert system's decisions might be accepted in blind faith, in the same way that computer programs are sometimes used without an appreciation of whether or not the output is reasonable given the data input. Thus an expert system could have the effect of reducing local decision-making capabilities. This would be more likely where an expert system was being used by a computer- or domain-novice who was unaware of its limitations.

The consistency provided by an expert system might not, in fact, be justified across space and time. The advantages associated with consistency might be inseparable from the disadvantages associated with rigidity.

An expert system might be written or adapted by an individual or organisation to suit their own (biased) viewpoints, which would more readily be accepted by non-experts because of the expert system's appearance as a "human machine".

It can only be proved that an expert system is not complete (in the sense that it does not take all relevant factors into account) but it can never be proved that an expert system is complete. Thus the conclusions reached by an expert system, or the conclusions reached by a non-expert with the aid of an expert system, should never be accepted uncritically. The reality of life is such, however, that an expert system's conclusions sometimes will be accepted uncritically.

5 A PROTOTYPE EXPERT SYSTEM FOR THE PRELIMINARY DESIGN OF A DRINKING WATER TREATMENT SYSTEM.

The tasks performed by human experts are defined by Stefik et al. (Ref. 27), as Interpretation, Diagnosis, Monitoring, Prediction, Planning and Design. For the most part, expert systems have been more successfully applied to diagnosis (or analysis) problems than to synthesis (or design) problems, because synthesis involves a large search space and it takes a great deal of knowledge to focus the search (Ref. 10).

However, it was argued in section 3.3 that, in developing countries, an expert system would be most useful at the preliminary design stage of a drinking water supply system in a developing country.

A design problem might be solved more easily by dividing the proposed system into components which are selected and combined at a strategic level and then designed in detail at an individual level. This approach has been adopted in the development of TREAT, a prototype expert system for the preliminary design of a drinking water treatment system. It has been implemented using the SAVOIR expert system shell (Ref. 18).

The program asks questions about the quality of water from a selected source, and the quality standards required for supply, in terms of: faecal coliforms, turbidity, iron and manganese content, colour, suspended solids, tastes and odours, schistosomiasis, algae, dissolved oxygen content and raw water quality variations. The unit treatment processes considered are: in-situ filtration (such as infiltration galleries), 48-hour storage, aeration, sedimentation, long-term storage, pre-filtration or roughing filtration, slow sand filtration and chlorination. The appropriateness of each component is generally dependent upon (1) the difference between the quality of raw water and the quality standard required for consumption (whose values are supplied by the user in response to questions asked by the program), and (2) the ability of the component to achieve the necessary reduction (which is represented in the expert system´s knowledge base). Some components have no effect upon a given quality parameter, other components are themselves affected by the parameter, and both the components and the quality parameters interact between themselves in a variety of ways.

TREAT creates a preliminary design by performing the task defined by Allwood et al. (Ref. 2) as "combinatory selection", described as the selection of plant to provide an adequate, inexpensive and flexible combination. Only a limited amount of expert knowledge was available to the author for implementation, and the expert system is correspondingly simple. It does not - as yet - contain elements of uncertainty, although the treatment components may be selected or rejected under more than one set of circumstances.

TREAT, therefore, is deterministic in the sense that a treatment component is either selected or rejected with absolute certainty. (Though if the user responds with "unknown" to one or more questions then the component may be neither selected nor rejected). The expert system could perhaps be represented by an algorithmic decision tree, but such a tree would either be very large with repetitive elements, or else be very complex with interlocking and looping branches.

When the knowledge contained in TREAT was formalised it was represented on paper as a matrix, in which the rows were quality parameters and the columns were treatment components. The components to be considered, and the order in which they were to be considered, were specified for each of the quality parameters in isolation.

The columns of the matrix were then implemented as conditional rules, bearing in mind the relationships between the components themselves.

The conditional rules which resulted are few in number but rather long and complicated. The knowledge base is such that the knowledge it contains appears to be procedural, in that the alteration of one of the rules requires the alteration of some of the others. In this sense TREAT is perhaps less characteristic of an expert system, because one of the features of an expert system is that its knowledge is declarative (i.e. separated from the control structure in the inference engine).

It is hoped that, over the next few months, a better understanding will be gained of the distinction between problem-solving methods in the knowledge base and heuristic methods in the inference engine, and that the knowledge base of TREAT will be both simplified and enlarged.

6 REFERENCES.

1. ALIM, S. & MUNRO, J., 1987. PROLOG-based expert systems in civil engineering. Proc. Instn Civ. Engrs, Mar 1987, Vol. 83, Part 2, pp 1-14.

2. ALLWOOD, R. J., STEWART, D. J., HINDE, C. & NEGUS, B., 1985. Report on expert system shells for construction industry applications. Dept. of Civil Engineering, Loughborough University of Technology.

3. BASDEN, A., 1984. On the application of expert systems. Chap. 4 in Coombs (Ref. 6).

4. BINGHAM, A., 1984. Helping to find the least-cost option for water supply. World Water, July 1984, pp 48 & 9.

5. BRAMER, M. A. (ed.), 1985. Research and development in expert systems. Proceedings of the Fourth Technical Conference of the British Computer Society Specialist Group on Expert Systems, University of Warwick, 18th-20th Dec, 1984. Cambridge University Press, Cambridge.

6. COOMBS, M. J. (ed.), 1984. Developments in expert systems. From a special issue of the International Journal of Man-Machine Studies. Academic Press, London.

7. DANGERFIELD, B. J. (ed.), 1983. Water supply and sanitation in developing countries. Manual of British Water Engineering Practice No. 3. The Institution of Water Engineers and Scientists, London.

8. GRAY, C., 1986. ´Intelligent´ construction time and cost analysis. Construction Management and Economics, 1986, Vol. 4, pp 135-50.

9. GROVER, B., 1983. Water supply and sanitation project preparation handbook. Vol. 1: guidelines. World Bank Technical Paper No. 12, The World Bank, Washington, D.C.

10. HART, P., 1986. Interview / Peter Hart talks about expert systems. <u>IEEE Expert</u>, Spring 1986, Vol. 1, No. 1, pp 96-9.

11. HAYES-ROTH, F., WATERMAN, D. & LENAT, D. B. (ed.s), 1983. Building expert systems. Teknowledge Series in Knowledge Engineering. Vol. 1. Addison-Wesley Publishing Co., London.

12. HAYWARD, S. A., 1985. Is a decision-tree an expert system? Chap. 18 of Bramer (Ref. 5).

13. HEBERT, P. V. & YNIGUEZ, C., 1986. Sensitivity of water distribution costs to design and service standards: a Philippine case study. Technical Note No. 16. UNDP Interregional Project INT/81/047. Technology Advisory Group, UNDP/IBRD, Washington, D.C.

14. HOFKES, E. H. (ed.), 1983. Small community water supplies / technology of small water supply systems in developing countries. IRC CWSS, The Hague, The Netherlands and John Wiley & Sons, Chichester, U.K.

15. HOWARTH, D. A. & COE, C. F., 1983. The role of development banks in international funding. Chap. 4 in Dangerfield (Ref. 7).

16. The International Drinking Water Supply and Sanitation Decade directory (2nd edtn). World Water Magazine, Thomas Telford Ltd., Mar 1984.

17. JACKSON, P., 1986. Introduction to expert systems. Addison-Wesley Publishing Co., Wokingham, England.

18. LANG, T., 1985. The SAVOIR expert system package / Users´ manual / Version 1.3. ISI Ltd., 11 Oakdene Rd., Redhill, Surrey, RH1 6BT.

19. LEVITT, R., 1986. Knowledge-based expert systems research in progress / expert systems in civil engineering. <u>IEEE Software</u>, March 1986, Vol. 3, No. 2, pp 57 & 8.

20. O´SHEA, T. & EISENSTADT, M. (ed.s), 1984. Artificial intelligence / tools, techniques and applications. Harper & Row, New York.

21. PACEY, A. (ed.), 1977. Water for the thousand millions. The Water Panel of the Intermediate Technology Development Group, Pergamon Press, Oxford.

22. PESCOD, M. B., 1983. Low-cost technology. Chap. 11 in Dangerfield (Ref. 7).

23. PESCOD, M. B. & KELSEY, G. R., 1986a. Design of low-cost water treatment and distribution. WHO Inter-Country Workshop on Low-Cost Water and Sanitation Options, Amman, Jordan, 13th-17th Dec 1986.

24. PESCOD, M. B. & KELSEY, G. R., 1986b. Institutional development, technology transfer and training. WHO Inter-Country Workshop on Low-Cost Water and Sanitation Options, Amman, Jordan, 13th-17th Dec 1986.

25. SELL, P. S., 1985. Expert systems - a practical introduction. MacMillan Publishers Ltd., Basingstoke.

26. SHALLIS, M., 1986. The end of intelligence. <u>New Internationalist</u>, Aug 1986, No. 162, "Patterns of Control / The Human Shape of Technology", pp 18 & 19.

27. STEFIK, M., AIKINS, J., BALZER, R., BENOIT, J., BIRNBAUM, L., HAYES-ROTH, F. & SACERDOTI, E., 1983. Basic concepts for building expert systems. Chap. 5 in Hayes-Roth (Ref. 11).

28. TECHNOLOGY ADVISORY GROUP, 1985. Microcomputer programs for improved planning and design of water supply and waste disposal systems. (Three floppy discs plus documentation.) UNDP Interregional Project INT/81/047. The World Bank, Washington, D.C.

29. TOPPING, B. V. (ed.), 1985. Proceedings of the second international conference on civil and structural engineering computing. Vol. 2. Civil-Comp Press, Edinburgh.

V GEOTECHNICAL DESIGN

A KNOWLEDGE-BASED APPROACH FOR THE DESIGN OF SPREAD FOOTINGS

Nabil A B Yehia, Structural Engineering Department, Cairo University, Egypt
formerly Assistant Professor, University of Pittsburgh, Pittsburgh, U.S.A.
and Ahmad H El-Hajj, formerly graduate student, Civil Engineering Department,
University of Pittsburgh, Pittsburgh, U.S.A.

SYNOPSIS:

A knowledge-based system for the design of general layout of reinforced concrete spread footings is presented. A database, sorting previous design cases is used to assist the user in obtaining different solutions
for each problem. Plotting capability is also incorporated to show all the reinforcement details as could be
obtained from a design office. The analysis of single and double footing is carried out using the convetion-
al methods whereas the mat foundation is treated as a plate on elastic foundation and analyzed by the bending theory of plates using finite element method.

1. INTRODUCTION

The use of computer has drastically altered the practice of civil engineering particularly in the area
of analysis. There are however, many aspects of engineering for which present programs provide insuffi-
cient assistance. These are the ill-structured problems in which the individual engineer's expertise,
aquired from years of experience, plays a key role
in the area of design. Such expertise is of particular significance in deciding which design is to be
selected, and interpreting the results produced by
the design algorithm.
In structural design problems, although the process
is subject to well defined rules of theory and practice, there are usually several possible correct answers to the same problem. The combinational nature
of the variables prevents the investigation of all
possible designs. In general, a solution path likely
to produce an optimum or near optimum result is taken.
This process is highly dependent on the experience
and memory of the engineer. Clearly, tools which can
help expedite the process of searching for good solutions are beneficial. A powerful tool can be realized if the knowledge of an expert can be incoporated
into it. A knowledge-based expert system (KBES) is a
tool of such kind. It is a computer program which
contains the knowledge and heuristics of one or more
experts and simulates the performance of those experts in problem solving in their domain. At a global
level, an expert system is also an effective mean of
collecting, organizing, preserving and propagating
valuable knowledge which has been developed and accumulated by experts through years of experience (Ref.
1).
An early attempt in this area was made by Roony and
Smith (Ref. 2) for designing simply supported steel
beams with the limitation to standard wide flange
sections. Since the wide flange rolled sections are
already listed in steel tables, a static database
was sufficient in that case. The approach was mainly
concerned with minimizing search time spent to find
an acceptable design. Adeli (Ref. 3) also outlined
an algorithm for development of a computer expert
system for CAD of structures with reference to stiffened steel plate girders where the problem solving
approach was based on the rule-based system paradigm
(Ref. 4). In their study, Roberts and Saiidi (Ref.5)
addressed the bending design of reinforced concrete

continuous beams using the moment as the primary
search criterion and the frequency of usage as the
secondary one. A knowledge based menu driven system
for the design of reinforced concrete rectangular
short columns under the action of combined axial and
bending loads has been recently presented by Bechara
and Yehia (Ref.6) where a more generalized approach
for search criteria is adopted. Since the search criteria depend upon the available information of the
specific consideration at hand it allowes obtaining
valid and practical designs for ill-formulated problems.
This study discusses the development of a computer
program called FOOT. The purpose of this program is
to provide the groundwork for the development of a
powerful computer-based system to aid in the process
of substructure type selection and design. It is actually presenting a part of a long term objective
for the development of an expert system which might
be able to design the foundation of any structure
where the loads and site conditions are the only
input. The present work is mainly concerned with the
spread footing design providing the ability to:

1. select the appropriate footing type for a given
   map of columns distribution and loading.
2. directly design the single footing and combined
   footing selected earlier. However, a mesh has
   to be defined by the user in order to design a
   mat foundation.
3. provide the user with a plotting of the selection made, and the reinforcement details of every
   single and double footing.
4. built a database for previous cases of design,
   based on the best selection specified by the
   user.

2. PROGRAM DESCRIPTION

For any given set of loads and geometry in reinforced
concrete structure design, there could be several
correct answers. There are well defined methods to
determine those. However, the best choice doesn't
necessarily correspond to the one with minimum material cost. To an experienced designer, the best alternative is the one which is: (1) more practical in
terms of placing of steel and concrete, (2) less
confusing to the draftsman, the engineer in charge of

shop drawings, and the site engineer, and (3) less likely to lead to problems in design for anchorage of reinforcement. No simple formula or guidline can be found to qualify these parameters (Ref. 2). The program described in this paper is an attempt to take most of these parameters into account. However, the best alternative is considered as the one which satisfies the user requirements. A databse is employed for this purpose. Each execution of the program will add a new deposit to the databank, making it richer. This phenomenon is similar to the pattern of human experience accumulation. Algorithmic routines were designed to select the appropriate type of footing for a given set of loads, material properties and bearing capacity of soil. Furthermore, they select the flexural reinforcement required for factored moments in accordance with the ACI-Code (Ref.7) limitations. A databank consisting of previous

execution results is utilized to assist the user in choosing the appropriate selection of reinforcement. This selection is based on one of the following criteria:

a. Select the minimum area of steel required by the ACI-Code, which in turn maximizes the depth of concrete section.
b. Select the bar size which furnishes the most exact flexural area of reinforcement required.
c. Maximize the area of steel by reducing the depth of concrete section to the limit specified by the ACI (shear criterion).

The program may be divided into four basic components: the decision making segment, the analysis and design of flexural reinforcement of footing, the plotting segment, and the database. The flow among different sections is shown in figure 1.

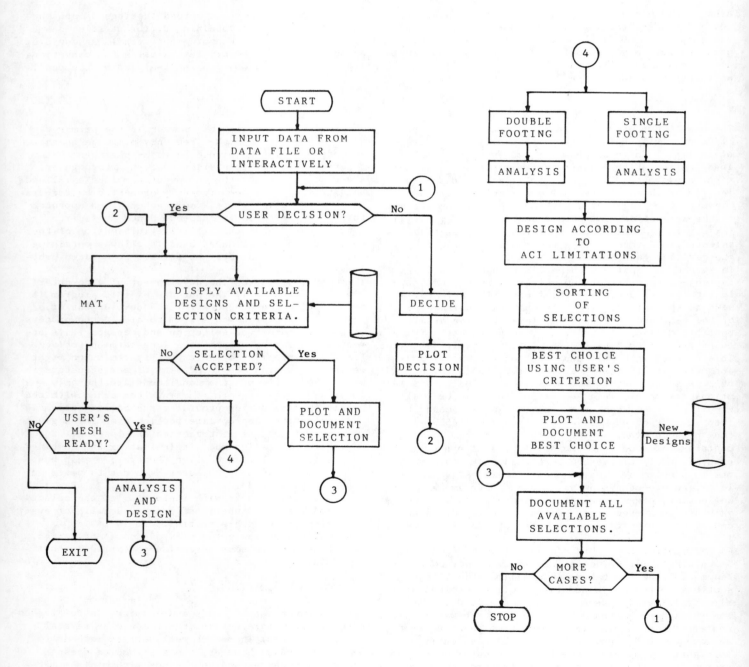

Figure 1: Basic flow of Program 'FOOT'

The program is capable of handling large problems defined by the user. In such case, a general map of column distribution is requested by the main program in a form of matrix data consisting of the coordinates of columns from two coordinates system. With these inputs fed to the main program, module DECIDE will select the appropriate footing type, and the design process will be transfered to module DESIGN. If a mat foundation is encoutered, the user will be asked to define his mesh for the finite element analysis of the mat. Nevertheless, the program will supplythe user with the approximate thickness and area to be furnished for the mat. Moreover, the user can select the type of footing he is willing to design by requesting an interactive data supply to the program. An inappropriate selection made by the user will not be accepted by the program, and a message in that sense will be displayed.
The cross sectional areas and diameters of standard rebars are already stored into the program, allowing it to determine different bar sizes that would satisfy the flexural strength requirements and the ACI-Code limitations. Shear reinforcement is not considered here. The program output takes the form of a table consisting of all possible choices which fall inside the code limits on different parameters such as steel ratio, spacing, development length,..etc. It should be noted here that a search will be made for every single and double footing, seeking a matching solution from previous executions. If such a matching solution exists, the user will be notified with the solution displayed. However, the user may accept the proposed solution or reject it calling for a full new run of the program.

3. PROGRAM FLOW

The program consists of four main modules and some different functional subroutines. The function of each module is briefly discussed in the following. (See Ref. 8 for more complete desciption)

3.1 Module MAIN:
Is the skeleton of the program which accepts the data directly from the user or from a data file prepared earlier. It perfroms some unit transformation and generates a code matrix which will be used later by module DECIDE to reach a decision. The code number and its location in the code matrix depends on the distance from center line to center line of each two columns and the footing dimensions of each column. The main program doesn't have a databank. Databanks are only provided in module DESIGN which will be described later.

3.2 Module DECIDE:
Which represents the inference engine, receives the code matrix and the numbering system of columns from MAIN. A 'zero' in the code matrix represents a discontinuity between two footings, which implies the identification of single footing. A 'one' represents an overlaping of two columns along x-axis or y-axis, depending on the position of the 'one' in the code matrix. The search inside the code matrix takes the form of an angle moving row by row along x-axis. A column previously identified may change its identification depending on its nearby column current identification.
Figure 2 shows a general map,prepared by the user, which consists of nine columns, one of them is fictitious. The fictitious column doesn't exist on the site map, however, it is required to be included in the data file, so that the columns distribution will always be rectangular. Ignoring the position of a fictitious column will affect the performance of the program resulting in a safe decision, but not a accurate one. For instance, if column5 in figure 2 is ignored, column 6 would be taking its place in the datafile, then, it will be checked with columns 2,4 and 8 for combination possibilities, where it is more likely to be combined with column 3 or column 9 if needed.

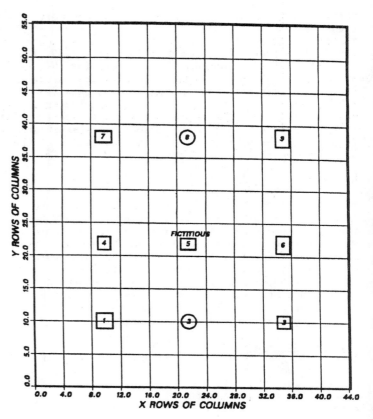

Figure 2: Column distribution map.

3.3 Module GRAPH:
It Utilizes a group of subroutines provided by DISPLA, an integrated software system and language available on DEC-SYSTEM 10 and VAX/VMS library. GRAPH will provide the user with a general map for column distribution and later on with the map of footing distribution. It also contains some arithmetic calculation procedures to be utilized by DISPLA software to plot the reinforcement details of single and double footings. Only the best choice will be plotted.

3.4 Module DESIGN:
It receives the input from MAIN or interactively from the user and starts the search fromsimilar cases in its databank. If a similar case is found from previous executions, the criterion for which the case wasbeing selected will be displayed. The intelligent segment of the program identifies only the best selection based on the user's criterion. At this point the user may request a complete detail of the design items which show all the available design possibilities in a matrix form and displays the best choice among these possibilities. The best choice will then be sent to module GRAPH to plot the reinforcement details. Through this process, the databank expands every time the program is used, and future selections are likely to improve. It should be mentioned that for the design of combined footing more input items will be requested, and so will be the output. At least five different locations of reinforcement will be taken care off in the databank, and, of course,

121

the search for similar solution imposes some more elements to be checked.

To perform the analysis of mat foundation, a program was adapted from the system described in Ref. 9. The program utilizes a nonconforming element for the analysis of flexural plates based on classical Kirchoff theory and it provides an automatic mesh generator for rectangular regions with rectangular elements. The results obtained from the mat analysis are sent to an algorithmic subroutine to sort the moments and their locations on the mesh for the completion of the design process.

4. DATABASE:

To prepare a database, it is necessary to know the input and the output parameters to be included there. These parameters are primarily the design variables. The structure of the databank affects the search time for best choice. In this study, the guide parameters are placed in first range, the best selection in the second, the user's criterion in the third, and finally the execution date. In general, the database consists of two main segments, the intelligent segment and the databank segment.

4.1 The Intelligent Segment:
The intelligent segment is utilized to consult the database and determine the available designs for the current case. Therefore, it selects the one that agrees with the user's criterion. This process involves a search through the databank that primarily satisfies the factored loads and the material properties, and secondarily the user's criterion. The best selection need not necessarily match all the parameters. The following tolerance limits were used on different variables:
3% difference in factored loads, 0% difference in each of the bearing capacity, steel yield strength and the 28-day concrete strength, one inch difference in concrete thickness, and three inches in footing lateral dimensions.

4.2 The Databank:
The search process inside the databank is performed quite similarly to a commercial banking machine. An identification number is always used to start with. The identification number, as in this case, might be the design selection criterion as specified by the user. Having the ID entered, the rest of the process might take one of the following two forms:
a) Compatible previous design:
    This form of search type inside the databank will be performed every time the program is executed. Having selected the design criterion, the material properties, and the bearing capacity of soil, a check for every item will successivelly take place. For instance, the factored load input will be compared with the one deposited first; if a difference within the tolerance limit is obtained, the comparison will continue for another item (yield strength of steel might be the other item). However, a complete agreement in value is required now otherwise the searching process will jump to the next set of data. If the comparison result comes out positively, the user will be notified that a similar case was handled by the program on the basis of certain criterion and on a specific date. A message in that sense will be displayed on the terminal and documented on an output file for later use to obtain a hardcopy. On the other hand, complete design details could be documentd if requested by the user. However, only the best choice will be plotted to save CPU time.

b) Design safety check:
    An alternative way of using the built database is to check the safety of an existing structure. the elements needed for that check are the existing dimensions of the proposed footing, the material properties, the bearing capacity of soil, and the area of steel furnished in different directions. The search in this case will take a longer time since more parameters are to be checked. Nevertheless, the safety of the structure depends on some more vital elements, like the current condition of the structure, which are out of scope of this study.

5. EXAMPLE PROBLEM:

In this example, the user inputs a map of columns, as shown in figure 2, with the factored loads assumed as: 391.5, 381, 288, 379, 0.0, 488, 299, 262.5 and 488 kips for columns 1 through 9 respectively. The selection decisions as concluded by the program are shown in figure 3. The design process took place for

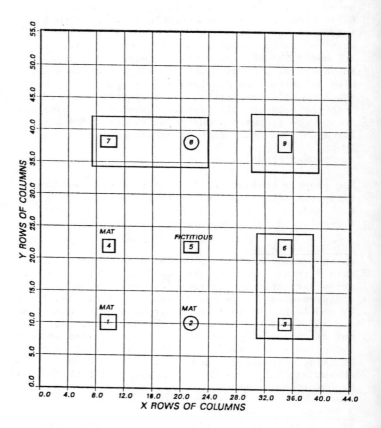

Figure 3: Selected footings map.

single and double footings first until it is altered by the presence of a mat foundation. A mesh had then been prepared, as shown in figure 4, to start the program again for the three columns mat and loaded by the loads of columns 1, 2 and 4 as nodal loads normal to the plane of the mat. The thickness of the mat was assumed 1.5 ft with elasticity modulus, shear modulus, and poissons ratio of 452700ksf, 19512 ksf and 0.16 respectively. The subgrade modulus is assumed 50 kcf. A maximum moment of 158 kip.ft/ft is found to exist between columns 1 and 4. A minimum reinforcement of 0.72 sq.in/ft, as recommended by ACI-Code is therefore adopted by the program. A Hardcopy of the designed single and double footing may be requested as shown in figure 5a and figure 5b. However, this facility is not yet available for mat foundation type.

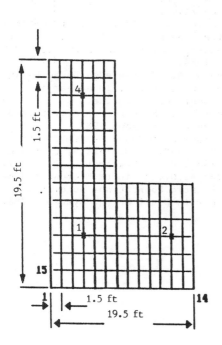

Figure 4: Generated mesh for mat of columns 1, 2 and 4.

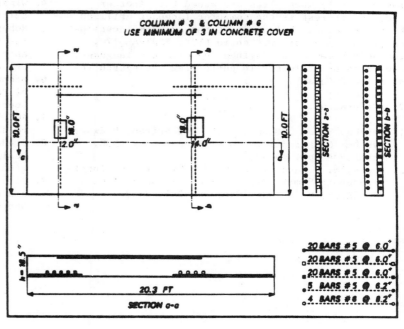

Figure 5b: Sample detail of double footing.

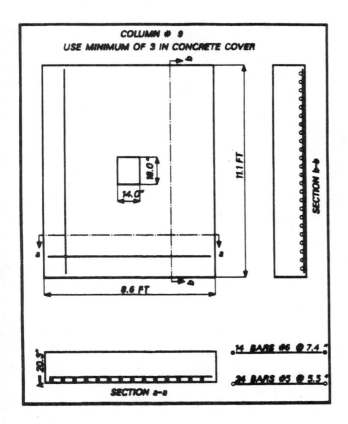

Figure 5a: Sample detail of single footing.

6. CONCLUSION

The paper presented herein can be considered as a preliminary study for the possibility of building an expert system that is capable of selecting and designing, eventually, any type of spread footing. Previous programs that dealt with footing design were almost always limited to a single type of footing. This however is impractical, since a footing design problem is most likely to have a column load map where a decision is to made before the real design steps can take place. Therefore, it was the idea of this paper to develop a program capable of making decisions, and furthermore, capable of handling single cases of design. There is however one part of the problem yet to be worked out. If the program delivers a decision that consists of mat foundations, the execution will be halt until a finite element mesh is supplied by the user.

Some of the published works that was referred to earlier (Ref.1 to Ref.5) have based their choice on the frequencies of previous acceptances. This sometimes resulted in limiting the options available to the user because after a certain number of program executions, the databank tends to become strongly biased toward certain selections (Ref.1). The concept discussed in this paper allowes the user to select certain design criterion and a best choice corresponding to the most matching area of steel will be based on that criterion. This process will enlarge the databank so that, at certain times it might contain all the design choices for a certain design case. However, the selection criterion used in the present work minimizes or maximizes either one of the concrete section or the steel area. Other criteria such as total material weight, market avalability or uniformity of steel bar size have not been taken into consideration in the present work. For the part of single and double footing design, the program is so efficient that it uses a vey little

CPU time. However, the explanation facilities, presented by the documented plots, enlarge the memory occupancy so much that the program could not be run interactively when plots are asked for. Another item of interest is the computer language utilized by the program. while most of the programs developed in this area are witten in LISP, FORTRAN-77 , commonly known as an engineering-oriented language, proved to be efficient in performing the search inside the databank.

7. REFERENCES

1. Fenves, S. J. , Maher, M. L. and Sriram, " Expert System: CE Potential", Civil Engieering/ASCE, Oct. 1984, pp. 44-47.
2. Roony, M. F. and Smith, S. E., "Artificial Intelligence in Simple Beam Design", Structural Division/ASCE, Vol. 108, 1984, pp. 2344-2348.
3. Adeli, H., " Artificial Intelligence in Simple Beam Design", Proceedings, Fifth ASCE/EMD Speciality Confernce, Laramie, Wyoming, USA, August 1984.
4. Winston, P. H., " Artificial Intelligence", 2nd edition, Addison-Wesily, 1984.
5. Roberts, P. and Saiidi M., " Artificial Intelligence for Design of R/C Beams", 2nd National Conference on Microcomputers in Civil Engineering, Orlando, Florida, 1984.
6. Bechara R. and Yehia, N., " Knowledge-Based Design of Reinforced Concrete Columns", to appear in Concrete International, ACI Magazine.
7. ACI 318-83, Building Code Requirements for Reinforced Concrete, Detroit, Michigan, 1983.
8. El-Hajj, A. H., " Knowledge-Based System For the Design of Spread Footing", M.SC. Thesis, Civil Engineering Dept., 1986, U. of Pittsburgh, Pa 15261.
9. Dick, R. E. and Yehia, N., " Finite Element Analysis of Plates on Elastic Foundation- Automated Approach", to appear in Civil Engng. Systems, 1987.

VI   MATERIALS ENGINEERING

COMPUTER ASSISTANCE FOR CONCRETE CONSTRUCTION

Kenneth C Hover, PE, PhD
Associate Professor of Structural Engineering
Cornell University, Ithaca, New York, U.S.A.

A small-scale expert system has been developed to assist in the planning and conduct of concrete-placing operations for slabs-on-ground. Assembly of the knowledge-base has illustrated the complex series of technical and managerial decisions which must be made by the construction professional. The program has considerable educational value through both its development and use. The industrial value of this type of program is discussed.

Introduction

Interest in the use of computers in the concrete construction industry is developing rapidly in the U.S. Our paper presented in Civil Comp '85 (1) detailed a computer program for determining material proportions for concrete mixes. This program has since been expanded (with the encouragement of conference attendees at Civil Comp '85) to become a small-scale expert system known as CONSLAB. In addition to determining mix proportions and costs, the program in its present configuration can assist the concrete contractor to plan a slab placing operation to include the selection of method of concrete placement, determination of manpower and equipment requirements, to evaluate the impact of weather conditions, and to monitor and report on progress.

The "Knowledge Base" for the expert system comes primarily from two distinct sources. Technical details are generally taken from established literature and the collected recommended practices published by the American Concrete Institute. This data base is supplemented with information from unpublished sources. The secondary, but also essential, source of knowledge comes from the author's familiarity with concrete construction practices. This information tends to be more administrative and procedural and less technical in nature. There is little in the way of "new" information or advanced expertise programmed into the expert system, therefore, making the primary benefit to the user one of rapid access to conventional information. This is in contrast to systems which provide the user with new information which is not otherwise available.

The following paper traces the development of CONSLAB, briefly describes content and output, and evaluates the merit and applicability of the final product. It is emphasized from the outset that the primary purpose for creating the

program has been educational and not commercial. The objective has been to experience the development of a small-scale expert system, and in particular to experience the translation of common but generally undocumented construction knowledge to a computer-oriented format. In so doing, it was discovered that a construction operation as simple as the placement of a concrete slab-on-ground is accompanied by a host of problems and decisions ranging from the tedious to the very complex. This particular program is merely a vehicle for exploring the broader issue of the use of computers to expedite decision-making on the construction site, and serves to demonstrate the kinds of information which can be made available to the fingertips of the construction professional. The program is therefore only an example of what can and perhaps should be done by others on a larger scale.

The Conslab Program

CONSLAB has been designed to address the solution to a variety of simple, yet time consuming problems which occur on the concrete construction worksite, and for simplicity its scope is limited to the issues involved in the casting of a simple, rectangular slab-on-ground. The concepts can be adapted to more complex constructions. The technical knowledge-base for CONSLAB is the collected committee reports and recommended practices of the American Concrete institute, found in the *ACI Manual of Concrete Practice* (2). (This is because of the author's familiarity with that set of documents, and not because of any inherent superiority.) While many construction professionals agree that this five-volume set of references is an invaluable document, the very bulk of the set and the literally hundreds of entries limit its utility in the field. While the program makes no claim to a complete adoption of the Manual of Standard Practice, several examples will suffice to demonstrate its inclusion.

To maintain simplicity the program is written in the BASIC language, without recourse to "shells" or "Artificial Intelligence" languages or systems. The program is organized into the following subsections, each of which is composed of one or more subroutines.

I.   Main Menu
II.   Common Input Information
III.   Preparation for Placement
IV.   Cost Estimate
V.   Assessment of Weather Conditions
VI.   Mix Manipulations
VII.   Ordering and Delivery
VIII. Progress Update
IX.   After-Action Report

Main Menu and Common Input

This is the entry point in the program, from which the operator can select the subsection of interest. All input information which is required by more than one of the subsections may be loaded at this point. Information which is not provided here and required at some other point will be requested at the appropriate time. Typical common input information includes slab dimensions, a reference to the concrete mix being used, the desired duration of the pour, and the anticipated method of placement. From this basic data the program calculates area, volume, perimeter, concrete quantity, and the desired rate of pour.

Preparation for Casting and Cost Estimate

The calculated area is used to estimate the required quantities of fine grading, gravel sub-base, and rebar or welded-wire fabric, as well as the required quantity of vapor barrier below and/or plastic curing sheets or blankets above the slab. The quantity of membrane-forming curing compound is also calculated, based on the slab area and the rate of application. The perimeter and depth values are used to calculate the requirements for perimeter bulkheads, expansion-joint filler, etc.

One of the most interesting aspects of the program is the prediction of the rate of concrete placement and the determination of the appropriate manpower and equipment requirements. The rate of placement may be considered as the independent variable which in turn dictates the manpower and equipment requirements. Alternatively, equipment, available crews, or the rate of concrete delivery may limit the placement rate. The program calculates 9 possible limiting cases and uses the slowest rate in all subsequent formulations. These simple rate and rate-limiting calculations are examples of the type of optimization and/or critical-path thinking which is not routinely part of "tactical" construction planning, while being fully utilized in overall project or "strategic" planning and management. This phase of the planning is completed by estimating completion times for placing and finishing operations on the basis of the start time entered.

Based on the selected rate of placement, the program then estimates the manpower requirements based on the data tables contained in *Means Concrete and Masonry Cost Data* (3). The same

reference is used to estimate the requirements for small equipment such as troweling machines. For example, Means suggests that placing concrete in 150 mm (6 in.) thick slab requires 0.50 manhours/m^3 if placement is by pump and 0.58 manhours/m^3 if placement is by crane and bucket. This is based on a placing crew of 1 labor foreman, 5 laborers, and 1 cement finisher. Installation of a hard steel-trowel finish will require an average of 0.16 manhours/m^2, presuming that each finisher has a power trowel.

The rate of placement is dependent on the method of placement, selected previously by the user. If a crane and bucket was selected, a routine in the program compares the rate of pour against the bucket volume and required frequency of lifts. Further, if the operator has preloaded information about crane capacity and overturning limits, the program can check for a safe distance from the center of the crane to the far edge of the slab, based on the size of the concrete bucket being used. Likewise, if the operator has preloaded information concerning pumping capacity and the rate of pouring, the program can check the selection of the concrete pump.

Prior to exiting this portion of the program, the operator can elect to modify his plan on the basis of extremes in weather as will be explained. Finally, the above information is output in the form of a pre-pour checklist, which includes small tools to include shovels, rakes, etc., and also advises on the number and type of vibrators, using the recommendations of ACI Committee 309 (4). For example, vibrators with a 30-60 mm head diameter are recommended for very thin slabs (say less than 50 mm) and 50-90 diameter heads are recommended for thicker slabs. Characteristic amplitudes and frequencies are also listed.

Once this planning data has been collected, it is a simple matter to take the materials, manpower, and equipment quantities thus calculated and multiply them by preloaded rates to obtain an estimate of the cost of the operation, expressed as total cost, cost per unit volume or unit area, and separated into labor and materials costs.

Assessment of Weather Conditions

The operator may input the predicted weather conditions for the day of concrete placement. This invokes several of the guidelines contained in ACI 308 (Curing Concrete (5)), ACI 305 (Hot Weather Concreting (6)) and ACI 306 (Cold Weather Concreting (7)). Using a modified version of the Menzel equation (8), the program estimates the predicted rate of evaporation from the slab surface. If the predicted rate of evaporation exceeds 5 kg/m^2, the program warns the operator that there is a risk of plastic shrinkage cracking, and will print the recommendations of ACI 305 for the reduction of such risk if requested. This includes provision for sunshades, windscreens, or fog sprays. To this list are added the options of using a film-forming evaporation retarder or modifying slab-finishing procedures.

If the weather forecast entered previously (in response to a specific prompt) includes a prediction of freezing temperatures, or if the mean daily temperature is likely to be less than $5^\circ C$, the warnings of ACI 306 are automatically invoked. This includes recommendations for insulation of all unformed surfaces, to include a recommendation for the R value of the insulating covering to be used over the slab.

Finally, using the equation found in ACI 306 (as well as in many other sources, e.g., Neville and Brooks (9), the final temperature of the concrete is estimated based on the temperature of the materials and the ambient air. This can be used to determine whether modifications to the concrete mix are necessary.
A truly comprehensive version of such a program would include at this point an estimate of the effect of temperature on strength gain, but this has not been done. The program will not predict the weather, however!

Mix manipulations

Based on weather conditions or other operational considerations the operator may wish to investigate modifications to the concrete mix proportions. While the mix-proportioning program developed previously is linked with CONSLAB, it is generally considered that mix proportioning is within the purview of the concrete supplier and not the contractor. Therefore, the common input section allows for transfer of mix data from the mix design program, or for direct entry of batch weights by the operator for a number of possible mixes.

For a complete reevaluation of the mix the operator can re-enter the mix design program, or he may simply examine the effects of heated or chilled mix-water (or ice) on the placing temperature of the concrete. Weather conditions may also dictate a change in cement type and/or admixtures.

Ordering and Delivery

Having already determined the total calculated volume of concrete and the rate of pour, this section formulates the order to the ready mix plant, including such details as a request for a small volume of grout to precede a pumping operation, and a slow rate of delivery for the first several truck loads. Additional information concerning truck capacity, haul time, and on-site/batch plant turn-around time, permits an estimate of the required number of ready-mix trucks. Start and finish times are carried from the input section for the concrete order. Special instructions such as the requirement to presoak lightweight aggregate are included.

The total volume of concrete to be ordered is taken from the slab volume, plus yield corrections (if known) plus an increment for wasteage (usually 2 to 5%). The program suggests to the person placing the order that it may be helpful to hold the trucks at some predetermined partial volume in order to check for final quantities.

Based on the quality control criteria contained in ACI 301 and 318, the required number of test cylinders is calculated, and the operator is reminded to contact the testing agency. Start and finish times are carried from the input section to complete a suggested order to both the testing company and the concrete supplier. Similarly, the user is reminded to contact the sawing subcontractor if joints are to be cut within the first 24 hours.

Progress Update

This section is designed to provide information while the pour is in progress. Having prompted for input for the actual start time, current time, yards placed, and approximate dimensions of the area yet to place and/or finish, the computer estimates the volume yet to be placed and the estimated time of completion of placement, finishing, and curing.

After-action report

At the close of the operation, the supervisor may load the actual quantities and times to obtain a report of the actual rate of pour, placement rate, finishing rate, and associated costs. These can be saved to form a basis for planning the next operation. The machine will also compare the actual volume to the calculated volume to estimate the yield of the concrete. The program ends at this point.

Educational Value of the Program

As was the case with the mix-design program, CONSLAB began as an academic exercise and shall continue to be used as such. The program is composed of multiple independent subroutines which have been developed independently, and shall be modified, updated, or replaced entirely as assignments for student working parties. Many of the sections described herein have been developed to only an elementary level, and will be made more comprehensive (and complicated) as the program develops.

The educational value of such an exercise is significant. First, in developing any type of expert system the student gains some familiarity with an important and rapidly growing computer application. Second, the student's first task is to understand the logic and technical background to the construction process and then to translate this understanding to computer code. This phase itself is highly beneficial in the learning process, as a seemingly complex and rather ill-defined construction operation is broken down into individual steps. Further, the practical application of information presented in the classroom and found in the references is reinforced.

Finally, having constructed such a system, the students can have the opportunity to use it in a series of construction simulation and optimization exercises. While these are not intended to replace field experience, such preparation can make subsequent field experience all the more valuable. The entire process of understanding, programming, and using the expert system to simulate the construction environment is therefore seen as a comprehensive training tool which may very well be the most powerful application of this type of program, and perhaps of the concept of expert systems in general.

Potential Use and Benefit to the Industry

If the program can assist in the training of young professionals, that in itself must be seen as a real benefit to the industry. More directly, however, the question arises as to who is the most likely user of such a system. This question was actually addressed early in the development of the program, as the writers of an expert system must continually focus on the background, needs, capability, and working-style of the user. A further question in the construction of an expert system is not only "who is the user?," but "who is the expert?". In other words, what is the level of expertise being delivered by the program.

Since it was intended that the program under development at Cornell was targeted for the construction site, it was initially presumed that the user would be a construction professional, such as the project manager or project superintendent. This person routinely solves multiple technical and administrative problems (often simultaneously) on a daily basis, generally having to make rapid decisions with limited time for data collection. In many cases a timely decision which is "almost right" is preferable to a considered response which is "precisely correct," particularly if arriving at the precise answer would cause delay in the critical path.

Targeting this construction professional as the user of the expert system implies that the program developer is going to provide expertise (in the form of a computer program) which is not otherwise available to that professional. In other words, it is anticipated that the user will seek the advice of an "expert in computer's clothing" in arriving at a decision. For several reasons the author came to the conclusion that such use of computers by construction mangers and superintendents is unlikely.

First, it is doubtful that an expert system which essentially comes to the same conclusion as the professional on routine matters is in much demand. Few of us in any profession are prone to seeking advice of any kind in routine matters. We seek advice only in special cases, or in cases in which the penalty for an inappropriate decision is more severe than usual. Therefore, a computer program which provides essentially the same answer as the experienced professional is unlikely to be used. Second, providing a level of expertise which is above that already possessed by the experienced construction professional would be difficult, and is certainly beyond the capability of the author or his students.

It does seem likely, however, that a system which tries to emulate the expertise of the construction manager or superintendent would be useful. Such a system could be used by subordinates in the project office to make

tentative plans for forthcoming operations. Such plans could then be reviewed by the experienced manager and modified as necessary prior to implementation. Such use would relieve the manager of having to do all of the planning, and would assist greatly in the training of assistants. Therefore, the "Expert" in the expert system is not an outsider with claims to a superior understanding of the construction process, but is a computer model of the thinking process conducted by the manager.

Future Developments

The program described is in its infancy, and indeed is not yet sufficiently comprehensive in content nor efficient in programming style. It will be improved with the help of students and graduate researchers over the next several years, and will be enlarged to encompass some new elements of construction technology. For example, recent developments in the ability to produce "flat" concrete floors are driving major changes in the ACI recommended practice for floor construction and in the concepts of construction tolerances. These new requirements and procedures are not yet part of the common construction knowledge, and the program could serve a genuine purpose in making new information available and understandable. The entire issue of slab shrinkage, curling, and cracking, to include recommendations for joint placement, etc. can be addressed as well. Finally, the expansion options are limitless if one considers extending this work on slabs-on-ground to other construction types.

Summary and Conclusions

What began as a simple demonstration program quickly became complex, primarily due to the underestimation of the thinking involved in planning and conducting even a simple concreting operation. This causes both the developer and the user to appreciate more fully the tasks of the construction professional. While the experienced construction manager may consider many of these factors almost unconsciously, or as "second nature," it is also likely that even such a manager will underestimate the task before him and occasionally fail to take all critical issues into account. If this is true, then the use of such an "expert system" may reduce the probability of error.

It also became clear in the development of the program that a useful system must provide its technical information in the context of the overall task and environment of the user. An expert system for construction application must reflect an understanding of the construction process which can rarely be developed anywhere but on the jobsite. Technical expertise "in vacuo" is likely to stay "in vacuo."

The educational value has been explained in detail. The industrial value may be in the training of subordinates, or as a guideline for the use by inexperienced construction planners for the development of tentative plans which will be reviewed by the project manager or superintendent prior to implementation. It may take an experienced professional to spot the errors produced or built-in to an expert system.

References

1. Hover, K.C. "Computer-Aided Concrete Mix-Design," Proceedings of the Second International Conference on Civil and Structural Engineering Computing, London, December 1985, Volume 1, pp. 233-238, Civil Comp-Press, Edinburgh

2. Manual of Concrete Practice, American Concrete Institute, Detroit, 1986, 5 volumes, 1500 pp. (approx.)

3. Robert Snow Means Co., Inc, Concrete and Masonry Cost Data, Smit, K., Senior Editor, Robert Sturgis Godfrey, Publisher, Kingston, MA, 1985, 372 pp.

4. American Concrete Institute, "Standard Practice for Consolidation of Concrete (ACI 309-72) (Revised 1982)," ACI Committee 309, Detroit, 1982, 40 pp.

5. American Concrete Institute, "Standard Practice for Curing Concrete (ACI 308-81) (Revised 1986)" ACI Committee 308, Detroit, 1986, 11 pp.

6. American Concrete Institute, "Hot Weather Concreting," Reported by ACI Committee 305, Detroit, 1982, 17 pp.

7. American Concrete Institute, "Cold Weather Concreting," Reported by ACI Committee 306, Detroit, 1983, 22 pp.

8. Shaeles, C. A., "Plastic Shrinkage Cracking in Mortar and Concrete," a thesis presented in partial fulfillment of the requirements for the degree of Master of Science, Cornell University, Ithaca, New York, 1986, 194 pp.

9. Neville, A.M., Brooks, J.J., Concrete Technology, Wiley, 1987.

VII   PAVEMENT DESIGN

PERFORMANCE OF CONCRETE PAVEMENTS USING "PAVEMENT EXPERT"

J G Cabrera and M Al-Shawi,
Department of Civil Engineering, University of Leeds, England

SYNOPSIS

Methods in use for the evaluation of performance of pavements are normally a mixture of observations of signs of distress and measurement of parameters like permanent deformations, crack length and width, area of patching etc. Data collection requires a system for storage and retrieval which is normally handled by available computerized systems. The usefulness of the data depends entirely on the correctness with which it has been collected. This paper reviews briefly the current methods used in the UK for evaluation of road performance and presents the development of an expert system named "Pavement Expert" which is operated by a portable microcomputer and which is mounted in the inspection car used for the survey of a pavement.

Pavement Expert guides the engineer on the selection of road sections for evaluation, and on the proper evaluation procedure ensuring that the evaluation is adequate and that it can be independently repeated by other engineers. The system also allows the engineer to ask for help on specific aspects of the evaluation process.

Pavement expert operates in two modes, i.e., dialogue and data logging modes. The dialogue mode is controlled by the Savoir shell interphase which controls the dialogue between the engineer and the system. The system makes decisions "Intelligently" concerning the length of the section to evaluate, extent and severity of some of the observed damages and calculates and stores the final indices for evaluation of performance. The system follows the information given by the engineer and checks for any inconsistencies. The data logging mode acts as an intelligent data logger recording specific observed damages. The engineer presses a particular key on the keyboard as soon as he observes a specific damage. The computer captures the key strokes, identifying them and recording their exact location. The system presents the information graphically on the screen to allow the engineer to make alterations if he wishes to do so. Five phases constitute the system developed. These range from identifying the road to providing a full report on the general conditions of the pavement. The system is operational on a IBM microcomputer under "MS DOS" operating system. The Savoir shell was used to develop the system and "Propascal" to write the external functions.

INTRODUCTION

Performance of a pavement is greatly affected by the type, time, and quality of maintenance it receives. Regular maintenance can slow the rate of pavement deterioration caused by traffic loads and adverse climatic conditions. Available information suggest that pavements are deteriorating faster than they are being restored because maintenance funds have not been sufficient (1). This problem is highlighted in the UK by the National Road Condition Maintenance Survey (2) which indicated that from 1977 to 1980 there was a trend towards improvement followed by a trend of deterioration from 1980 to 1985. The net result is that the condition in 1985 was significantly worse than in 1977.

Data for the assessment of concrete pavement performance and for the implementation of adequate maintenance policies requires trained engineers and demands intensive labour allocation. The methods in use for the evaluation of performance are normally a mixture of observations of signs of distress and measurement of parameters like permanent deformations, crack length and width, area of patching etc. Data collection requires

a system for storage and retrieval which is normally handled by available computerized sytems. The usefulness of the data depends entirely on the correctness with which it has been collected. Young engineers which have little experience on evaluation of pavements find that the interpretation of the signs of distress and their causes are not very easy to recognise for allocation to a particular type of distress which is specified in the method of evaluation being used. Because the speed with which these surveys have to be conducted it should be of great advantage to give an engineer some expert guidance during the assessment stages and also during the decision making process with regard to the formulation of maintenance policies.

This paper reviews briefly the current methods used in the UK for evaluation of road performance and presents the development of an expert system named "Pavement Expert" which is operated by a portable microcomputer and which is mounted in the inspection car used for the survey of a pavement. The expert system is based on a method of assessment developed in USA and which in comparison to the methods in current use in the UK is very simple.

Current methods of pavement evaluation

Prior to 1970 most highway authorities in the UK had simple rating methods to assess pavement conditions. Following the publication of the Marshall Report (3), more complicated rating systems have been developed. The most widely used systems at present are CHART (4) and MARCH (5). Both of them were developed in such a way as to minimise subjective judgment and optimize an objective, numerate quantitative approach. The measured condition of defects is related to standard criteria which are a development of the Marshall standards. Both systems incoporate computer processing and have a variety of outputs portraying road condition and priorities for remedial treatment (6). The current application of these systems are poor, about one third of the highway authorities are using one of the two systems (7,8). This is apparently because the application of these systems requires time and much engineering experience.

In the USA, the Pavement Condition Rating (PCR) system was developed by a private engineering consultant for the Ohio Department of Transportation and the US Department of Transportation, Federal Highway Administration (9). The PCR is a simple method which provides a procedure for uniformly identifying and describing pavement distresses in terms of severity and extent. The numerical expression of the PCR provides an index reflecting the composite effects of varying distress types, severity and extent upon the overall condition of the pavement. It is based upon the summation of deduct points for each type of observable distress. Total deduct points are subtracted from 100 to yield the PCR. The scale used for the PCR is shown in Figure 1, with a PCR of 100 assigned to a pavement with no observable distress.

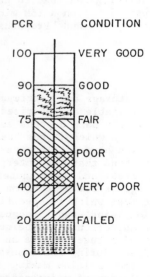

Figure 1 Pavement Condition Rating Scale

Deduct values are a function of distress type, severity and extent. Deduction for each distress type is calculated by multiplying distress weight times the weight for severity and extent of the distress. Distress weight is the maximum number of deductible points for each different distress type.

This evaluation procedure is easy to apply when engineers with experience and knowhow used it for assessment of performance. The final rating does not give detailed information regarding the origin of failure or the necessary corrective action as it does any of the other detailed methods like CHART or MARCH. However it is very easy to use with the aid of the Expert system presented in the following paragraphs.

It is envisaged as a method which can be used with advantage as a preliminary assessment procedure where the critical sections of a pavement are earmarked for further detailed studies.

In its present form it can be used as a front end of either the CHART or the MARCH SYSTEMS.

Computerized methods for pavements evaluation

Pavement evaluation procedures are tedious and subjected to random errors while coding and typing information into the computer, if the computer is used for analysis. These errors are expensive to correct as they are not normally detected until the information has been analysed and the corrections usually involve a return visit to the site. The Transport and Road Research Laboratory (TRRL) (10) has developed a hand held microcomputer to record inspection information for the CHART highway maintenance system. A programme loaded into the memory of the microcomputer guides an inspector through a CHART inspection by displaying a series of prompts on a screen. Inspection records are entered on the keyboard and stored in the device. The stored data then can be transferred to a main computer for processing by the CHART programme. This method simplifies data collection especially in damp or windy conditions. Also, it eliminates the transcription and punching stages of the data preparation.

In the USA, a feasibility study was carried out on a system which fully automates the evaluation procedure (11). The system consists of three electronic sensors and associated optical equipment to scan a lane of a road. The equipment is mounted in a van which can be driven at a speed of 90 km/h. A sophisticated software written for the system recognises each type of pavement damage, a crack for example, among the mass of data recorded through the sensors. The study showed that the system is successful under laboratory conditions, but it has not been tested under real field conditions.

Pavement expert

The primary objective of Pavement Expert (12) is to enable any user to make accurate PCR evaluations with maximum efficiency. This implies extensive help facilities to allow the inexperienced engineer or technician to learn "on the job". As the PCR system is well documented, the knowledge base is accessible and therefore, Pavement Expert has been based on an expert system shell.

A detailed functional analysis indicated that Pavement Expert should have a dialogue mode when the car is stationary and a data logging mode while on the move. Particularly when in the latter mode, procedural logic is required to:-

* Capture keystrokes made to record observations
* Maintain animated screen displays
* Update a database of all observations for future use.

In contrast to manual PCR rating, it was decided that Pavement Expert should maintain a detailed record of all observations. To assist in this aspect the production version of Pavement Expert will be linked to the mileometer of the car to allow accurate changes to be associated with each observation.

The Savior shell was selected to implement Pavement Expert, this shell allows the use of external functions written in pascal. Other than providing overall control and the help system, the knowledge base is employed to make decisions regarding the partition of the road into sections, the extent and severity of some of the observed distresses, the final PCR indices and to check the observations and ratings for inconsistencies.

The internal structure of Pavement Expert is shown in Fig. 2.

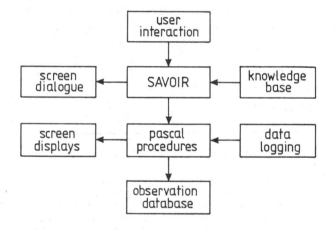

Figure 2   Internal structure of "Pavement Expert"

It comprises a Savoir model with which the user normally interacts in dialogue mode plus a number of procedures written in Pascal. These procedures enable Savior to interact with the observations database and generate animated displays of the observations as required. When data logging mode is entered, control passes from Savior to the external Pascal procedures and keystrokes are captured and the display updated until the car stops and control returns to Savior.

Pavement expert structure

The evaluation procedure used by the Pavement Expert can be divided into five stages:-

Preamble

An initial pre-site dialogue during which new or uncertain users can request an overview of each stage of the rating process and guidance on how to interact with Pavement Expert. The system asks the user for details of the road to be evaluated. Information such as the country name, road name, project number, start and finish

chainage, pavement type and details of any known landmarks are requested. The system then represents this information graphically as shown in Fig. 3 and allows any corrections to be made. Finally the user is asked to drive to the start of the road to be rated.

Preliminary inspection

An initial data logging run over the whole road at 60 km/h during which preliminary observations are recorded. A starting dialogue enables the user to request an explanation of this stage and guidance on the observations to be made. Once the car starts moving control passes from Savoir to the preliminary inspection data logger which maintains the display shown in Fig. 4 and captures any keystrokes made to record observations.

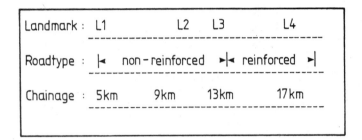

Figure 3   Preample display

```
Drive down the whole road to be inspected at
60 km/h and record your observations by
pressing the specified keys.....

Current chainage = 17.86 km

                                           5: excellent
Current subjective quality of ride (SQR) = 4: good
                                           3: fair

Press : [F9]   to increase SQR
        [F10]  to decrease SQR
        [F1]   to record EVIDENCE OF PUMPING
        [F2]   to record CRACKING
        [F3]   to record LANDMARK

For assistance stop the car and press [?]
```

Figure 4   Preliminary inspection display

Function keys [F1], [F2] and [F3] are used to record evidence of pumping, cracking and landmarks, respectively. A measure of the Subjective Quality of Ride (SQR) as felt by the observer is also recorded on a scale of 1 to 5. The current value is highlighted on the screen. The adjacent values are also displayed to assist the user. Function keys [F9] or [F10] are pressed in response to a change in ride to increase or decrease the current value.

During the inspection the rater can stop the car, causing control to return to Savoir, and ask for help by pressing the [?] key. A help menu will appear on the screen containing several options:-

* Describe the distresses being observed
* Describe the current stage of the evaluation
* Display graphically the observations made so far
* Interrupt the inspection
* Start the initial inspection again

On terminating the dialogue the inspection is resumed.

Preliminary evaluation

When the preliminary inspection is completed the observations including the partioned sections are displayed at the top of the screen as shown in Fig. 5.

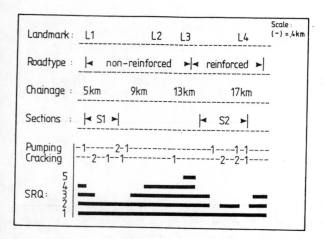

Figure 5   Preliminary evaluation display

The objective being to select sections of not more than 5 km in length such that the road within each section is in a similar condition. At this stage it may be decided not to proceed further with those sections whose condition is good.

The display, which remains at the top of the screen during the dialogue, shows the current section boundary locations together with landmarks, roadtype information, chainages and the observations recorded during the preliminary inspection all expressed in graphical form. The distribution of Pumping and Cracking is represented by the number of recorded incidents for each linear scale increment while the SRQ is represented as a histogram.

At the start of the dialogue, section boundaries suggested by Pavement Expert are displayed. The system can be asked to justify this arrangement or to verify an alternative arrangement favoured by the user. The user may also seek help on the terminology or request a description of the current stage of the evaluation.

Detailed Inspection

The aim of this stage is to inspect each section to be rated in sufficient detail to enable the PCR index to be determined. Pavement Expert will restrict the detailed inspection of any long sections to one or more sample panels, i.e. short sections being regarded as a single panel.

A starting dialogue directs the rating team to the start of the first panel ready for the second data logging run and enables the user to request an explanation of the stage and guidance on the observations to be made. The team then drives over each panel in turn at a speed of 20 km/h recording the incidence of Corner Breaks, Pressure Damage, Surface Defects, Joint Defects and Settlement or Faulting by pressing particular function keys. While on the move control passes to the detailed inspection data logger and the screen display will be as shown in Fig. 6. The user may stop the car at any time to gain access to help similar to that described for the preliminary inspection.

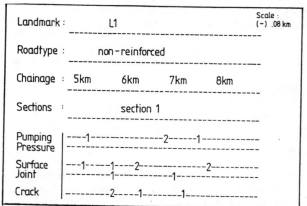

Figure 6   Detailed inspection display

During the inspection of each panel Pavement Expert will request that the car be stopped to enable a closer inspection to be made. On stopping the car the observations made so far will be displayed as shown in Fig. 7 and a dialogue conducted below. This will ask the user to get out of the car and inspect the road and then Pavement Expert will seek to establish the nature, extent and severity of the distresses suggested by the previous observations. The knowledge base minimises the questions to be asked while ensuring that items are not overlooked or miss-interpreted. Help can be requested at any stage using the [h] key to display a menu thus:

Landmark :	L1			Scale : (-) .08 km
Roadtype :	non-reinforced			
Chainage :	5km	6km	7km	8km
Sections :	section 1			
Pumping Pressure	---1-------------2-----1----------			
Surface Joint	---1----1----2------------2--------			
Crack	---------2-----1--------1---------			

Figure 7   Detailed inspection display when stopped. (To determine the nature, extent and severity of the observed distresses)

* Summarise the agreed distresses in tabular form.
* Give details of the distress currently being investigated.
* Describe the current stage of the evaluation.
* Interrupt the inspection.
* Start the inspection of this panel again.

When the dialogue is finished the remainder of the panel is inspected prior to moving to the next panel.

Postscript

When all the panels have been inspected a final dialogue allows the user to review the results and adjust the section boundaries if required. The results are summarised as in Fig. 8. In addition to the PCR index the system also computes the related Structural Damage (STD) index for each panel. Finally a detailed report of the inspection and evaluation is presented.

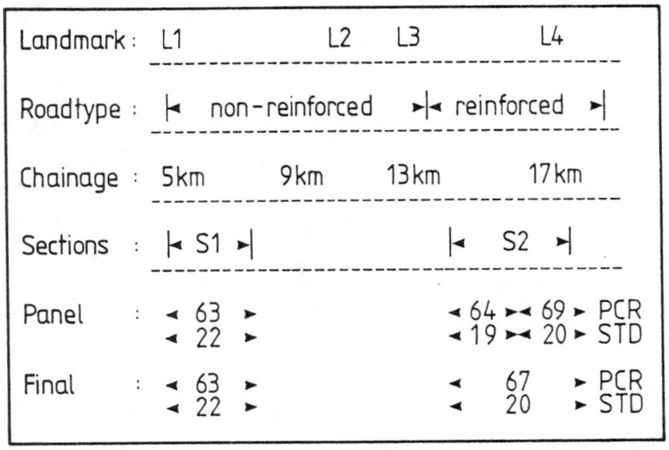

Figure 8 Postscript Display

Summary

Pavement Expert has considerable potential as an economic means of obtaining reliable evaluations of road condition. It currently exists as a working prototype, most of the features described have been implimented except the maintenance of an observation database. To form a practical tool the system would also need to be extended to be able to cope with flexible (i.e. blacktop) pavements. This would require a knowledge base similar to but slightly larger than that which exists for concrete pavements.

The authors consider that significant advantages have been gained by basing the software on an expert system shell. It is anticipated that the greatest benefit will prove to be the relative ease with which the behaviour of the system can be adjusted in the light of operational experience.

REFERENCES

1. Transport Research Board, Evaluation of Pavement Maintenance Strategies, NCHRP Synthesis of Highway Practice, 77, (1981).

2. Standard Committee on Highway Maintenance, National Road Maintenance Condition Survey Report of the 1985 Survey, Feb, (1986).

3. Ministry of Transport, Report to the Marshall Committee on the Organisation and Standards of Highway Maintenance, TRRL Report LR366, Crowthorne, (1971).

4. Wingate, P.J.F. and Peters, C.H., The CHART System of Assessing Structural Maintenance Needs of Highways, TRRL Supplementary Report 153UC, Crowthorne, (1985).

5. MARCH Group, MARCH Highway Maintenance System, MARCH 2, Suite Engineering Manual, June, (1979).

6. Pell, P.S., Development in Highway Pavement Engineering-2, Applied Science Publishers Ltd., London, (1978).

7. Nicholas, J.H. and Thompson, P.D., Highway Maintenance Development and Innovations, Highway Engineer, March, (1979).

8. Snaith, M.S. and Orr, D.M., Pavement Assessment in North Ireland, Highway Engineer, Jan., (1980).

9. Majidzadeh, K. and Luther, M.S., Development and Implantation of a System for Evaluation of Pavement Maintenance, Repair, Needs, and Properties, Interim Report, National Technical Information Service, Virginia (1980).

10. Pynn, J. and Weller, D., An Improvement Data Collection Method for the CHART Highway Maintenance System, Department of the Environment Department of Transport, TRRL Lab. Report 1084, Crowthorne, (1983).

11. Curphey, D.P., Fronck, D.K. and Wilson, J.H., Rating Pavement by Computer, Civil Engineering, ASCE, October, (1985).

12. Al-Shawi, M.A., Evaluation of the Performance of Concrete Pavements: Data Analysis, Empirical Models and Expert System, PhD Dissertation, Civil Engineering Department, University of Leeds, England, (1986).

VIII   EDUCATION

A KNOWLEDGE-BASED EXPERT SYSTEM FOR TUTORING IN STRUCTURAL ENGINEERING

David J Gunaratnam, BSc, PhD, CEng, MICE
Department of Civil Engineering
University of the West Indies, St. Augustine, Trinidad

The paper deals with the design and implementation of a knowledge-based expert system for tutoring in Structural Engineering. The tutoring domain is limited to plane truss structures, however, the concepts and problem solving skills learned have broader application and are essential for mastering more advanced material. Two tutoring strategies are considered, but the framework exists for implementing more advanced tutoring strategies. A rule-based programming paradigm was selected and the system was implemented on a VAX 11/750 Supermini computer running under a UNIX operating system. The programming language is OPS83, which is primarily rule-based, but permits procedural or imperative coding and interface to modules in other languages. The powerful pattern matching capability of OPS83 is exploited to provide the tutoring system the ability to recognize complex structural arrangements and make sophisticated decisions. The parser for interpreting student input was developed using the YACC program. The graphical display is on an IRIS terminal and the communication program is in C.

INTRODUCTION

Computers have been used in the past, in a variety of ways, to create an environment that enhances the learning process. The basic approaches that have emerged, from applications within structural engineering, can be classified as alogrithmic, structural modelling, simulation-demonstration and interactive exploration of structural response. The last approach is identified as contributing to the development of insight and a feel for structural behaviour and derives its power from the graphical capabilities and analysis languages developed (Ref. 1). These approaches focus on different of aspects of the problem solving process in structural engineering, and the numerical processing power of the computer and the constructs provided by the programming languages, permit the student to consider (i) a broader class of problems, (ii) different cases within each class and (iii) the effect of parametric changes in each case.

These learning environments, however, are mainly confined to well structured aspects of structural engineering and are not sensitive to individual student needs. The introduction of artificial intelligence techniques adds another dimension to the computer-based learning environment and provides a means of addressing both the ill-structured aspects of structural engineering as well as individual student needs. Intelligent tutoring systems, based on artificial and expert system techniques, can be developed that capture expertise not only in the subject area, but also in student modelling, tutoring strategies and effective communication (Refs. 2, 3, 4, 5, 6).

There are three distinct ways in which artificial intelligence and expert systems techniques are used to enhance the learning process. The first is by requiring the students to organize the knowledge base and build a small knowledge-based system, for a given problem domain, using a suitable expert system tool (Ref. 7).

Expert systems usually function as consultants in a problem domain and can also explain their inference process. Students can thus interact directly with the system and learn the contents of its knowledge base and problem solving process for the different situations the system recognizes. This approach, however, has two drawbacks, (i) it requires the student to ask an exhaustive set of questions to discover all of the reasoning paths considered by the system and (ii) at present there are not many expert systems in structural engineering that are well tested and in commercial use, suitable for this approach (Ref. 8). Further, the knowledge base of these systems may consist of compiled knowledge that lacks low-level details and relations necessary for learning.

The third approach is to provide a reactive learning environment by building intelligent systems that can tutor effectively on both well structured and ill-structured aspects of structural engineering. Considerable research effort has been directed towards the design of intelligent tutoring systems that are sensitive to student's strengths, weaknesses and preferred style of learning and permit the tutorial dialogue to be driven by the student's interest and misunderstandings (Refs. 3, 4). Implementation of this approach has been demonstrated in domains such as medical diagnosis, debugging electronic circuits and programs, algebraic simplification and symbolic integration. Most of these developments have been based on cognitive and artificial intelligence techniques and only recently has an attempt been made to capture and use the knowledge of good human tutors (Ref. 6). The present work reflects a similar attempt, but in the area of structural engineering, to provide a framework in which the expertise of human tutors can be captured.

In general, the goal of tutoring is to clarify a body of knowledge to which the student has already been exposed, either through lectures or reading. To achieve this goal and to function as an effective tutor, tutoring systems require knowledge of the subject area, student information, how to teach and how to communicate (Ref. 5). Typical intelligent tutoring systems are built around modules that embody knowledge about problem solving, student modelling, tutoring strategies and effective communication.

The first module, which is also referred to as an expert module (Ref. 5), contains knowledge of the subject area, that the system tries to impart to the student. In addition it translates student's input into a form that can be evaluated against the expert's knowledge and also provides possible rationales for the student's answers. In some cases, this module generates the problems to be solved.

The second module, referred to as student model, contains information about the individual student, indicating the student's level of understanding. Different theoretical constructs have been used to represent explicitly the state of knowledge in a student. Of these, the overlay model represents the student's knowledge as a subset of the expert's knowledge and the student model is generated by comparing the student's behaviour to that of the expert model. Another approach is to view the student's knowledge not as a subset of the expert's knowledge, but as a perturbation or deviation from the expert's knowledge and is characterized by the existence of bugs.

Observations of problem solving behaviour of experts and students in the area of mathematical programming indicate that both types of differences identified above exist, between the expert and student models. The expert's concepts are more differentiated than those of students and it is this differentiation that enables the expert to categorize problem description accurately into standard archetypes and to attribute correct meanings to problem features (Ref. 9). This obser- is true for many other domains as well.

Tutoring strategies, that help to remodel the student, is the focus of the third module. This module essentially controls the system's interaction with the student and determines which material is to be presented. It deals with issues such as when assistance should be provided in the form of hints or how far students should be allowed to go along unproductive paths.

The communication module provides the necessary interface for the tutoring module to interact with the student and carry out its function. Because of the size and complexity of these tutoring systems, not all of the components are fully developed in every system, usually the focus is on a single module (Ref. 3).

PROBLEM DOMAIN

The main considerations in selecting a suitable tutoring application for development is that the subject area should represent an educational watershed, in that mastery of concepts and skills in that area is essential for progress to be made in the study of subsequent material. Computation of Thevanin equivalents in Electrical Engineering (Refs. 6,11) and static equilibrium of determinate systems in Civil and Mechanical Engineering (Ref. 10) are two applications that fall into this category.

Thevanin equivalents in basic electric networks

is a topic that is brief, difficult and important. Many students fail to master the skills involved in assembling Thevanin equivalents early in their programs and are hampered in their ability to appreciate succeeding material. The domain is narrow and the payoff is considered high enough to warrant the building of expert systems for tutoring (Ref. 6). In the second application, rigid body dynamics is considered to provide a similar class of problems, where a good understanding of the methods and underlying concepts is essential for subsequent work. Treatment of this topic by lectures alone may not ensure the mastery of concepts and hence the need for a tutoring program to provide in-depth personalized assistance in learning the material (Ref. 10).

Similar considerations apply in selecting a suitable domain for tutoring in Structural Engineering. Focus should be topics that need to be introduced early in the program but the concepts and skills learned find a variety of applications and is important for learning subsequent material. The present tutoring application focuses on truss structures and considers the three topics:- classification, force distribution and displacement.

Information on topology and geometry of structure, support positions and load arrangements can be used to classify the different structural situations that can arise in practice. A variety of concepts such as statically determinate and indeterminate, statical and kinematic indeterminacy, stable and unstable structural arrangements, symmetric and antisymmetric loadings can all be introduced under the topic of classification. Simple, compound, complex and redundant truss structures and the basis for modifying complex and redundant trusses to simple trusses can also be considered. The latter forms the first step in some analysis procedures.

Classifying helps to identify a given structural description as belonging to a particular class of structures, for which certain analysis methods apply or simplified approaches can be used to determine structural response. Though the classification has been developed in the context of truss structures, once the concepts at this level are mastered, transition to other skeletal structural types should not be difficult.

Force distribution within a simple truss is given by method of joints and method of sections, the latter method can also be used to determine individual member forces. By using suitable structural modifications, the force distribution in other truss structures can be determined by combining the principle of superposition with one of the above methods. Finding statically determinate force distribution has wide application in structural engineering. Most of the approximate methods used for preliminary design as well as the membrane theory for shell structures require equilibrium equations to be set up for various parts of the structure to determine the force distribution.

Displacement at any joint in a truss structure can be determined by using the principle of virtual work. This is a very powerful tool and has wide application in structural analysis (Ref. 12). It requires the determination of force distribution and is applicable to structures with non-linear material properties.

The three topics selected for tutoring represent three different levels of knowledge and represent three different, but important aspects in structural engineering. The problem domain, though partitioned, is broader than those considered previously. It is felt that too narrow a focus can result in problem domains far removed from real world situations (Ref. 13).

Partitioning the problem domain into different levels permits trapping the student's errors and misconceptions at the appropriate level and to correct them, before moving to the next level. Too narrow a domain and a simple student model, that is based on what the student knows and does not know, may require the tutoring system to carry out deep probing to determine the source of the student's misconception. This involves encoding more knowledge into the tutoring component and a sophisticated communication module, both of which require considerable development work.

PROGRAMMING REQUIREMENTS AND LANGUAGE FEATURES

To function effectively as a tutor, the tutoring system must (i) be able to solve all the problems it poses to the student, (ii) use methods that the student is expected to know and use and (iii) decompose the problem solving process into a sequence of short steps, so that the student's problem solving efforts can be tracked fairly closely.

In a state space representation, the problem solving process is considered as applying a sequence of operations in order to move from an initial state to the goal state. The problem solving efforts of both the system and the student can also be viewed in this manner. Each student input can then be viewed as the application of an operator to move in the state space and the system can diagnose the student input by checking whether the operator (i) is legal, that is the context permits it (ii) is correctly applied and (iii) moves the student towards the goal. A rule-based programming language is particularly appropriate for implementing this approach.

The problem solving component should encode knowledge to classify the structure, determine member forces using the method of joints and method of sections and apply the principle of virtual work to calculate deflection at any joint. To solve classification problems, the system should be able to recognize instability, redundancy and symmetry in structural arrangements in addition to identifying simple, compound and complex trusses. The system must also know how to modify or decompose a truss structure to arrive at simple trusses and to introduce members to stabilize unstable structural arrangements. These require using topological information and geometric relationships, some of which can be reduced to numeric calculations. Rule-based programming languages are also appropriate for classification type problems, however, a fairly powerful pattern matching capability will reduce the number of rules required to recognize the different structural arrangements.

To determine member forces, the system should initially set up the overall equilibrium equations and solve for the unknown reactions. The method of joints then requires (i) determining a suitable joint to consider, (ii) generating the equilibrium equations for the joint and (iii) solving the equations to obtain the required member forces. For the method of sections, decisions like, where to section, which free body to consider and which equilibrium equation to use, have to be made prior to setting up the equilibrium equations. Similar considerations apply in encoding knowledge required to apply the virtual work method to determine deflections. In both these cases, a programming language with rule-based and procedural components would be suitable.

The communication component should display the structure and provide problem description, interpret student inputs either in the form of equations, conclusions or request for assistance and permit students to recover from input errors. The tutoring component is required to select a suitable problem from a problem set based on student needs, activate the relevant tutoring strategy, diagnose the problem solving efforts of the student and provide information for student modelling. In diagnosing student inputs, the system should recognize solution paths that are valid, but not necessarily those the system uses. In addition to these requirements, the system's response should be reasonably fast.

OPS83 (Ref. 14) was selected for development of the tutoring system as it meets most of the requirements identified. It is the latest in the OPS family of domain independent production system languages and immediate predecessor of OPS5 (Ref. 15). Although it is primarily a rule-based programming language, it also incorporates a procedural or imperative language component.

OPS83 permits the use of powerful rules. The LHS of a rule may contain expressions and function calls; the function may perform arbitrarily complex calculations provided there are no side-effects. This permits the rules to match complex patterns and make sophisticated decisions. The RHS of the rule can perform any action that can be performed in the body of the procedure, including calling subroutines, or even recursively invoking itself or another rule. This is in addition to the actions like creating, modifying and removing working memory elements and input-output operations. Since OPS83 uses conventional data representations and standard subroutine linkages mechanism, it can be interfaced to analysis programs and graphical front-ends written in another language. Most of these special features are exploited in the development of the present tutoring system.

TUTORING SYSTEM AND IMPLEMENTATION DETAILS

The tutoring system was implemented on a VAX 11/750 supermini computer running under a UNIX operating system. The OPS83 program is constructed in terms of modules and each module is compiled separately by the OPS83 compiler. In the present implementation, all type declarations, procedures and functions were placed in a single module and the dependencies are specified by the use statement. The rules for the problem solving, tutoring and communication components are placed in six modules, the size of the modules are limited to reduce recompilation time at the debugging stage. The parser to interpret student equations is generated using the

YACC program and the communication program to the IRIS graphics device is written in C, and both are declared as external functions of the OPS83 program. Once declared as external, these are thereafter treated as any other OPS83 procedure or function. The result of compilation is a synopsis file and an assembler file. After assembly, all the resulting object modules are linked together with the OPS83 C run-time system. The compile-assemble-link sequence is handled by the UNIX make command.

The program is organized around goals with a subroutine-like control structure. The default conflict resolution strategy of OPS83, selects the rule, from the conflict set, whose first pattern matches the more recently added working memory element. By making the goal element the first LHS element, the program is made goal oriented. Within a set of rules matching a given goal, however, the control is data-directed.

Initially the student interacts with the top level tutor control module. It queries the student as to the problem type, level of difficulty and tutoring strategy required. The control module then sets up appropriate goals and the conflict resolution strategy ensures the transfer of control to the different modules required to achieve these goals. Depending on the context, each module that is activated then sets up its own set of goals and sub-goals to achieve the goals identified by the control module. At present, not all of the components of the tutoring system are fully developed. A brief description of the modules developed and their capabilities are given below.

Problem Solving Module

The classification tree for truss structures is shown in Figure 1, and indicates the different structural arrangements the system can presently identify. The system uses the condition for statical determinacy and other topological information like number of unbraced panels, overbraced panels etc. to provide a topological classification.

Figure 2 shows four structural arrangements consisting of nine members, six joints and two supports. They all satisfy the condition for statical determinacy. The system can correctly classify them as simple, unstable, complex and compound trusses. In addition, in the case of the compound truss, the system can decompose it into simple trusses and indicate the joints at which the trusses are connected. For complex and unstable configurations, the system can suggest rearrangement of bars to arrive at simple trusses. The knowledge required to perform at this level is encoded into the problem solving

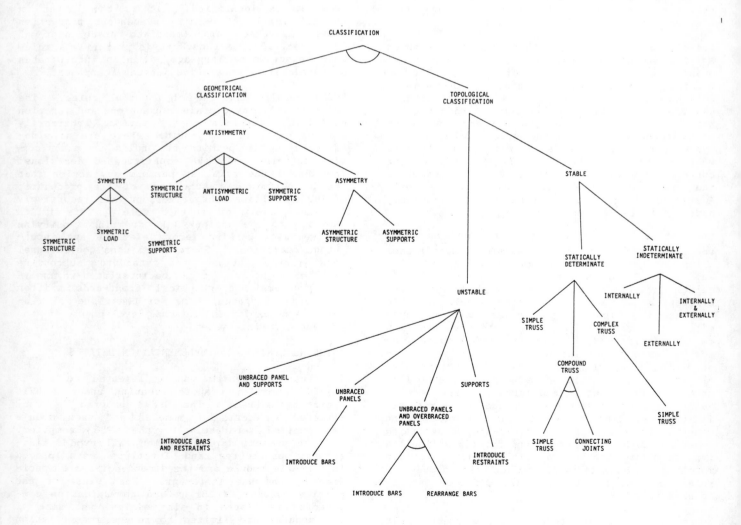

Fig. 1 Classification tree for truss structures

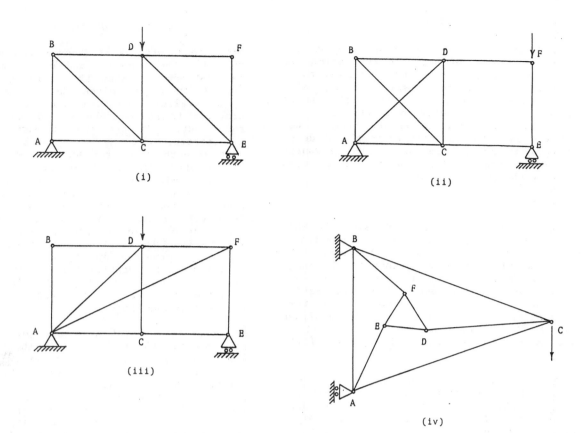

Fig 2. Trusses with nine bars, six joints and two supports - Four different classifications.

module and is essentially in the form of rules which permit the system to look for specific structural features and to combine these features to arrive at the final classification.

The knowledge required for the method of joints and method of sections include substantial procedural components, and these are placed in the RHS of the rules. The context determines when the procedures will be invoked. Knowledge to make decisions as to which joint to consider next, where to section, which freebody and set of equilibrium equations to consider are all encoded in rules and are general enough to be applicable in most situations. The system considers special structural features such as panels, diagonal members, chords etc. in making these decisions, though more general rules that use sophisticated alogorithms, to determine minimum cut sections in a graph, could be developed. In the present work, the intention, however, was to provide problem solving knowledge at the same level as those the student is required to learn.

At present, the knowledge required to apply the method of virtual work to calculate deflections has not been encoded. As the system knows how to determine the force distribution in a truss structure, the additional knowledge required to apply the method of virtual work can be encoded using a set of few rules and this is planned for the next stage of development of the system.

User interface

This part of the program performs two functions, it (i) displays the structure to be studied on a graphical device and provides a problem description to the student and (ii) accepts student input, interprets it and provides the information in a form the system can process. This program recognizes two forms of student input: statements or conclusions and equations. It recognizes all statements and conclusions by matching keywords that define the domain concepts and equations by considering its form and context. At present, the program recognizes inputs for the classification problem only.

Graphics

After a suitable problem is selected from the problem set, the top level control module sets up a goal for the display module to achieve. This module then displays, labels and dimensions the structure based on the problem description provided. In addition it also displays the location and magnitude of the loads and the position of the supports. The module consists of a set of rules that write the necessary drawing commands, based on the problem description, on to an output file. A communication program, written in C, then transmits this information from which the display is generated on an IRIS terminal.

Keywords

At the beginning of the tutoring session the system defines a set of keywords from which the student is expected to construct his responses. These establish a common vocabulary and also indicate to the student the concepts that should be known. A set of procedures accept, scan and check the student input to ensure that proper keywords are used and to indicate to the student, the words that do not belong to the keywords set. The pattern matching capability is used to interpret the student input.

Equation Parser

The equation parser was generated using the YACC program. This is a program for converting a grammatical specification of a language into a parser that will parse statements in the language. YACC requires (i) a specification of the syntax of the language, (ii) what action is to be performed, if an instance of the grammatical form is found and (iii) a lexical analyser to read the input being parsed and break it up into meaningful chunks (also called tokens) (Ref. 16).

The equation parser developed can evaluate expressions and parse equations. The tokens are placed in a file, from where an OPS83 procedure reads the information to create working memory elements for student equations. This permits the system to capture the form of the equation, that is variables present, as well as the numerical coefficients and signs. The working memory elements are then matched against the appropriate LHS of the rule that defines the form of the equation. The RHS of the rule checks the coefficients and the corresponding signs.

When the procedure for accepting student input encounters the string eqn or exp, the equation parser is activated and another procedure then creates the working memory elements from the token file. The string exp creates a calculator mode for students to carryout intermediate calculations.

Tutoring Strategies

Two tutoring strategies are presently available, both are for classification problems. The first is aimed at making the system's problem solving knowledge explicit. This is achieved by entering a demonstration mode that also provides different levels of explanation. The explanation is provided by examining the intermediate results obtained by the problem solving module, and the first level of explanation is such that it requires the student to infer some of the intermediate steps in the problem solving process. If the student is unable to infer the intermediate steps, the second level of explanation is provided, again by tutoring rules that examine intermediate results for further details. The explanations are thus given at different levels of abstraction and lower level details are provided only when further explanation is requested.

The inability to infer intermediate steps gives an indication of the student's understanding and this information can be used for student modelling. The tutoring strategy and level of problem difficulty selected are both useful indicators for infering the student's confidence level in the problem domain.

The second tutoring strategy requires the student to solve the problem, and errors are indicated as they occur. When this strategy is selected the system first solves the problem, then sets up a parallel data structure to track student's progress in state space and prompts the student for input. If the student input is accepted as correct, the system updates the student's data structures to reflect the present position in the state space. Otherwise the type of error is indicated. This can be an incorrect equation, a statement or equation for which the necessary preconditions have not been established or an incorrect interpretation of the problem. The system can also prompt the student for additional information, if required and is of a form that cannot be provided by keywords. For instance, if the student identifies a structure as a simple truss, the system would prompt him for the base triangle and the sequence used in generating the rest of the truss.

The data and control structures used in the program provide the necessary flexibility to implement and test other tutoring strategies as well. It is also possible to change tutoring strategies during a session. In terms of the two tutoring strategies implemented, this requires resetting the tutoring goal and data structures to reflect the student's 'state of the world'. The problem solving module would then proceed from the point at which a change in strategy was requested. This is useful in situations where the student's knowledge is only sufficient to partially solve the problem posed.

The tutoring component generates considerable information useful for student modelling. This information can be used to generate suitable problems and remedial material. These aspects, however, have not been considered at present, but are to be included in the next stage of development of the system.

CONCLUSIONS

The present work represents the first stage in the development of a knowledge-based expert system for tutoring in structural engineering. The main focus at this stage has been in identifying a suitable problem domain, building an efficient problem solver, developing user interface that permits meaningful communication, designing a program structure that is flexible enough to implement and test various strategies and implementing two of the strategies. The language features of OPS83 were essential for the implementation of this system, to provide the above capabilities and reasonably fast response.

Student modelling and tutoring strategies, for remodelling student's problem solving behaviour, based on the expertise of experienced human tutors are important aspects that are to form part of the future development. These are in addition to extending the system's problem solving and diagnosing capabilities.

The ability to incrementally extend the knowledge base without major restructuring is one of the advantages of knowledge-based expert systems. The proposed future development could therefore be implemented without much difficulty.

ACKNOWLEDGEMENTS

The author is grateful to Prof. S.J. Fenves for providing the opportunity to work on this project and for the valuable advice and discussion sessions. The author is also grateful to the Department of Civil Engineering, Carnegie-Mellon University for providing the computational facilities and access to OPS83. Mr. Nelson Baker's assistance in providing the communication program for IRIS is also acknowledged.

REFERENCES

(1) Haritos, N., Computer Aided Education in Structural Engineering, Proceedings of the Second International Conference on Civil and Structural Engineering Computing, Vol. 2, 1985, 443-447.

(2) Slater, J.H. and Connor, J.J., A Computer Aided Teaching System for Structural Engineering, Proposal to project Athena, MIT, Feb 1985.

(3) Barr, A. and Feigenbaum, E.A., (Eds.), The Handbook of Artificial Intelligence, Vol. II, Ch. ix, 1982, 223-294.

(4) Sleeman, D. and Brown, J.S. (Eds.), Intelligent Tutoring Systems, Academic press, Inc., 1982.

(5) Woolf, B. and Mc Donald, D.D., Building a Computer Tutor: Design issues, Computer, Sep 1984, 61-73.

(6) Joobbani, R. and Talukdar, S.N., A Knowledge-Based Expert System for tutoring in Electrical Engineering, Proceedings, 8th International Computing Symposium ICS – 85 Florence, Italy, March 1985.

(7) Starfield, A.M., Butala, K.L., England, M.M. and Smith, K.A., Mastering Engineering Concepts by Building an Expert System, Engineering Education, November 1983, 104-107.

(8) Rooney, M.F., Expert Systems in Structural Engineering, Survey of the State-of-the-art Expert/Knowledge-Based Systems in Civil Engineering, Maher, M.L. (Ed), Department of the army-CERL report, Sep 1986.

(9) Orlikowski, W. and Dhar, V., Imposing structure on linear programming problems: an Empirical Analysis of Expert and Novice Models, Proceedings of the AAAI, 1986, 308-312.

(10) Slater, J.H., Petrossian, R.B.P. and Shyam-Sunder, S., An Expert Tutor for Rigid Body Mechanics: ATHENA CATS-MACAVITY Proceedings of the IEEE/CS Expert Systems in Government Symposium, Mc Clean, VA, Oct 1985.

(11) Joobbani, R. and Talukdar, S.N., An Expert System for Understanding Expressions from Electric Circuit Analysis, 9th International Joint Conference on Artificial Intelligence, Los Angeles, Aug 1985.

(12) Davies, G.A.O., Vitual Work in Structural Analysis, John Wiley & Sons, 1982.

(13) Kennaway, A., Does the Elite Think Any Better Than A Computer?, CME, Dec 1986, 40-42.

(14) Forgy, C.L., OPS83 User's Manual and Report, Production System Technologies, Pittsburgh, PA, 1985.

(15) Brownston, L., Farrel, R., Kant, E. and Martin, N., Programming Expert Systems in OPS5, Addison-Wesley, Reading, MA, 1985.

(16) Kernighan, B.W. and Pike, R., The Unix Programming Environment, Ch 8, Prentice-Hall Software Series, 1984.

PANDORA'S BOX:
AN AUTOMATIC GENERATOR
OF STRUCTURES

R L Sack, BS, MSCE, PhD, FASCE and **R D Schroeder, BSCE, MSCE**
Department of Civil Engineering, Univeristy of Idaho, Moscow, Idaho, U.S.A.

PANDORA'S BOX is micro-computer software that can provide an unlimited number and wide variety of two-dimensional truss, beam, and frame problems; different types of structures are available within each category. The user establishes limits for the range of number of nodes, boundary conditions, loads, element lengths, and material properties. Also s/he selects condition parameters to control the type of loading, statical indeterminacy, and cross-sectional properties. The user has output options including hardcopy, screen display or disk storage. PANDORA'S BOX produces problem solution files with the appropriate sequence of commands that produces a solution when imported to a matrix interpretive program. Faculty using PANDORA'S BOX select the types of exercise problems, and the program responds with a graphics display of the structure, the problem data, plus the solution. With slight modifications, the program could be used by students as a prolific source of exercise problems, and subroutines could be added to accumulate and store student performance.

INTRODUCTION

The availability, power, and speed of microcomputers have made them an invaluable engineering tool, and compelled engineering educators to infuse computer usage throughout the curriculum. Are we in education enhancing our pedagogical methods by exploiting the intrinsic characteristics of computers, or are we simply automating old approaches to teaching? Faculty members currently use personal computers (PC's) primarily as an aid in developing problem solutions, but there are many areas where we can take advantage of todays' computer capabilities to enhance the learning process and increase faculty effectiveness. The field of artificial intelligence intimates that computers may be tomorrows' pedagogue, and some expert systems already augment learning, but only in very specialized areas [1]. The contemporary student has the capability to analyze complex problems and study the behavior of entire systems; therefore, we must offer the challenge of an abundance of exercise problems with a broad range of complexities beyond that offered by most textbooks.

In problem-oriented classes, engineering educators face the constant dilemma of assigning and grading a new set of exercise problems every term the class is taught. Without new problems, students may succumb to the temptation of using solutions from old files, which are typically archived. Relying upon experience, faculty members must develop appropriate new problems and accompanying solutions; in this sense the educator is the expert. Although s/he may have considerable experience in the practice of engineering and methods of education, the task of producing exercise problems is, nonetheless, difficult and time consuming. The instructor must develop problems that are appropriate for the course work, and those exercises must: a) be relevant to current problems of engineering practice; b) require use of the latest solution techniques and tools (i.e., PC's); and c) not be available to the student in archived solutions files. These incessant demands place a tremendous burden on the instructor's time and imagination; a better approach to this component of learning would be invaluable.

PROGRAM DESCRIPTION

At the University of Idaho we have developed a computer software package to help faculty members meet these educational demands. The program, PANDORA'S BOX, will generate an unlimited number of exercise problems, and their solutions, for courses in structural analysis; it is written for PC's using Fortran 77 and is portable between microcomputers. Unlike the mythical Pandora's box that unleashed a swarm of evils upon mankind, our version can be controlled and will: allow faculty to use their time effectively; prevent texts from becoming obsolete because of limited availability of exercise problems; and give students the opportunity to investigate a wide variety of structures of varying complexities.

PANDORA'S BOX handles structural problems for two-dimensional beams, frames, and trusses. The user has three options: 1) load a problem of her/his choosing; 2) retrieve a stored problem from the library, or 3) request that problems be generated. The program incorporates a tree system of menus consisting of: a) an opening screen; b) a structural category menu; c) a main menu; and d) several submenus that depend on the structural category and the user's selection from the previous menu (Fig. 1). The opening screen gives the program title and author credits. The structural category menu signifies that beams, frames, and trusses can be handled by PANDORA'S BOX. The main menu indicates the operations that can be performed by PANDORA'S BOX: specify a problem; library retrieval; generate problems; and parameter designation. The submenus are dependent on the main menu selection and reflect options available to the user. For example, if the user selects the operation "library" from the main menu, the submenu allows the user to either: retrieve a previously stored problem; store a problem; edit a problem; plot the structure; or solve the problem.

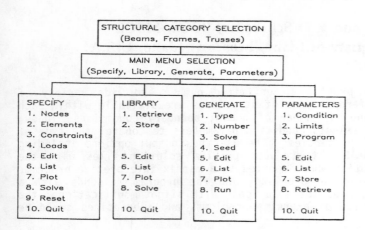

Fig. 1 Menu tree for PANDORA'S BOX.

Along with each menu, the program gives instructions for selecting options from the current menu. Also, headings shown on the screen give the operator an indication of her/his current location within the program. These indicators simplify the task of moving from one task to the next. Each menu selection displayed on the screen is accompanied by a brief description of the operation that will be performed by making that selection. Again, the intent is to make the program easy to learn and efficient to use. A person familiar with computing and structural analysis, but without experience using PANDORA'S BOX, can efficiently run the program after minimal instruction.

Throughout the program development we wanted PANDORA'S BOX to replace problems/solutions manuals. To realize that goal we believe it is necessary to have the format for problem description selectable by the user. Problems consist of descriptive data defining the structural configuration and applied loads; therefore, presentation of that data can take many forms. We have incorporated the following five different options into the program: 1) a screen listing of the problem data; 2) a screen plot of the structure, with loads applied; 3) a printed/hardcopy of the problem data; 4) a plotted/hardcopy of the structure, with loads applied; and 5) a file stored on disk containing the problem data. Any combination of these formats can be selected by the user.

A sixth option for distributing and recalling problem data also exists but is more subtle. PANDORA'S BOX utilizes a random number generator to produce a random problem from limit files. During generation the random number generator is called several times. At the start of a problem, the generator has an initial value called the seed, which is available to the user. To recall a problem generated from a particular limit file,

the user can reenter the seed value and the problem will be regenerated. Utilizing this method the instructor could select problems, record seed values, and give those seed values to students who have access to the problem generation portion of PANDORA'S BOX. Thus the amount of handout material is reduced while still providing the student, and teacher, with a complete problem statement.

We have made extensive use of graphics within PANDORA'S BOX, both in the form of output to the student and as an aid for entering and selecting problems. Problems, either generated or specified by the user, can be displayed from any of three menus using a function key. The generated structural plots are to scale and consist of: the structural elements; boundary conditions; applied loads; and nodes. Loads and nodes are numbered on the screen for clarity. We made no allowance for the user to control the content of screen plots. Graphics have also been used to produce printer plots. For printer plots we incorporated a screen dump subroutine into the program so that "what you see is what you get."

PANDORA'S BOX uses parameter files to control problem generation and output [3]. The operator is required to specify: condition parameters; limit parameters; and program parameters. Condition parameters control the configuration and complexity of problems to be generated. The user specifies multiple loads, multiple element sections and material properties, boundary conditions, and redundant elements by toggling the status of these parameters. Limit parameters are those values that actually control the magnitudes and dimensions of the generated problems. The user can select the range of the number of nodes, member lengths, load magnitudes and number, and material properties. Program parameters are used to select the format for the problem statement. By selecting the desired output the operator can produce a problem statement that is both clear and complete. The program allows the user to review, edit, store, and retrieve parameter files. Therefore, an instructor could conceivably have different files for individual courses, various topics within courses, and each student in a course.

Initially, it was our desire to write a program that would also produce solutions to the problems; this was not possible due to the complexity and size of the problems generated. To overcome this limitation we wrote a single, short subroutine that produces a solution batch file which, in turn, can be loaded into a matrix interpretive package [4]. Using this approach we kept the program size within desired limits and efficiently produced reliable problem solutions. Using the program documentation [3], the user can interface PANDORA'S BOX with other solutions software packages by incorporating appropriate subroutines.

PANDORA'S BOX has been broadly described elsewhere [2], and we have provided documentation for the user and programmer [3]. The expertise embodied in the program to generate tractable exercise problems resembles that of an experienced professor of structural analysis; the objective of this paper is to provide insight into some of the system algorithms with that knowledge base.

KNOWLEDGE BASE FOR GENERATING PROBLEMS

Configurations of generated structures are repeatable and expandable; they have between 3 and 100 nodes, plus a corresponding diversity and number of boundary conditions, loads, and elements. We have limited the structural configurations and variations in the interest of restricting program size and complexity. For beams and frames, we have limited the number of elements per span, the number of spans, the orientation of the elements, and the type of end constraints. We imposed limitations on trusses by controlling the general configurations, allowing only point loads, and restricting the orientation of elements.

The user has control over the generated problems by entering limits for nodes, loads, element lengths, and boundary conditions. The structures generated are limited to 100 nodes, 200 elements, 40 boundary conditions, and 20 applied loads. For all three structural categories the user must also enter at least one value for the material modulus of elasticity, E, which cannot vary. The program contains checks to insure that the user has not entered a limit that could produce an unstable condition. For example, a stable truss requires three independent constraints, but if the user has specified a maximum of only two boundary conditions, PANDORA'S BOX will ignore the requested maximum and impose three constraints.

In generating the different types of random structures, the program must establish: 1) the number and location of the nodes; 2) the type, number, location, magnitude, and direction of the applied loads; 3) the number, location, and direction of boundary conditions; and 4) the element properties. PANDORA'S BOX uses modified forms of accepted structural design equations to develop the member geometric properties from load magnitude ranges specified by the user; we believe the user can envision appropriate applied load magnitudes more accurately than element sizes. Generation of each of the four groups of data is not the same for trusses, beams, and frames.

Thus after the user has indicated his/her problem bounds, the program assigns the structural parameters. The rationale embedded in the program for making these various assignations is the system knowledge base. The subsequent sections describe the expertise and logic of the program for generating problems. We have emphasized the algorithms for truss generation, with a cursory description for beams and frames. The reader interested in more detail should consult reference [3].

GENERATING TRUSS NODES

Node generation consists of assigning: a) the number of nodes; b) the x and y coordinates for each node; and c) the element connectivity. The final task is included herein because, within a structural category, the algorithms for generation rely upon various patterns of element orientation, which in turn influence the number of nodes.

PANDORA'S BOX generates three different truss configurations: bridge; roof; and multistory (Fig. 2). Bridge trusses have parallel upper and lower chords, and the vertical height is determined by the length of the vertical element. An isosceles triangle, with the lower chord horizontal, defines roof trusses; furthermore, two- and three-story (i.e., multistory) trusses are formed by stacking bridge trusses. Unlike beams and frames, nodal assignment for trusses is dependent upon the configuration; therefore, the algorithm to generate the nodal coordinates and define the element ends is different in each case.

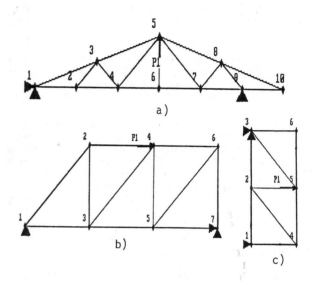

Fig. 2 Generated trusses: a) roof; b) bridge; c) multistory.

Using the range of nodes supplied by the user, the program establishes the number of nodes for bridge and multistory trusses, nn, as follows:

$$nn = nnmin + integer((nnmax-nnmin)*aran) \qquad (1)$$

where nnmin and nnmax are the minimum and maximum number of nodes, respectively, and aran is a decimal value between zero and one that is produced by a uniform random number generator. Roof trusses are symmetric; consequently, the program insures that there is an even number of nodes.

Bridge truss nodes

There are two basic bridge truss configurations; one is produced by combinations of right isosceles triangles. Horizontal and vertical element lengths (hl and vl, respectively) are generated as follows:

$$hl = hlemin+integer((hlemax-hlemin)*aran) \qquad (2)$$

$$vl = vlemin+integer((vlemax-vlemin)*aran) \qquad (3)$$

where the user initially stipulated the limits for maximum and minimum lengths. Diagonal elements have horizontal and vertical projections of hl and vl, respectively.

147

Generation begins at the origin using a right triangle with horizontal and vertical legs hl and vl, respectively; the right angle is on the horizontal axis and a distance hl from the origin. We generate the truss using two basic right triangles: one oriented as described, and a second of the same size obtained by turning the first triangle upside down and rotating it about its vertical axis. By alternating these two triangles we generate the truss (Fig. 2b). We calculate upper chord nodal coordinates by adding vl and hl to the previous lower chord nodal coordinates. Lower chord coordinates are simply the previous lower chord coordinates with the x value increased by hl. Node numbers are assigned such that all vertical and diagonal elements have consecutive end node numbers and horizontal elements have end node numbers that differ by two..

The second general bridge configuration consists of isosceles triangles. The base of the basic triangle is twice hl, and vl defines the height. Trusses are generated by combining basic isosceles triangles that are alternately upright and upside down. Nodes on the upper chord are located by adding vl and hl to the previous lower chord node. Nodal coordinates on the lower chord equal the coordinates of the previous lower chord node with the x value increased by twice hl. Element end nodes for diagonal elements differ by one; whereas, element end nodes on the chords differ by two.

Roof truss nodes

PANDORA'S BOX will generate two types of roof trusses: a Pratt truss, wherein the diagonals are in tension and the number of nodes is divisible by four; and a modified Howe truss in which the total number of nodes is not divisible by four (Fig. 2a). The algorithm for assigning nodal coordinates and element connectivity is similar for the two configurations. The program calculates the vertical height at the peak using a form of Eq. (3). The horizontal dimension of elements depends upon the total number of nodes and is established by determining the number of nodes along either the upper or lower chord, depending upon the configuration. The lengths of upper and lower chord elements depend upon the number of nodes along those chords, which is a function of the configuration and total number of nodes. To maintain symmetry node numbers on both the upper and lower chords are simultaneously assigned from both ends of the truss, with numbers increasing toward the center on the left and decreasing toward the center on the right. The centerline node on the upper chord is numbered nn/2 and that on the bottom chord is nn/2+1. The program assigns coordinates for the nodes on the upper chord as increments of the height and width of the truss. The program assigns element numbers starting from each end and progressing toward the center. With some exceptions, nodes on both chords increment by two; whereas, diagonal elements, especially those near the center, require special logic.

Multistory truss nodes

PANDORA'S BOX uses right triangles to generate two- and three-story trusses (Fig. 2c); the

approach is similar to that used for bridge trusses. The program calculates hl and vl from Eqs. (2) and (3). The total number of nodes, nn, comes from Eq. (1); incomplete bays (i.e., bays without the full number of stories) are produced since nn, as produced by Eq. (1), is not adjusted. A number produced by the uniform random number generator determines the number of stories. The algorithm for assigning nodal numbers and coordinates is similar to that for the bridge truss with right triangles. The program assigns node numbers starting at the lower chord and numbers consecutively vertically until the highest node for that bay is reached; subsequently, the numbering continues starting from the next node on the lower chord. Nodes on a vertical line have the same x coordinates, and nodes are separated vertically by a distance vl. When beginning a new column of elements, the x coordinate is hl greater than the previous node. Node numbers at the ends of elements differ by: one for vertical elements; nstor+2 for horizontal elements; and nstor for diagonal elements (where nstor is the total number of stories). Incomplete bays require unique numbering schemes.

GENERATING BEAM NODES

Beam problems are limited to a horizontal linear arrangement of elements. This structural category allows from one to four elements per span (i.e., the structure between two supports). Using the range of nodes supplied by the user, the program establishes the number of nodes for the structure using Eq. (1). The program selects the number of nodes per span, spnn, using the equation:

$$spnn = 2 + integer(4*aran) \qquad (4)$$

Note from Eq. (4) that 2 is the minimum number of nodes required per span. Because the random number generator can not produce a value exactly equal to one (0.999999 is possible), determining the integer value from the multiplication, 4*aran, produces a number between zero and three. Thus, the number of nodes per span can be two, three, four, or five. Using integer math again, the program divides the number of nodes by the number of nodes per span to obtain the number of complete spans (nspan). At this point, we may have a contradiction between nn, spnn, and nspan; therefore, the adjusted value for the total number of nodes is

$$nn = nspan*(spnn-1) + 1 \qquad (5)$$

If the user requested only one span, the number of nodes is set to the number of nodes per span. PANDORA'S BOX generates nodal coordinates using the randomly selected horizontal length of elements, hl, which is computed using an algorithm similar to Eq. (2). Since beams are horizontal structures, all y nodal coordinates are 0, and the x nodal coordinate is that for the previous node incremented by hl. Figure 3 shows an example of a generated two-span beam.

GENERATING FRAME NODES

Establishing the number of nodes, nodes per span and total spans for frames follows the same logic used for beams. The term span for frames refers to the structure between: two supports; or two joints (i.e., points where the structural members change direction). Unlike beams, frames typically have spans that are not horizontal. Progressing from a nodal point, frame spans can be directed in one of five coordinate directions: 0; $\pi/2$; $3\pi/2$; the first quadrant; and the fourth quadrant. Limiting progression to those five directions allows control over the growth of the structure as more nodes are added. The program computes limits on horizontal and vertical element lengths, hl and vl, respectively, using an algorithm similar to Eqs. (2) and (3).

Fig. 3   A two-span beam.

Controlling structural growth of a frame during generation involves mapping the location of elements as they are added. From a defined node, the frame theoretically can extend in any one of the five prescribed directions, but complications can arise. PANDORA'S BOX checks all five growth directions to establish if any choice would result in: a) two elements occupying the same end coordinates; b) two elements crossing; or c) two elements overlappping. The program performs a final check to insure that the last span does not have the same orientation as the previous span. Completion of all the checks yields a minimum of two possible growth directions and a maximum of five.

After establishing feasible growth directions from a node, the program chooses one direction at random. The direction, along with the horizontal and vertical element lengths, the number of nodes per span, the starting coordinates for the span, and the first new node number to be assigned within the span, are all used to assign the nodal coordinates for the new span. Vertical spans are assigned by adding or subtracting vl to the starting coordinates for the span. Horizontal spans are assigned by adding hl to the starting coordinates. Diagonal elements use both hl and vl. The process of adding element lengths continues until the number of nodes per span are filled. Finally, the ending node number is added to the span array.

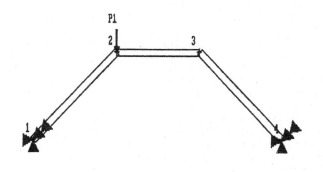

Fig. 4   A frame example.

Prior to generating the new nodal coordinates for the span, PANDORA'S BOX notes whether or not this span will be a sideshot. The term "sideshooting" indicates that growth does not continue from the terminus of a span eminating from a node on the frame. Such sideshot spans represent a structural leg, crossbracing, or simply an auxiliary support. If the span is a sideshot, the previous starting node will be used for the next span; if not, the ending node for the generated new span will be used for the staring node of the next span. It is not necessary to redetermine the possible directions each time a sideshot span is generated. Figure 4 illustrates a generated frame.

TRUSS BOUNDARY CONDITIONS

After assigning nodal points, PANDORA'S BOX generates boundary conditions, which are a function of structural category, the structural configuration, and the user's limit parameters. The type and direction of each boundary condition are randomly selected, but sufficient numbers of boundary conditions are assigned to remove rigid body motion. Although stability is insured by the algorithms for assigning boundary conditions, large displacements can occur if the boundary conditions are sufficiently close together; this problem can be severe for trusses.

The program uses basically the same process to assign boundary conditions for all three truss configurations. Two dimensional trusses have two independent degrees of freedom at each node, and they can exhibit three independent rigid body displacements (i.e., rotation, and translation in each of two orthogonal directions). PANDORA'S BOX assigns all node numbers to a temporary array. Subsequently, the program fills a boundary condition array by randomly selecting node numbers from the first array. If the user has not selected redundant supports (i.e., statically indeterminate supports are requested by setting the appropriate condition parameter), the boundary condition array will contain only two node numbers. If the redundant support option was selected, a random number of boundary conditions will be determined using the random number generator, together with the maxiumum number requested. The boundary condition array is sorted so that the nodes farthest apart are the first and second elements of the array.

The first node of the array is constrained in both the horizontal and vertical directions. Subsequent nodes in the boundary condition array may have either horizontal, vertical, or both constraints imposed. Constraints for the second node in the boundary condition array are assigned to stabilize the structure. For example, if the second node is located on a vertical line through the first node, the program imposes a horizontal constraint to the second node. Redundant support conditions are assigned to nodes in the boundary condition array with one or zero imposed constraints. All displacements for constrained degrees of freedom are set to zero.

BEAM AND FRAME BOUNDARY CONDITIONS

Beam structures are generated using one of the four basic beam segments: fixed - fixed; simple

- simple; fixed - simple; and cantilever. In general each node has one translational and one rotational degree of freedom per node; we assume that beams are constrained against translational along their lengths. Multiple span structures are generated by combining several of the four basic segments, and the program checks combinations of the basic segments to insure structural stability. Since each segment has boundary conditons implied, PANDORA'S BOX does not impose additional constraints.

Frames have two independent translational and one rotational degree of freedom per node. The program only imposes boundary conditions on the first node, the last node (but not always), and the ends of sideshot spans. Intermediate supports along the continuous portion of the span are · not permitted. PANDORA'S BOX applies redundant constraints if the user has set the appropriate condition parameter.

LOADS ON TRUSSES

To generate loads the program must: 1) determine the number of applied loads; 2) identify nodes where loads are to be applied; 3) establish load magnitudes; and 4) specify load directions. The number of loads to be applied to a truss is dependent on the maximum number permitted (i.e., the total number of nodes minus the number of constrained nodes) for the structure and the maximum number prescribed by the user as a limit parameter. Loaded nodes are randomly selected from the array of candidate nodes (i.e., those that are unsupported). Loads on roof trusses are limited to nodes along the upper chord. This restriction is not rigidly enforced, but it increases the likelihood of loads on the upper chord. Using the limit parameters, the load magnitude is

$$\text{load} = \text{minmag} + (\text{maxmag} - \text{minmag})*\text{aran} \qquad (6)$$

where minmag and maxmag are the lower and upper load limits, respectively, requested by the user. PANDORA'S BOX offers the user the option for randomly choosing load directions from either: a) the four coordinate directions (i.e., 0, $\pi/2$, π, and $3\pi/2$); or b) 10 degree increments of a full circle.

LOADS ON BEAMS AND FRAMES

PANDORA'S BOX also assigns loads to beams and frames using the four-step approach described in the previous section. Trusses can support only point loads; whereas, beams and frames can be loaded with point loads, uniformly distributed loads, and applied moments. Point and uniform loads are applied normal to the elements. Point loads and moments are assigned to randomly selected available nodes (i.e., those without boundary conditions), and uniform loads are applied to randomly chosen elements.

TRUSS ELEMENTS

The final task in problem generation is to establish the cross-sectional properties of the elements; this is a crucial task in producing structures that display realistic displacements and stresses. Element lengths and connectivities are established during nodal point generation; furthermore, load magnitudes, directions, and points of application have been defined in the previous step of the process. Therefore, this task requires the program to choose element geometric properties commensurate with problem parameters previously defined to yield a structure that will help the student to visualize authentic behavior.

We obtain an estimate of the largest load that elements must sustain. During generation of applied loads, the program sums the absolute values of the vertical and horizontal components of each prescribed nodal load into two registers. The maximum of these two loads is the maximum expected load. Assuming that all loads could pass through any one element, we initially used the maximum expected load to calculate the element section properties. This assumption probably approximates structural behavior for small trusses, but we found that, in general, this approach resulted in very stiff structures. Consequently, we are presently using an average of the horizontal and vertical load magnitudes to give the average expected load; this yields trusses that are more flexible than those previously generated.

We obviously produce two values of the average expected load: one from the horizontal components, and another from the vertical. We use the largest of the two, but these two average loads can differ markedly. Elements are either horizontal, vertical, or diagonal; therefore, we calculate the components of the average expected load associated with each orientation of element. For example, if the average expected load, aeload, is produced by the vertical loads:

$$\text{eloady} = \text{aeload}$$

$$\text{eloadx} = \text{aeload}*(\text{hl}/\text{vl}) \qquad (7)$$

$$\text{eloadd} = \text{aeload}*(\text{dl}/\text{vl})$$

Assuming that the most critical element is in compression, the relationships of Euler's buckling load yields the area of a circular cross-section required to sustain the load, e.g., the area associated with the expected load in the y direction is

$$\text{areay} = (4*\text{eloady}*\text{vl}**2)/(E*\pi**2) \qquad (8)$$

Since all elements are not in compression, this approach produces elements with areas larger than would be required for a final design. The element lengths for Eq. (14) are dictated by truss type. For bridge and multistory trusses, all horizontal lengths equal hl, and all verticals are vl long; the Pythagorean theorem gives dl. Roof trusses assume vl is the height at the centerline, and hl is the length of lower chord elements. The program calculates an area for the longest diagonal element and another for the upper chord for roof trusses. If the user entered three different values for E (i.e., the maximum number) and selected the multiple section option, each of the three element types can have different E Values.

The program assigns either a single or multiple element cross section(s), depending upon condition options selected by the user. If only one cross section is requested, the program assigns the area based upon the average expected load and maximum length of diagonal elements. If the user selected the multiple cross section option, a separate cross section is calculated for horizontal, vertical, and diagonal elements using the associated characteristic dimensions for each. If the user chose the multiple E value option, the program assigns the first E value entered to diagonal elements. The algorithm uses the second and third E values for various elements depending upon the truss type. The Euler buckling formula, admittedly characterizes bending behavior, but matrix structural analysis assumes no element bending. Therefore, after the program assigns element cross-sectional areas, it makes the tacit assumption that element moments of inertia are zero.

The program assigns the appropriate area to elements within three loops for bridge and multistory trusses: one each for vertical, horizontal, and diagonal members. The logic uses the fact that element end nodal points are consistent for each type of element. The program categorizes roof truss elements as either: upper chord; lower chord; or web (i.e., located between upper and lower chords).

If the user has requested redundant elements, they are added at random in an alternating pattern starting from opposite ends of bridge and multistory trusses, thus producing cross-braced bays. The number of redundant elements for these two truss types is randomly selected from the total limit specified. PANDORA'S BOX introduces redundant elements into roof trusses by assigning one additional element to each of the two bays adjacent to the centerline. The number of redundant elements is a random event; structures with large numbers of nodes are the most probable candidates. Therefore, there may be no redundant elements even though the user requested them.

BEAM AND FRAME ELEMENTS

For beams PANDORA'S BOX can produce up to three different rectangular cross sections with an aspect ratio of three. The program calculates actual beam dimensions assuming lateral torsional buckling behavior. The loads are transformed into moments at midspan and over supports using influence envelopes at critical points on four basic beams. After the program establishes moments at critical points along the beam, it calculates the cross-sectional properties using the maximum moment. If the user requests multiple cross sections, the program uses a random number, along with the size established from the maximum moment criterion, to calculate the largest cross section. A third section is assigned midway between the two extreme sizes. PANDORA'S BOX assigns cross sections to each element based on the critical bending moments assigned from the influence envelopes. Alternatively, the program assigns multiple beam cross sections using the maximum moment and multiple E values in the lateral torsional buckling relationship.

PANDORA'S BOX also assigns cross sections for frames using the basic moment envelopes and assumes lateral torsional buckling behavior for a section with an aspect ratio of three. Description of frame members requires a cross-sectional area, in addition to the moment of inertia; therefore, the program determines the area associated with the calculated moment of inertia.

DISCUSSION

The extremely powerful generation capability of the program has the potential to be unpredictable. PANDORA'S BOX can produce eight different types of random structures; for one structural category as many as six different types of problems can be generated. The user can modify the features of the structures produced by setting the limit and condition parameters. An unrestricted number of random problems can be generated for one set of parameters, and revising the parameters can significantly alter the nature of the problems produced. Selecting a different type or category of structure will result in a new, completely independent, set of random structures.

The current version of PANDORA'S BOX has been tested for input/output and logic errors. We have run the program many times to establish that meaningful data are produced for the various structural categories. Inspite of these checks, we recognize that the possibility exists for creating errant structures. For example, testing revealed that generated trusses were overly stiff; this prompted a change to using average expected load rather than maximum expected load in assigning element cross-sectional areas. Further testing may reveal that additional truss flexibility is required; this could be accomplished using a scaling factor that is based on parameters such as the number of nodes and number of boundary conditions.

PANDORA'S BOX may produce beams that are too stiff by: a) assigning element cross-sectional properties with the aid of influence envelope equations; and b) using lateral torsional buckling behavior to translate the bending moments into section dimensions. The influence envelope equations were developed for a single span, and a load can have considerable affect outside of the span in which it is applied. Therefore, it may be necessary to modify element cross section design by: a) using the average (rather than the maximum) bending moment at key points; and/or b) incorporating a scaling factor into the lateral torsional buckling equation.

Frame problems have the greatest potential for deviating from the expected results. The possibility of long, unsupported frames with no intermediate supports exists; the assumption that individual spans have some means of support at each end is based on the probability of sideshot elements acting as intermediate supports. Also, the assumptions used to translate element generation algorithms for beams to frames may not be valid.

We propose an extensive testing program for all structural categories. The prime controlling factor of the configuration is the number of nodes. Statistical sampling should be performed across the limits of the program (up to 100 node structures) for all categories of structures.

The results should reveal trends in the characteristics of the randomly produced structures and point out embedded logic errors.

PROGRAM EXTENSIONS

From the beginning we have considered other uses for PANDORA'S BOX. We anticipate subroutines to be written that fall within the current three structural categories. We also expect that users may wish to dispense with paper work and simply distribute the problem generation portion of the program to students. Only one subroutine is used within the program to produce solution files. Although the SOLVE subroutine is called from several locations within the program, that subroutine is not absolutely required. An instructor need only remove the SOLVE subroutine, or more elegantly, rename SOLVE and create another subroutine, called SOLVE, that acts as a gate to produce solution files.

It seems logical that a program could be written to analyze homework, check it for solution technique and completeness, and assign a grade. The philosophy behind automated grading centers around controlling the flow of the solution. For a structural analysis course, the best method for controlling flow may be to produce an interactive program capable of informing the user of correct steps or misguided directions. Another possibility may be to have the user develop the entire solution and submit it to the grading program. The grading program would check to determine if the appropriate commands have been issued, the data placed in the correct order, and if the data and commands have been assembled correctly.

SUMMARY

Under the control of the user, PANDORA'S BOX will produce two-dimensional beams, frames, and trusses with a variety of hardware-dependent selectable outputs. The complexity and size of the problems are controlled by the user. The solution file generated by PANDORA'S BOX interfaces with a matrix solutions package to produce nodal displacements and element forces.

PANDORA'S BOX is an initial attempt to develop a program to aid instructors with problem/solution creation in structural analysis courses. It approaches the capabilities of an expert system in that it is controllable by the user, incorporates both experience and technology, and reduces the time and effort required by the user. It is obviously not a substitute for the professor. The program provides the faculty member with a source of original exercise problems/solutions, which can be easily generated to complement lecture materials. These plentiful and diverse problems will help students to strengthen and extend their understanding of structural analysis. PANDORA'S BOX is a comprehensive attempt at producing a viable instructional assistant, and it is written to be adapted for diverse applications by revision, modification, and extension.

REFERENCES

1. Kostem, C.N. and M.L. Maher, Ed., Expert Systems in Civil Engineering, American Society of Civil Engineers, New York, 1986.

2. Sack, R.L. and R.D. Schroeder, "Auto Creation of Structural Analysis Exercises," UPCAEDM87 Proceedings, 1987.

3. Schroeder, R.D., "Random problem generation for courses in structural analysis," thesis presented to the Univ. of Idaho, Moscow, Idaho, in partial fulfillment of the requirements for the degree of Master of Science in Civil Engineering, 1987.

4. Wilson, E.L., "CAL-86, Computer Assisted Learning of Structural Analysis and the CAL/SAP Development System," Rept. No. UCB/SESM-86/05, Dept. of Civil Engrg., Univ. of Calif., Berkeley, Calif., 1986.

THE APPLICATION OF ARTIFICIAL INTELLIGENCE TECHNIQUES TO CIVIL AND STRUCTURAL ENGINEERING